DIVINE TREASURE

DIVINE TREASURE

MEMORIES OF BELOVED ENCOUNTERS WITH MY ANCESTORS

GRACIELA THOMEN GINEBRA

GREEN ORB & WHITE FAWN, LLC

To my children
André Emin, Alexander Murat and Victor Ali

May the love of your ancestors enfold you
May the strength of your ancestors accompany you
May the power of your ancestors protect you

For wherever you are, they are too
Irradiating love and strength
In your heart

Because where your heart is, your treasure is there also.

— THE BIBLE

CONTENTS

PREFACE

Puerto Plata. 1912

The wind arrived in time for the farewell. Pigeons huddled in the cracks of the Victorian transoms, sleepily watching the first light of dawn. A couple comes out of the main door of Hotel Europa pausing at the threshold. She faces him, flanking the exit. Patiently, the man takes her hands and bends down to murmur in her ear. He promises that he'll be back soon; that he chose the smaller suitcase as a promise that the trip will be short. The woman shakes her head, refusing to listen. Her curls blow loose, and the breeze ruffles them. Last night, a premonition dressed as a dream took her by surprise.

This is how I imagine the farewell of two of my ancestors in that gloomy dawn. Isidoro, susurrating a thousand reasons, his eyes seeking understanding. Bianca turned her gaze on the horizon and pulled away from his embrace. Her complaints are pointless now. The ship is about to leave.

My vision is so vivid and so clear. I believe I am there in person as a seven-year-old girl, an omitted, clandestine witness to the farewell of two of my ancestors. I have come running, my bare feet full of sand. Feeling the cold from the pavement in my ankles. I have stopped at the opposite corner peering at them in disbelief; it's an unknown scene but I feel I've seen it a thousand times. But the moving mist blurs my eyes. And I fear any movement of mine will dissolve the enchantment and make me wake up to oblivion. Maybe this time, I will see something new; perhaps, I will know something more, something I've missed before. I realized, this is not my memory and yet it seems mine. *Are memories inherited? If not...who told this to me?*

With her chin raised and without deigning him a glance, Bianca bypasses him, enters the home and closes the door, unaware that she has denied him a last goodbye. The pigeons nervously move and some swoop down while others take flight. He sighs and picks up his suitcase. When he lifts his gaze to the street, I think he's going to see me...he's coming towards me...we're going to see each other! My heart clenches and I hold my breath. I wait for him but the pigeons at his feet take flight and obscure my sight. In the blink of an eye, he passes me quickly. The shadow of his hat covering his face. I turn around trying to make the words, "Wait, don't go!" but they can't come out of my throat. Yet, when I see him stopping, a hope catches me. If he heard me, he'll turn back and...he won't pass the threshold of oblivion. But he only fixes his hat and resumes his pace. The mist envelops him and divides us. I'm left alone...in that empty street of Puerto Plata.

PART 1

THE ABANDONMENT

PUERTO PLATA. 2008

"*And* how many family members are traveling with you?" asked the officer behind one of the Customs windows at Puerto Plata's international airport. His voice mingled with the echo of the loudspeaker, the music of drums, and murmurs from other travelers. I weighed his question.

He was tall and thin, with closely shaved black hair, and his uniform was starched and pressed within an inch of its life. Beneath the light at his station, he was checking our passports. At that moment, Mappy and I were standing together, leaning close to his window. We were dressed almost identically: jeans and a white shirt. Our jackets were different; hers a royal blue with gold buttons and mine a light brown with golden threads. We wore them folded over our arm so as not to get overheated. Carryon suitcases were at our sides. She wore her black hair in a modern cut, and I had left mine long and highlighted blonde. If it weren't for our smiles, and similar laughs, no one would know that we were related. We're descended from Isidoro and Bianca; she, by her grandmother Mafalda, born and raised in Bologna, sister of my grandmother Chela, born and raised in Puerto Plata.

We had met up in Atlanta before getting on the plane. Mappy had traveled from Arizona and I from Virginia. It had been fifteen years since we had last seen each other! As we greeted each other,

She was laughing as I was crying, overwhelmed by how much time had passed. Before boarding, we asked to sit together so we could talk about family stories. She brought photos inherited from her grandmother and I brought genealogy research documents. As we buckled seat belts, we unbuckled our words and anecdotes came tumbling out in gushes of laughter. As the plane flew over the ocean, we cherished what brought us together: our family stories, each from our own perspective. As we landed, we agreed it was far too fast for everything we wanted to share.

And now, we were both answering the questions of the customs agent. As a consummate professional, he had waved Mappy over to present her documents. But because I didn't want to be separated from her for even one second, I linked my arm with hers, hopefully signaling to the agent that we were family traveling together.

The officer's voice brought me back to reality. I felt like the list of normal questions on the entry form were getting steadily more esoteric. He had started with a simple, "How long is your length of stay?" He tapped the sheet with the tip of his pen waiting for our answer and raised his head to glance at us briefly. As accomplices, Mappy and I looked at each other. We were both past our third decade, but we couldn't stop giggling like teenagers. I mentally calculated, based on the plan: *We'll arrive and go directly to a welcome party. Tomorrow we will have a tour of Puerto Plata where we will inaugurate Doña Blanca's alley (that's what Bianca was called in this town). We will return together on the same flight on Sunday; we will separate in Atlanta to return to our daily lives with our husbands and children. How many hours does that add up to?*

"Forty-two hours." Mappy answered before I finished my calculation. I was amused by the precision of her mathematics.

"What is the reason for your visit?"

It was logical; there were many passengers, and the officer was meticulously doing his job. These were the preformulated questions asked on arrival at any airport in the world. The normal response would be: "recreation or business." But I was so giddy at that point, I was more than willing to give him the full story. *"Our common ancestors, Isidoro and Bianca, arrived in Puerto Plata in 1898. One day, he left, never to be seen again..."* adding in how my great-grandmother was left alone more than 80 prior, life happened, and here we were, following a catalytic summons from our Uncle Frank for this family reunion! I wanted to explain everything to him for some reason. To tell him that when our family gets together, it seems as if magic unfolds; the air is electric and a current of love envelops all. I wanted him to understand that I often wondered if our grandparents, now all passed on, also enjoyed our gatherings too, through the parts of them that lived on in all of us, their descendants. As though, in a mysterious way, we keep them c close and they're able to delight in our laughter and conversations. Yes! What if they laugh from another dimension and bless us? In simple terms, his question was, *"Why did you travel here?"* But I thought to myself: *What do you mean why did we come? To receive that blessing and to feel that family love that we have for each other and that manifests itself in every encounter—What else, of course!*

But before I could open my mouth, Mappy won over again. With simplicity, she answered:

"We're here for a family reunion."

The officer continued:

"Are you from Puerto Plata?"

In this, we contrasted, answering at the same time.

"No," said Mappy.

"Yes!" I exclaimed.

That is my custom reply for inquiries about my provenance. Although I was born and raised in Santo Domingo, as were my four sisters, I say I am from Puerto Plata because I *feel* it. As a child, the quotidian boredom of school and home was just a passing of time for me. I was just waiting for Fridays, when my family would take to the road and start living! We sing at the top of our lungs to the songs on the radio, as we drove along to Puerto Plata. Once we arrived, we'd all spill out of the car to play with my cousins, share with my grandparents, and finally breathe the air of freedom which inflated my whole being. I've always maintained that Puerto Plata is where life itself begins!

The sweetest childhood memories come from there. One such memory always calms me every time I relive it: *I am sitting on a low branch of a tree dangling my bare feet. It is a "Bishop's Hat", so called because its branches spread everywhere like an umbrella. These strong branches accommodate me like my grandparents' large, soft arms. Our house was at the top of a peak surrounded by the sea on three corners. If I look to my left almost 180 degrees, the horizon showed in a blue gradient as the backdrop of an infinite row of coconut trees in a grove. If I look to my right, I can see the house terrace, and hear the music that lifted the adults to dance and party in a chercha.*

But it is the wind that I remember the most. *It gathers strength as it moves towards me, then passes by while caressing the leaves of my tree. It continues towards the hundreds of coconut trees, tousling their long leaves, which roll and unroll, flapping each other and producing the sound of applause. Applause for the perfection of nature in this sublime moment! I wish I could fly and get tangled up in them, with them. So, taking advantage of a buzz in the air as it blows harder, I leap and land on my feet making the fine sand rise on my heels. As I run, I wriggle my feet to avoid stepping directly on the tiny thorns of the morivivíes until I reach to the smooth grass. And then I leap. And the wind lifts me up, tangling and untangling me among the long, slender leaves. My outstretched arms spread like wings ready to fly with the wind. And as it elevates me, I become as light as a feather and the breeze takes me to the next tree to tousle me playfully among the leaves.* This reminiscence is of infinite sustenance to me. It is imprinted within me as is every rock in this place, every grain of beach salt, every drop of dew on the leaves, every breeze that lifts me. Puerto Plata lives in me.

Once again, the officer interrupted my thoughts with his questionnaire.

"And... How many family members are traveling with you?"

That is it! The precise question with which we started this story. The one that triggered all my imaginary trips. I looked at him with compassion; he was naive to the knowledge of all the lives that live in me. Unbeknownst to him, of all the questions, that was the most profound of all. The one that holds the hidden secrets of the ancestral lineage of our own souls. It is that...all the time, my family travels with me, in me, in my mind, in my thoughts...Not only my children but my four sisters, my parents...But beyond them, far beyond the immediate ones, there are also my ancestors. My grandparents are still with me, as alive in my mind as if they were by my side. Just as present as Mappy is now. I didn't know it until this adventure disguised as genealogical research began. Now I am sure of it. In fact, I affirm it.

Mappy winked at me, ready to answer. We talked on the plane about our grandparents who were sisters, but above all, about our great-grandparents, Isidoro and Bianca. She already knows what I think and agrees. Although she lives in this world more than in mine and to make me laugh and make the joke, she answered:

"About ninety."

Quite seriously, the agent looked up and hesitated, looking behind us, then at us, back, and again...looking for ninety. Finally, he realized it was a joke spreading his mouth into a pleasant smile and, with no more questions, he stamped the entry seal on our passport pages.

"Welcome to Puerto Plata!" he said to us, his voice quickening. He alluded to the fact that our whole being had just arrived, never suspecting that, eternally, part of us has always been here.

There is something mystical about Puerto Plata. An innate preservation of time immemorial. The place itself is a canticle of mysterious narratives. Its history has a poetic nuance. Puerto Plata had been a *Taino* settlement where its first inhabitants felt protected from the annual hurricanes between mountains and sea. But the place did not protect them from the real danger that lurked. It did not warn them of their fate at the hands of a Genovese, Christopher Columbus, who took shelter in its bay to ride out a storm. From his ship, he observed up that the mountain was silver and for this reason he called it Puerto Plata. Was he disappointed when he approached it and discovered that what turned the mountains silver were the leaves of the *yagrumo* tree? Trees that cheerfully announce the arrival of the rain by turning over their leaves on the silver side. I think they are enchanted!

There are things unseen by the eyes but not by the soul. And when I was a little girl, I imagined that the *yagrumo* trees had invisible eyes that could read the clouds and feel the arrival of water from the sky. As if dancing in joy, they'd raised their branches to receive the clouds blessings. Despite the beauty and originality of this species, I imagine that, in his greed, the admiral was not at all amused when he got off his ship and saw that what he thought was silver were only leaves of a tree in devotion to the rain.

Now admiring green mountains from the road, Mappy and I reunited with the family at the town's plaza. Amidst enchanted and imaginary ancestors and ninety living and lively relatives, we showed up at the center of the center, between the *glorieta* (gazebo) and the cathedral. It was the place where my grandmother and her siblings enjoyed the music and the moon in the days of yore. Now, their descendants cherishing each other in this, I believe, consecrated and blessed space.

Eighty years ago, Isidoro and Bianca's children listened to accordion, violin and drum songs played by elegantly dressed musicians in the *glorieta*. Today, their descendants can't stop hugging, talking, laughing...And my memory changed the scene between two times, as I imagined my beloved grandmother Chela, barely seventeen years old, standing next to me, observing, like me, the family scene of the present. She, with her dark, soft curls falling like a waterfall over her shoulders and those eyes of sky mixed with sea, whispered in my ear.

"When from the hotel we listened to the swaying of the violin notes, Yolanda, Mayú, Ana and I would rush here. Then, once Queco and Mafalda arrived from Italy, they would also come to enjoy the melodies. We would go out together, arms linked, hurrying so as not to miss a minute of music and joy."

An old musical note introduced its tone and I searched left and right for its source. But my eyes could only detect the merriment of my cousins hugging each other and taking pictures. And I sighed in nostalgia...it seemed like a daydream. My grandmother's voice came back to my side as if carried by the breeze. Her words illuminated the images before me, and I enjoyed this borrowed memory:

"We would cross to the square to cool off and walk around the gazebo. Sometimes, someone dared to invite us to a dance."

Among the animated figures of descendants, shadows from other times mingled. Past and present merged in translucent silhouettes of hatted gallants bowing, inviting to dance. The ladies, in their pompous dresses, curtsey in acceptance. Then, paired together, they began the dance. I watched as a silent witness of two different times.

Do places hold memories? Do stones on the ground, which have witnessed so many steps, have been imprinted with memories?

My eyes blinked, making the past disappear in front of me and leaving a beautiful present with my cousins. I was overcome with joy and belonging. In marvel, I reflected that all of us descendants, together in the square, belong to the hope of cells of a couple. A couple that looked into each other's eyes right here in this space. A couple who walked together to pray at this very church. All of us, proud of the legacy, now arriving here in remembrance of a woman who one day found an empty bed and who had to raise her small children all alone. Because of *her* and in her honor, our dear Uncle Frank was inspired to bring us together. Tonight promises to be a magical night.

So, just as her descendants are walking hand in hand to the hotel door, 80 years ago my grandmother and her siblings walked this same path. I feel they are marching with us. We soon arrived in front of the plaque with our great-grandmother's photo. This is the alley where she sat every afternoon for her tea. This is the place where she last took her breath.

We surrounded Uncle Frank, who spoke:

"My grandmother Bianca, who was called Doña Blanca, was a woman full of mettle and tenacity. When she was left alone, she raised her children to be good men and women. She instilled in them honesty, integrity and love for work. People ask me: "What is the key to success?" Family unity is the key to success. The secret to happiness is family togetherness. I am fortunate to have both: success and happiness. But more than that, I am fortunate to have all of you. To have this family united, as my grandmother always wished. All of us supporting each other, wishing each other well, loving each other. We must carry on her legacy. Pass it on to our children. Set an example for them. It is her love that instills it. It is love that binds us together. Her strong love continues in us from generation to generation.

We clapped enthusiastically, hearts bursting with happiness for being descendants of this great woman. Huddled in that space, close together, we formed a line so that each one of us could see the photo and the plaque on the wall that baptized the space. I took my place to wait my turn. But as I approached the image, I began to feel a new companion...as if a sadness stood beside me.

When I approached, I examined the coppery metal inscription, touching with the tip of my fingers the numbers: one, nine, one,

7

four...1914! The noise of joy began to fade behind me as if I were in a movie and the volume had been lowered.

Since I started family genealogy, it became common for dates to trigger images in my mind. This date was no exception. I knew it was the inherited memory of Isidoro's abandonment...but something was amiss. I was feeling the unanswered question that lingered in the family, up until this day of the family reunion in 2008.

In a *flash* memory, I recalled Mappy's question a few hours earlier. Still on the plane, it was my turn to tell her my side of the story...based on found documents. I tried to describe to her what I had discovered, but she gripped her arms of the seat tightly. Her eyes were wide as she bluntly and energetically asked me,

"So, *did he or didn't he abandon her?*"

My smile had frozen at that question. Their energy transported me to a scene in a black and white movie. It was as if Mappy was grabbing me by the lapel saying, "Answer me! *Did he truly abandon her?*"

Did he abandon her or not? I wanted to be sure! I wanted to tell her the whole story...to include the opinion of my heart. But I couldn't answer her because this is not a movie. This is a life. Two lives and more. A couple, and their descendants. Is *their* story, a story of love or a story of oblivion?

And my cousin's honest eyes staring intensely at me...eyes with dark lashes reflecting the light from the airplane window...demanding the truth. The truth and nothing but the absolute truth! The truth that now has turned into an ancestral longing.

Standing in front of the sepia image of my great-grandmother Bianca, the wind interrupted my reverie bringing me a whisper. I thought someone had called me and I turned to look back. But those behind me were still engrossed in their conversations. With a shiver running down my spine, I turned and looked for eye connection in my ancestor's photo. I received her confident Italian matronly and eerily quiet smile. I moved my fingers away from the silent numbers. Tonight, I was to open a document in front of everyone and read...and let the past speak. And let each descendant listen with the ears of the heart. And witness how their own heart responds.

8

However, first I had to tell the truth of my discoveries and bring Isidoro alive to this family puzzle so that all of you, non-descendants, would also perceive his being like I do. And to feel in your bones, if you can, the truth of the heart.

So I will begin, as it was told to me...the story of the abandonment.

THE ABANDONMENT

*T*he darkest time of the night is just before the first rays of dawn. The genesis of the story of abandonment is no exception. Abandonment existed in the family history as a sorrow buried among the flowers of oblivion. I remember the place and the moment, I remember the awl in the center of my chest. A metal key in my thymus igniting the mystery. Darkness is sadness. To know the truth, you have to dig it out from the soil of the land of sorrows. To do so, one must be brave and have a strong-hardened heart, not a soft one, as *softie* as mine. If I don't dare to step in the darkness of the unknown and plunge the shovel into the earth with a single movement to discover it, why did it occur to me to dig it up in the first place? My only excuse: a compelling feeling that overcame me in a time of sorrows.

After my father's death, Mami sold her house. It was my childhood home. As a farewell, I wanted to visit it before she gave it away. It had a large yard with many flowers and fruit trees. In the corner, near the terrace, there was an orchid garden. It was a small square kaleidoscope of color. The purple ones hung from the palms, and others, bright orange, bloomed almost all year round. I insisted that I would come to say goodbye to the house, but... it all happened so fast! She tried to explain to me over the phone. She did it because the pain of the loss was so deep. She told me that she had to move to a new place without any sad memories. I kept quiet, with the receiver in my hand, biting my lips, for I was going to tell her that I had learned that... it was impossible not to pack up the sorrows. No matter how much one closed the boxes and sealed them, one should not trust. At some point, perhaps at night, when one was not looking, the sorrows would come out of their hiding places and crawl like viscous gel into the suitcases through the tiny, paper-thin like cracks of the already closed boxes. I wanted to warn her. I wished...closing my eyes as if in prayer, that if *I* had been there to help her pack, I'd have drawn out a sharp sword to fight any sadness that wanted to lurk, taking advantage of any distraction, to get into the boxes. But I couldn't make it. Geographical distance prevented it. I resided far away in Virginia with my husband and children. It was not so easy to travel whenever I wanted. Work and family obligations demanded planning in advance. On that occasion, I could only go with my children after Christmas. So I did. By the time we arrived, she was in her new home.

Mami had settled in a condo near a park. It was the second floor of a comfortable and spacious apartment with opposite balconies, freshening the space. The land on which the building was located was filled with glorious flamboyant trees whose branches spread covering the grass and kept the lawn cool. Under their trunks were ferns placed as ornaments. The paths between the residences were full of flowers and, through one of the windows of the room, a Ylang-Ylang could be spotted, and its perfume could reach us, despite the distance. The thing I liked most in this new space was that, on the outside, my mother had hung a cheerful wind chime that tinkled when the breeze blew in. Thus the tune of little bells in the tone of a xylophone were heard sporadically, all morning, all night.

I arrived with the plan to ask her questions about her childhood and her family, specifically, her grandparents. My idea was to save those memories, jot them down for posterity.

I had done just that with my father two years before. When in New York I suspected that the end of his presence of this earth was closing in and the days were marching on, I asked him all the questions I could think of. They were interview-type questions. His answers, recorded in ink, I would pass them on to my children so they would not forget him. Whenever they wanted to read about their grandfather, they'd had it written, and for all upcoming descendants too, should they come to grace my life. They too would have written records of scenes from the lives of their ancestors. The questions to my dad ranged from his favorite color to his favorite meal; as in, which dish as a child he loved the most and who'd prepared it for them. That's how I got to know some of my paternal great-grandparents. Seeing that my dad was so entertaining in answering in detail, I became even more dedicated. Those last meetings became a flowing litany of words at all hours, like an eternal conversation between the two of us. Secretly, they were an excuse for me to make him to talk to me while I tried to make sure I'd never forget the sound of his loving voice. I loved my dad with all my heart.

And now, it is necessary to give a report of the issue with my heart: when my dad died, my heart broke into pieces. It seems logical, expected, without too many twists and turns, but in reality, it was not so simple. Every time I saw him in the hospital bed, my heart squeezed. With each visit, it squeezed once more. So when all the fluid dried up, my heart crystallized. My heart ended looking like a heart-shaped ruby hanging in my left side of the cavity of my chest. A fragile red crystal on the left side of my sternum. The moment he died, the heavy hammer of sadness hit it and it burst into pieces. Its glass fell in a heap, in there. The piercing points of that mountain of broken glass stayed there as I was unable to get it out, and so it lacerated the inside cavity of my flesh; if I moved too much, they'd pierced me in the inside. Even deep breathing felt like a cut into my living flesh, and... it hurt.

Two years later, still carrying the pieces of my broken heart in that cavity, I curiously entered my mother's new home. Thus, entered the questioner about her and her ancestors. The meandering interview of rescued memories would fall in long paragraphs on my notebook. As far as I could recall, I haven't heard my mother talk about her grandparents. Well... only one of them... her maternal grandmother, whom she held up on a pedestal. This preference intrigued me. My mom being a reserved personality, I suspected that asking her anything would be like asking a pigeon. I would have to spoon-out the answers in small units, as if little pieces of rice.

It was the day of my arrival when I decided to begin interviewing her. I took a small, lined notebook, one that had been left over from my children's schoolwork. I had torn out the pages that were full and was ready to its new use. Its pages would receive my mother's answers. I'd clearly write her anecdotes.

I found her sitting in the living room knitting under the coolness of the ceiling fan blades. Her feet were tucked up. My mom had cut her hair short and left the gray out, now that my father wasn't around. Her sad eyes were olive green and turned the color of a warm river water when they rested on her grandchildren. She was knitting in a combination of light green and violet, which looked like flowers in a garden. She told me she was making a blanket for someone's baby. She spoke without looking up or slowing down her art. Her fingers twirled like soldiers under her orders. Her short nails were oval and beautiful as she knitted evenly, with precise and diligent gestures.

"Mami, I'd like to ask you a few questions...."

I sat down next to her and leaned my head on the back of the chair waiting for her to finish calculating something with her finger. Slowly, she raised her eyes, focusing on mine.

I resumed:

"Let's see." I reviewed my list of questions. "Tell me, what are the earliest memories you have of your grandparents... what were they like? Let's say you were about four or five years old. Give me your first impressions..."

My idea was to start at an early age and take it little by little down the line. That's how it had worked with my dad, in a linear way. This time it wasn't the same.

"Why do you want to know?"

She tangled a yarn around her finger, which she then caught with the needle. She could be talked to while knitting; she didn't mind. I smiled because I knew she would negotiate her words and came prepared.

"It's for my children's project...for grandparents' day at school," I replied.

This was half the truth. I wasn't going to tell her, "Hey, Mom, I want to save your words for your grandchildren in case you die too soon for my children to have memories of you." I mention the latter because I grew up hearing stories directly from my grandparents that seemed like colorful fantasy fables. At family gatherings, enlivened by my questions, I would hear them recount their experiences in their own voices. It was an honor and a delight. If my children were not going to get this from their grandparents' own voices, they would get it from my written voice. I would become the rescuer of remembrances. I will be the keeper of memories.

Approaching again, I started with her grandmother Bianca, also called Mamma Blanca, the Italian. That would be the easiest place to start since her love for her grandmother was palpable and immense.

I asked her, "What is the earliest memory you have of your childhood with your grandmother Blanca?"

I was delighted to see her countenance turn dreamy as she began to speak.

"Every summer of my childhood, my parents (Chela and Joaquin), would take me to my grandmother's house in Puerto Plata. From an early age, I spent my summers there with my cousins. First it was Billy and I, as the oldest cousins... We were inseparable. We called our grandmother Babi. That was our endearment to her. She cooked delicious food especially made for us... whatever we liked."

The soft look in her eyes dissipated as she noticed the notebook I was writing in as she talked. Clearly curious, she craned her neck to see what I had put down upon the paper. To calm her curiosity and keep her from stopping, I recited the words as I wrote them.

"Puerto Plata...with her grandmother Bianca...nickname Babi...summers with Uncle Billy Harper...they played in the garden...."

Her attention was drawn back to her needle and I thought she wasn't going to go on, so I started making things up.

"Naughty cousins... playing with dirt and water in the garden... Grandmother who would get mad and beat them with broomsticks."

"She wasn't like that," she protested, holding up her index finger, and then pressed her lips in a semi-smile. "But Billy's antics were..." She looked up at the ceiling as if remembering something funny.

The anecdote that she gave me was about summers with Billy, who had some hilarious outings. She said that when Billy found little spiders or some small toads lost inside the house, to save their lives, he would slyly throw them in his pockets and leave them free in the garden, because if Babi found them, she would throw them out with a broom, but she'd do that only to the little spiders and toads... never to them, her grandchildren. I had to make a good note of that, she insisted.

I was delighted to hear her evoking her childhood with her semblance illuminated. She told me that, every afternoon, her grandmother liked to sit in a rocking chair to enjoy the Puerto Plata breeze, watch the people go by and enjoy a cup of tea. She'd spent long hours reading books, which she enjoyed, but she enjoyed most giving her grandchildren treats, like when they wanted to climb into the rocking chair with her to be rocked like on a swing!

In my mind, I would conjure up the image as if I were watching it live and direct. I could see Babi pause her reading and put the book to the side when her grandchildren approached her, and, sitting each one-on-one knee, she would rock as if they were going to take a flight of three. It was a garden full of flowers, there..., where the alley was now located. I admit that this image of a happy grandmother contrasted with the image of a stoic heroine that had been instilled in me of my great-grandmother. And I welcomed in my mind this new image of Mamma Blanca. So I expressed so to Mami.

"How different this idea from the one I had of that tough, high-tempered woman!"

Mami immediately defended her grandmother:

"She had to be strong to raise her children.. She had to be! She was a business owner, and she was a woman in a country that wasn't her own. And she was all alone. Yes...maybe she was tough on her children as they were growing, but not with us, her grandchildren. Never with us.

Her finger pointed to the sky and I understood that she didn't want me to get the wrong impression of our ancestor. Family loyalty demanded that all her grandchildren present her in the best light. . .always!

"And your grandfather Isidoro?"

My question was innocent but found not answer. If the evocation of her grandmother's memory was a pink cloud, at the mention of her grandfather, that glorious cloud soon dissipated with a poof! My mother twirled her yarn, tangling and untangling as only she knew how.

When she didn't answer me, I wanted to make up words to poke at her memory, but even that felt uncomfortable. Suddenly, I vaguely remembered something my own maternal grandmother had told me years before. It was an anecdote that came to my mind inadvertently. It was something about Isidoro. The memory danced in front of me, and I repeated it to her:

"Mamma Chela remembered Isidoro very fondly. She once told me that he played with them and that he was always in a good mood..." I stopped when I noticed she was shaking her head, frowning. Before she could deny it, I hurried to say: "That's what my grandmother told me...." Note that when I said my grandmother, she was Chela, who is Mami's mother.

"That couldn't have happened like that," she answered sharply. Her tone had changed. "Mother was a toddler when her father left!"

Suddenly, something had woken up to protest inside me. A rumble of voices thundered in my head. I had to shake it off "what?" I shook my head to deny her statement. My voice jumped to fight my grandmother's memories against hers:

"Mamma Chela told me that, when she and her four- or five-year-old sisters got up early, they would go downstairs and go to the hotel's office. There he was, Isidoro, working since dawn... The little girls would play at interrupting him... *him*... Isidoro. Why not?" I asked a little annoyed when my mother kept shaking her head denying the story that Mamma Chela had given me.

I insisted, "That's what she said! She used to describe him to me...she used to refer to him as a happy person, very hardworking, loving and cheerful. He was never angry. He was always in a good mood. He laughed all the time."

I thought of adding *in contrast to Bianca*...but I dared not go there. Still, I contained myself and insisted with my borrowed memory,

"Mamma Chela told me that she remembered that he, Isidoro, would play around the hotel... Yes?"

Mami's voice hardened. Looking at me fixedly, she clipped her words.

"That Isidoro was not my grandfather! She was *not* referring to *her* father, but to her older *brother*, who was also named Isidoro."

I fell silent and held my breath to hear her better. As her yarn kept twirling, Mami finally looked up and I met her green eyes. My heart was alert and I felt determined.

"He abandoned her! Isidoro took a ship and never came back. My grandfather abandoned my grandmother."

The word abandonment pricked the skin of my chest, pierced it and twisted. It was an internal crack. As if an invisible metal object had buried itself in my thymus. I ran out of air. The shards of glass from my broken heart crammed into its cavity felt as if they sutured the living flesh. I had to stop and gently touch my fingers to my chest and took a slow breath in. The echo of a resounding *no* buzzed back in my ears.

"No... I don't think so," I murmured, breathing in slowly, with a feeling of faintness.

Mami looked up and her eyes softened when she saw me so affected. To soothe me, she tried to play it down.

"For what it's worth..., it doesn't matter. That happened so many years ago. In 1914."

She waved her hand as if shooing away bad memories like flies. Then, tugged at the wool, unraveling a few more strands from the ball, caresses it, and tied to the needle.

A thousand questions crowded my mouth. I rummaged for any memory that my grandmother could have given me to refute this information. I remembered pieces, but none of them gave an answer.

"You say he sailed away. Where to?"

"New York."

"But...why did he go to New York, to then go on to Italy? But...did he really abandon her or did she just feel abandoned?

What evidence is there of such abandonment? Did he leave a farewell letter? Where did he die?"

My memories combined with a scene from about two years earlier in New York, when my dad died precisely in New York. What would it be like to transport a corpse at the turn of the century? What happened if someone dropped dead on a ship in those days would they get thrown overboard?

My strategy of getting her to talk delicately *did* go overboard. Now, I demanded answers from her. I repeated my last question.

"Of course he died!" replied my mother, as if *she* was offended.

But by her tone, *I was* offended. She looked at me as if I had the ridiculous idea that I'd be expecting to arrive in New York almost a hundred years after his departure and find him alive. My semblance must have looked badly for her that I saw her collecting her thoughts and added:

"I don't know the date. I don't know where he's buried. His whereabouts were never known. But so much time has passed, I suppose it doesn't matter anymore."

"How come you don't know where he was buried?"

"I don't know."

"But isn't he buried next to Bianca, in Puerto Plata?"

My mother took a breath of air and let it out slowly. Finally, she said,

"In my adolescence, every time we traveled to Puerto Plata with mom and dad, we would stop on the way and go to the cemetery to see Babi's grave. We would bring her flowers. Isidoro's grave was never by her side. You could hardly ask about him. He was never mentioned."

"In conclusion..." I said as I opened my notebook and wrote furiously in it. "One day, Isidoro boarded a ship and left. He abandoned Bianca, either willingly or unwillingly..."

I looked up so that she could see that I didn't believe what I was saying, that I challenged even the sharp pain I felt in my chest from all of the emotions swirling around inside it.

"And, what happened next?" I asked insistently, stabbing the pen on the paper.

Mami looked at me again. I felt as if someone had lit a fuse inside me; my cheeks were burning. I stared back at her hard. I would have liked to enter her brain and searched for any memories that might have been lurking within its labyrinthine fibers. For her, the conversation was over. For me, it had only just begun.

"If anyone knew what date he was buried and where, it was lost in family history."

Her eyes rested on me this time in tranquility. She was not one to dwell long on things that could not be resolved. She had received this information when she was young, and it had stayed carved in her memory. Family stories are not questioned. They are accepted as they come. As they are told, they are consented to. They are not doubted or contested. Likewise, hadn't I accepted the ones I received from my grandparents before now? Why couldn't I swallow this one? Even I was amazed at the commotion in my chest!

I stood up. I needed to breathe. But as I did, my heart felt tender. Slowly, so it wouldn't hurt, I moved to the window. I had to open it wider to take in the fresh air. To make matters worse, there wasn't even a breeze. It was as if the whole apartment had become silent and the little brightness of the afternoon had been extinguished. As I took a deep slow breath, my mind kept wandering and searching for anecdotes that might disprove what it had just heard. "Can't be true," I kept repeating to myself.

But I come from a family of women who own no mistakes and where absolute certainties reign. What my mother said, which probably came directly from Bianca, had to be true. I tried to convince myself. But the more I pushed that reality into my chest and looked for a way to resign myself, the more it hurt. "It's just... it must be a misunderstanding. Something's wrong," the voice in my mind fired.

Black and white images of ships approaching and leaving ports flashed through my head like an old movie. For the rest of the afternoon and evening, I was analyzing in my memory any details of some forgotten story my grandmother Chela might have told me. Unlike my mother, she was an avid storyteller. She loved to recount tales, and my sisters and I loved to listen to them. When she told them, she acted them out in different voices. And when she burst out laughing, it was open and true. She'd laughed at her own witticisms and her own misadventures so many times. Why hadn't she told me this one? Maybe my grandmother didn't tell sad stories. Maybe I heard it and wasn't ready to receive it. I don't know. Truly it felt as the saddest story of abandonment. The abandonment of abandonments.

I excused her silence. Who could have asked my stoic great-grandmother? Perhaps Bianca, had buried her grief with nothing more to say. If, growing up, my grandmother could have heard the story her own mother but from neighbors or older sisters. It would have come in whispers so as not to talk about it in front of the abandoned mother.

Suddenly, the image of Bianca, the warrior everyone in the family consorted, the matriarch of great mettle and temple... aroused sympathy. She was a young widow. A mother left behind. In a country that was not hers. How deep must her grief have been as more time passed without his return? How and when did she learn of his death if it took place in another city, even another country? Did she learn of his death immediately or did it take months to find out?

"He left her." Distant whispers were heard among the shadows in Puerto Plata.

"No!" I retorted energetically inwardly making an echo inside of me.

With my head on the pillow, my grandmother's stories danced like movies in my head; but as much as I searched, not even one was about Isidoro, her father. It dawned on me that I had never even seen a picture of him. In my mind, I could easily turn to the image of Bianca, because in my great-aunts' houses there has been always a picture of her. In a place of honor on their ancestral altars. Among white candles and pictures of saints, were portraits of loved ones and never-forgotten loves reside, there she was. But I never saw one of Isidoro.

That night, I dreamed of my grandmother. It was a memory I experienced as if I had been an eyewitness. I was a young girl, and I was standing on the threshold of a door. It was the main entrance to the Hotel Europa. I had my back to the street, as if I had just arrived. The skirt of my dress swayed against the floorboards. I scanned the lobby carefully. Just a few steps away and in front of me, there was a high table with an open book. It was the guest book. It had long lines with names written in cursive handwriting in beautiful calligraphy and rested next to a lamp that was against the wall. Behind that high plateau, there were nails arranged in rows from which hung the long wooden key rings painted gold. The room numbers were carved on them and I could see some of them: 4, 17, 19...

The morning was warm. I observed each space around me with curious eyes. In the carpeted area to my right was a table that held a basket with magazines and newspapers, surrounded by a couple of armchairs with high padded backs upon which guests could sit and wait to be served. Others simply enjoyed relaxing there as they read newspaper after the delivery man dropped them off at the front desk. But today, at dawn, the place was silent. I wanted to see beyond this room and stood on tiptoe. The main dining room was visible. It had perfectly placed chairs and tables.

To my left, beyond a door under the stairs, a rustling of pencil on paper caught my attention. Inside this room that served as an office, I saw a young man sitting. I couldn't see his face; but observed his silhouette from behind: he was wearing grey pants and a white shirt rolled up, and he was wearing characteristic braces that came out from his waist. Like a dream clearing, he leaned over the thick wooden desk, writing on a green-lined ledger pad with the sharp point of his pencil. I could see his profile to admire how handsome he was. His hair fell over his forehead in a spike.

Suddenly, he straightened up...as if he had noticed my presence. I stepped back a little. Out of pure instinct, I didn't want him to see me..., lest the spell dissipate. But he only turned his head a little, and then ran his fingers through his hair, leaning back again to continue concentrating on his task.

A sound, something similar to a ting...! A hotel bell awakened the action just as the scene unfolded.

Little voices sounded from upstairs. Three girls came down, crowding each other every step of the way. They looked like little bunnies in search of adventure, coming and going and stopping at every corner. They wore long white pajamas and whispered on their way to the office door. On tiptoe, they skimmed the floor and

21

tried not to make a sound. They covered their mouths saying, "Ssshhh, Ssshhh!" and twittered like little birds.

Four-year-old Chela was the most precocious. She was the first one to peek around the doorframe into the office. With a mischievous smile and sparkling eyes, she urged the other two to come closer. Was she the one who had this idea from the start? She probably was! I was fascinated by that thought. A young child coming to play a prank on her older brother. Seeing that he, Isidorito, was concentrating, they came in singing a rhyming song in jest.

"Isi-doro, Isi-doro, Isi-doro, where did you leave the *tesoro*, he's got a heart of *oro* (gold), but his name rhymes with the W.C."

They burst out laughing and pushed at each other to run away when he jumped up from his chair, playing at being angry. The young teenager stood up with his arms bent and imitated the voice of an ogre.

"Who dares to disturb me? Who dares to chant my name in jest?"

Amidst squeals of horror and delight, the little girls hid behind the furniture in the reception room. Ana, the youngest, ran and hid under the table between the two chairs. She covered her eyes, believing that this way she would not be found. Isidorito, pretending not to see them, passed by them all. The twins, hidden behind the armchairs, squeezed their little hands together to cover their mouths.

"I'll find you!" said the older brother, purposefully looking only where they were not.

The sound of footsteps coming down the stairs interrupted the game. It was Blanquita, their older sister. When she discovered that it was the hiding place, she admonished them, ordering them to be quiet:

"Ssshhhh...! Stop making a racket, for God's sake! It's not even full morning and you'll manage to wake up the guests."

She gave her brother an accusing look as she took Ana by the hand. The little girl burst out laughing as Blanquita tried to shoo the others out from their hiding places while Isidorito made faces behind her back. With firm whispers, she ordered them to go upstairs and not to make a racket as they did so. The older brother, playing along, returned to the threshold of his door, grabbed the doorknob with great drama and said over his shoulder,

"Someday I'll find you and then.... You'll see!"

And lest they forget, he craned his neck up the stairs giving a funny but menacing look, which caused the girls to laugh even more and run upstairs, forgetting the older sister's admonition. He closed the office door thus avoiding another eventual interruption.

I awoke in the wee hours of the morning with the joke song echoing in my mind like a faded echo. The dream had been delicious and sweet, but I knew that there, in that hotel entrance hall, that had been their home too, had been more than just one farewell and many more sadness. I hugged my pillow trying to organize my thoughts. "How do you even start looking for a great-grandfather who one day shipped out and left, never to return?" I made plans inwardly. Almost unwittingly, I set about diagramming a plan with the conviction to go in search of answers. I would look for cemeteries of the time. I would investigate all the sites... Italy, New York... I would interview experts. I would use my creativity for more. I would search for the forgotten stories of my ancestors inside me. I would recall the ones Mamma Chela had told me. She'd told me many... Surely some clue would slip in among them. I would examine them all. And a promise came from me to them all. A promise to my mother, to my own grandmother and also to Bianca.

"I'll look at every registry book of names in Italy if I have to, And if perchance he had traveled and died on the way, wherever my imagination takes me, I'll find him!"

I stopped hacking my head in my pillow, because... I stood with a thought, because... I had the strange conviction that, somewhere, he was waiting for me to trying to find him.

"Why did you go, Isidoro? What happened that you didn't come back?", I said to myself referring to the father of them all. "Where were you when your children were growing up between Puerto Plata and Bologna? Why did Bianca feel abandoned?"

I waited in silence; my inner ear wanting an answer. But the emptiness of the night enveloped me. I let myself be overcome by tiredness and a reverie enveloped me as I repeated internally:

"I don't believe it...!"

ONLY TEARS COME FROM ITALY

*T*he night was short. Sunlight was streaming into the room. I awoke with the sensation of having a memory floating like a cloud in front of my closed eyes. In the haze of dreams, as I drifted in and out of the real, something drew my consciousness. I felt as if beside my bed there was an iridescent image, a vestige of a tiny, curly-haired, mischievous giggling girl. Finally, when I opened my eyes to look at the picture, it seemed to slip away with a big crackle and slip like water under the slid of the closed door.

Mami was already up, and her bed was made. The light coming in through the blinds illuminated every corner of the room. I raised my head slightly and caught a glimpse of the cat's furry tail approaching out of the corner of my eye. I raised up on my elbow, calling by her name:

"Come, Preciosa. come!"

I wanted her to come closer so I could pet her. Her tail wafted elegantly over my pillow. I reached down so she could rub on my hand, sinking my fingers into her fluffy fur. Her softness passed through my fingers and in an instant I felt happy because it is a pleasure to give pleasure. She would say to me, "Meow!" and I would respond in kind, because I think I speak Cat and they understand me. While she purred and cuddled with my hand, I mused over the incomplete memory that had awakened me. "Who spoke to me in my sleep?" Absentmindedly, as Preciosa settled close to me, I moved my fingers to reach her neck and scratch behind her ears. She turned her furry face toward me, looked up with her beautiful eyes and suddenly, an image popped into my head.

A surprising and unexpected evocation, but, above all, funny and typical of my grandmother. I smiled as I recalled magical realism that always seemed to follow my dear Mamma Chela. Now it makes me laugh to think that it was just a humorous coincidence. Preciosa, my mother's cat, had one blue eye and one yellow eye, just like my grandmother had two eyes in different colors.

I recalled another memory, this one time I had gone to visit Mama Chela at her apartment, number 1 of Building 1;as I climbed the staircase, it was even the first door! I had come to say goodbye, as I was moving to college in the U.S. My older sisters had lived this experience and now it was my turn as I was seventeen. Entering her light-filled house, I found her in her rocking chair watching *novelas*. Immediately, nimbly as ever, she got up to turn off the television and pay attention to me. After I greeted her with a kiss, she asked me to sit across from her. She turned her chair around so that we were facing each other and, as always, she exhibited a knowing, mischievous smile.

Mamma Chela was not the typical devoted, gentle grandmother. On the contrary, she had a strong character, she always found humor in her experiences, good or bad. She was eccentric like that —a fascinating whirlwind of stories turned into fables. There was nothing more entertaining than listening to tales of her youth. She spoke fast and sometimes ended each punch line by pursing her lips to make a characteristic sound (she was an expert in *chuipiti*, the art of making herself understood with funny grimace, on the form of a pout and a short whistle).

In that visit, she asked me questions about my upcoming trip and I was deep in relating my plans to her when, in a moment of impetus, she leaned her rocking chair forward precariously. If it had been anyone else, I would have thought she was going to fall. But my grandmother was an acrobat in that rocking chair! She stood it up on the front tips while at the same time pointing to her own eyes.

"I have one eye blue and the other green. Hardly anyone notices, but I do! I see it in the mirror. Look!"

She pointed to the left one. "Blue!"

She pointed to the right one. "Green!"

Then lifted her chin and pursed her lips triumphantly with her mouth making an acute short sound: *"Uh-hoo!"*

I admired the colors and noticed the difference. They looked like rings that ranged from a deep turquoise to a fantastic aquamarine. A sea of colors of the same hue, as deep and unique as that of the waters of *Sosua*.

Agreeing, I told her I'd noticed and this pleased her. She pulled back, rocking back and forth enthusiastically.

I appreciated all her witticisms. She was very hands on with her grandchildren and loved our shenanigans. Out of my mother's sight she would give us chocolates. Anyone, known or stranger, who came to visit her home, she would invite for coffee. Any child or teenager who would just salute with a polite, "good morning" or "good afternoon", would leave with 5 *pesos* that she would magically produce from the square pocket of her flowery gown. She was always ready to give to others. She was as excellent in the cook as all her sisters, in the kitchen she was equal to them, but there was something different in her, she was the only one of them who did not want to speak Italian. Growing up, Italian was the language of the household, but Chela refused to answer back in the language of her family.

I distinctly remembered a gathering with her sisters in their garden at home. They were all sitting under a thin tree that, despite its skinny trunk, held large long branches that gave a wide pleasant shade. The chairs and rocking chairs were made of iron and painted white, which made the yellow poppies that surrounded them stand out. Orchids, which my mother had lovingly strung together and tied to the branches of the tree, fell in floating rainbow colors. Then, I listened as Mafalda and Mayú, two of her sisters, exchanged words in Italian. My grandmother answered them in Spanish. And when the other two, Yolanda and Blanquita kept adding more Italian phrases to the conversation, my grandmother would keep up the pace, but in Spanish. I had always thought that very strange and somewhat rebellious of her.

So I took advantage of her good humor during my present visit before leaving for college and dared to ask her a direct question, which I knew was one of those things that should not be asked.

"Mamma Chela, why don't you like Italy?"

"*Uh-hoo!*" she exclaimed at my nerve.

With amused arched eye-brows, she leaned the rocking chair precariously forward again to fix her eyes on mine. I think she wanted to scare me, but her impish smile gave her away.

"Because..." She raised her eyebrows as if wanting to shock me even more. "Only tears come from Italy!" And without looking away, she pointed to her eyes and drew lines down her face to mimic crying. "Only tears!

I was ecstatic because, honestly, I can't think of anything more Italian to say than, "Only tears come from Italy!" My grandmother was undeniably Italian! She didn't tell me what it was that made her cry, instead she expressed herself with profound poetry. It was so like her.

Looking back, I realized it had stirred something within me and awakened some kind of dull ache. She did continue eventually and told me a tale of how someone in Italy had cried, packed their tears in a little box, and mailed them to Puerto Plata. And in the foyer of that Victorian hotel stood Chela, in her summer dress, and the first to receive the mailman. "A parcel from Italy, what a thrill!" She untied the rope and pulled off the wrapping with great care. She uncovered a seemingly empty and at first glance did not understand what was inside. Was it water? Her smile waned and sadness crept up her throat. She moved her face closer to get a good look and discovered they were tears. Tears in a box!

And from the entrance of the hotel, that was also her home, she shouted her disappointment to the world, not giving a damn if everyone knew. "I knew it! Only tears come from Italy! Only tears!"

I was fascinated by this story. At the look of rapt expectation on my face, she told me another. She said that when letters arrived from Italy, she hid them. It was clear to here that only bad news arrived from Italy; bad news which would cancel any joy in the house, sometimes for weeks or even months. More than once, after a letter, she had to dress in black. For her, mourning was superfluous. It did not bring anyone back to life. But it was customary.

When her mother learned of this mischief, she threatened her with a beating. "If you hide the letters from Italy again..."

At that time, Bianca was already alone and had her children separated on two continents: at the family business, the hotel in Puerto Plata, and at her home in Bologna, where Mafalda and Queco still remained. If letters arrived from Italy, they might well have been marred by tears!

Bianca did not find Chela, with her witty and vivacious style, an easy daughter to raise. She possessed a beauty that, together with the impetus of youth, attracted the attention of others.

Which, of course, happened at a party, an event that could have ended badly.

In context, this story speaks to the innocence of the time, when danger lurked and no one knew its consequences. There was a celebration held at the Puerto Plata Club. I assume around 1932. This elegant event was attended by a man who was rising in power to become a dictator. In the ballroom, Rafael Trujillo asked Chela to dance. He was twice her age and married. Would it be impolite to refuse to dance with him? That's definitely what modern girls of today would do. But Chela wasn't afraid of anything. She laughed at caution. At eighteen, she thought the whole thing was just funny.

Curious as it may seem, this story has two different versions depending on the relative who tells it. Some of my cousins, having passed on the anecdote from their grandmothers, Mafalda in particular, say that my grandmother refused the invitation and did not dance with him. Period.

Others, however, cling to the same plot she told us. I heard it from her and this is what she told me.

Apparently, before inviting her to dance, the dictator-in-making had asked about the "Italian girls". Mayú, Chela and Ana, the younger sisters, were being chaperoned by their older sisters, Yolanda and Manuel, who were already married. I understand that the club manager would have answered him with, "Those are Doña Blanca's daughters."

Curiosity piqued, he wanted to meet them.

My grandmother remembered how well he introduced himself. His good manners. The perfection of his dress.

Trujillo was a celebrity in those days even before his terror unfolded and was considered by many at that time to be a hero. In addition, he was supported by the great power to the north.

When he invited Chela to dance, according to her, she graciously accepted.

And, as the violinists got into position to play, other couples got up to dance, and she found herself being led by the arm onto the dance floor. However, the music had barely even begun when the electricity suddenly failed. The music stopped abruptly, and silence ensued. Moonlight streaming in through the windows kept them from total darkness. The lit cigarettes of the guests who stood around them looked like little stars. Immediately, the bodyguards approached: "Don't worry boss, it's something with the cables. A normal malfunction." Hearing the report, he turned to Chela who was still next to him on the dancefloor; neither she nor anyone else dared to move.

"Don't worry, Chela, know that you're with me," he managed to tell her in the half-light.

"Don't worry, Don Rafael, know that you are with me," she replied. The confidence of her youth made her the mistress of humor in Puerto Plata.

This witticism fills us with admiration and makes her descendants laugh, more for the jocular and detached way in which she told it. Sometimes, we argue that it was probably her who said it first. Because that was our Chela. The great humorous heroine, innocent and ignorant of any danger.

Before the electricity came back on, Trujillo and his henchmen sped away leaving a blanket of dust on the road, but the story did not end there. It continued the next day at the Victorian hotel, the family business. The whole family were sat, shared lunch at a long table, and Chela, with all her acting skills, was telling the story of what had happened the night before. How would Doña Blanca have received this anecdote? With her usual gravity, she listened to her daughter in silence, but held a muffled cry in her soul.

She was always concerned with maintaining the dignity of her entire family. And while the others laughed with Chela, Doña Blanca focused her eyes on her daughter. She observed her delicate appearance and her detached laughter. She was before an adolescent who feared nothing and no one. But to her mother this seemed like a scandal waiting to happen. Chela, in the rails of her youth, had been seen by much of Puerto Plata society dancing with a married man, who had a family, and was twice her age. Not only that, but with a man who, was on a dangerous path in his political career. To Doña Blanca, these facts made her daughter a target and added a security problem for the entire family.

Would it be an exaggeration on my part to think that this situation led Doña Blanca to think that Chela should be married off? As long as her younger daughters did not have a man to represent them, they were vulnerable. Beauty and youth could attract the attention of many dangerous men, including those who were married.

It must have been a great relief for Doña Blanca when, a couple of months after this incident, Chela met Joaquín Ginebra. The man who would become my grandfather came into Chela's life. Fortunately for me, I know the story of how they met.

My Aunt Elsie (whose daughter would end up marrying Chela's son), told me how she and Joaquin met. Elsie and I chatted very often when I was a student at Marymount University in Virginia and she lived in Bethesda with her daughter and my uncle. Thanks to these frequent phone calls, and my questions about her youth, she once told me something about my grandmother which stuck in my memory.

"When Chela arrived, joy itself entered the room. She would light up every corner of the garden like a ray of sunshine."

The scene took place in Elsie's own house. It was a Victorian building with an inner courtyard and a flower-filled path leading to a bower at the back patio. Under the hanging leaves, there were chairs, tables and refreshments: a little piece of paradise to enjoy. Elsie loved to receive guests. She constantly held gatherings and evening *cherchas* for her family and friends. That day Joaquín had arrived for a visit and was abiding in that inner courtyard, enjoying a fresh lemonade to cool off from the heat. A small, informal get-together had spontaneously happened and those present were engaged in a great conversation.

Then Chela arrived.

He saw her approach through the entrance to the garden, all the way on the other side of the courtyard. She had cut off the long braid of dark curls she had worn over her shoulder until then and had a modern hairstyle. That change made her look more womanly, more grown-up. Her nose was long and imperfect, her eyes were colorful and they sparkled under her black eyelashes. The glow of rosy cheeks and her laughing face completed the picture of joyful youth. That is how my Aunt Elsie described her tome as she told the story. And my heart filled with emotion to see her so clearly in my mind's eye: her small frame walking gracefully, like a ballerina parading down the flower path.

Joaquin was struck by her conspicuous beauty. He was sitting on the edge of his seat as she approached. From afar, he watched the contentment in her broad smile. An arrow touched his heart.

The sun shone brightly on that day and illuminated the moment like a celestial spotlight. The breeze danced, lifting the leaves in a pirouette and clearing the path as she walked along it. I pictured her entering in a white dress whose skirt is decorated with delicate flowers, some painted and some embroidered, surrounded by soft green leaves in light tones. The breeze, as it played with the flowers on the path, also seemed to make the leaves on her dress come to life. As they opened and unfurled splendidly, the natural and the ethereal seemed to blend together in a single movement. The petals, animated by the magic of the moment, turned and twirled as the leaves fell, guarding their walk. In their wake, spring came to life... pink on violet, green on green.

"Who is she?" asks Joaquín, spellbound.

"It's Chela," I pictured the little birds twittering, equally bewitched.

"It's Chela, Doña Blanca's daughter," Aunt Elsie clarified, enchanted.

As she moves along on the path of polished stones, I liked to think that her dancing shoes awakened the trees, and that they leaned in towards her, imitating what Joaquín himself was doing. He couldn't take his eyes off of her. Chela, according to my aunt, did not suspect that she was marching towards her future. Towards the arms of the man who would be her husband.

And this story would have remained here as a happy ending if life had frozen in that instant like a fairy tale. But life went on and time passed, and destiny did its thing. That's how today I know that tears don't only come from Italy. I know because there are no photos of my grandparents' wedding. Or, at least, I never saw one. I never enjoyed seeing her her at the foot of the church, dressed in white, her youthful exuberance adorned with flowers as she leaned on the arm of her beau. She herself had destroyed them one by one...without crying. She tore them with her fingers, strong and determined. The little pieces that fell to the ground she trampled on even more, as if it were necessary to fully impart her bitterness. Even the pieces she could not tear any smaller she took to a bonfire and burned.

Their three children, Socorro (my mother and eldest daughter), Nelson, and Blanca, grew up during a time of tyranny when Italians were viewed with suspicion and envy. My aunt Blanca, my mother's sister, told me a story that illustrated how serious it was.

Joaquin had bought a piece of land in Haina. It was a property full of coconut trees lined up along the seashore. He had made an *enramada* (gazebo style house) in which to spend Sundays with his family and friends. My mom and her brother were very young and, although Chela was on her third pregnancy, she fixed and served food in the pleasant countryside. She loved the place because of the sea breeze that lulled the palms all afternoon. Apparently, her Sunday family trips to this beautiful piece of land didn't last long. One day, some friends came to visit Joaquin at their city home conveying the wishes of the "Boss". He had seen the land, like it, and offered to buy it.

"My property is not for sale," Joaquín said, lifting his chin in pride. He didn't like when others tried to push him around..

In every house a sign had to be hung on the wall that said, "In this house, Trujillo is the boss." Every time Joaquín saw it, his throat swelled and he felt the urge to throw it out furiously. But Chela, cautious, kept the sign in a drawer and, depending on who knocked on the door, she would take it out and hang it on the wall.

During this particular visit of friends, the sign was hanging up and Chela had retired; it was not smart to be near when strange men arrived, even if they were acquaintances, and even less so if they came from the "Chief". They calmly urged Joaquín to sell the property. "There is no reason to displease the Boss."

A few years later, after this situation had passed, Chela had an atrocious experience when a bullet came through the window of the Elite Theater, her husband's business, where she also worked. A stray bullet shattered the window, whistling over the transparent, half-round jars where the candy was kept for sale. It blew one of the jars to smithereens. She and her assistant fell to the floor amidst shattered glass. And that wasn't the worst of it! The worst part was that she had to keep silent about what had happened. They couldn't even report it to the police without fearing retribution. All that was left was to pick up the broken pieces and pretend that nothing had happened.

And the hardest part was yet to come; betrayal, rejection, abandonment. The rebuffs of Joaquín's infidelities. After having endured them all, he ended up being the one who asked her to dissolve the marriage union.

Joaquín divorced Chela, putting one last nail in his story forever, consciously hammering the box of broken loves, filling it with more tears. And that's how I know that not all tears come from Italy.

WIND CHIME

"What happened here...magic?" I asked my mom when I entered her room. The atmosphere was filled with an energy of joy. When I opened the door, I found her laughing, sitting in front of her new computer monitor. I was stunned.

I had just come from the beach with my children. I had already bathed them to wash off the sea salt. They were exhausted and their red noses were smeared with after sun lotion. I had left them comfortably reclining in the living room in front of the TV.

I had already suspected that something was wrong with Mami. During my stay, her moods would transform with no warning. It wasn't that I wanted her to be sad about my dad for the rest of her life. No, it wasn't that. It was that I didn't understand what the fascination was with the new computer. Rather, it seemed that not only she, but the whole room was happy. Oblivious to my suspicious thoughts, Mami invited me to come closer.

"Come take a look at this."

She had a baby smile on her lips. It had been more than two years since I'd seen her smile like a schoolgirl.

Her present to herself on Christmas was this object, which she placed on top of the mahogany desk set against the wall in the now cramped side of her room where I slept. I had tolerated this new intrusion in the evenings, despite the tangle of ugly wires hanging near my feet.

Before that device appeared, that corner was, for me, small, yes, but an illuminated space with a special aura. Through the window, green leaves elongated their stems, blurring and refreshing the brightness in the evenings. The breeze brought a soft perfume that made the bells on the wind chime dance with a *tin-tin* for each dream or angel's pass. I often found myself enchanted as I stared at that tableau. And by the rainbow of light reflected inside the room by the metal on the wind chime as well. Every morning, tucked in my little bed, I relaxed in delight. This space was the only thing I considered mine in this new home of Mami's. And there was nothing better than watching Preciosa make her presence known and snuggle up next to me. Needless to say, my partner in crime didn't like the mess of cords under the desk either. On several occasions she tried to push them out with her paw. However, they were thick, hard and stiff...not suitable for a cat to play with.

We liked to play, and I, to lure Preciosa into a game, used a ball of yarn that Mami used for knitting. As she caressed me with her tail, I'd show her the ball of yarn in my hands. Then I would throw the balled up yarn and Preciosa would run after it. That's how we spent some entertaining mornings. I would play like a little girl and she would play like, well, like a cat.

In fact, just that morning I had been playing with Preciosa, and that's when I had realized things had *really* changed. I picked up a ball of yarn and threw it to Preciosa to play with, as usual, and it rolled on the floor with Preciosa chasing to catch it. Unfortunately, I'd picked the wrong one As Preciosa ran off with it, I saw the yarn in the basket move. Oh, no! A sweater that Mami had almost completely knitted, was now it was in half, it was fraying! Each tug from the happily playing cat unraveled it more. I ran after her to prevent further damage.

"Oh, Preciosa! Oh, no! Come back, it's going to unravel more!"

But she thought it was all part of the fun. Seeing me chasing her, she batted at the yarn with more haste and ran out of the room. Preciosa was older than me (in cat years), but more agile and I couldn't catch her quickly to take it back from her. When I finally did catch her and untangled the yarn from her nails, I thought, *If Mami finds out what happened, we're both going to be in trouble.* I hurriedly put the bundled yarn back in the bottom of the knitting basket. I arranged other colored wool on top hoping my mother wouldn't even notice. I pretended that nothing had happened, confident that Preciosa couldn't tell on us and that Mami wouldn't notice.

And that's exactly what happened...nothing.

She never found out!

Apparently, her knitting days were over. She had traded the motion of her knitting needles for the clacking of letters on the keyboard.

So back to the moment when I said to her, "So what happened here?" The wind chimes outside tinkled as though trying to answer me. Not noticing the happy tune, Mami just turned her chair around for a second and replied with a smile,

"It's just that they sent me a joke...and it's soooo funny!" She began to read me the joke she had received.

I hesitated, because I didn't find it particularly humorous, and I approached her a little annoyed. I laid a hand on her shoulder as she watched me for my reaction, I graced her with an *"uh-hoo"*, as I finished reading, noticing out of the corner of my eye that she was clearly waiting for me to laugh. To enjoy it. Into her email inbox came another email that was sure to be another joke.

"Who is this Milagín?" I asked her, curious about the sender of the new message.

She replied, "It's from Milagros! We made up usernames according to our initials. Hers is Milagín, for Milagros Ginebra. Mine is Sogitho."

"Sogitho?" I asked, knowing it was the initials of her first name combined with dad's last name: Socorro Ginebra de Thomen. I had to admire her creativity: "Wow, Mami!" I exclaimed in surprise, "I like it!"

Finally, I left her alone and went to take a shower, weighing in my mind what was going on. I remembered that the first time she plugged in the computer, she introduced it to me as if it were a person. "Look, meet my new computer." She was so proud! On another occasion, she asked me to give the computer a *tour* of the Internet. "To use it the way you would use it," she'd said. Actually, she was referring to my job. I replied to her, a bit haughtily, "I use it mostly at work to do research." I took the mouse and demonstrated search engines and *browsers for her*. Immediately, I softened my voice as I watched her write down *Google* and *AltaVista* on a piece of paper next to the keyboard. I was touched by her humility.

Not that there was anything wrong with her spending her days reading jokes on the internet. It's just that I thought I had come to share a few days with her and didn't want to be around computers. After all, it was my vacation, and I didn't want to lay my eyes on the light of a screen. Although I had to admit, seeing her happy like this, perhaps it was me who needed a change of attitude. Her new joy increased with every joke. The smile took years off her face. The blessed computer filled her with laughter!

I also decided to appreciate another good side of having this computer available in our lives. When Mami told me about her grandparents, Isidoro and Bianca, I had vowed to find his whereabouts no matter what. Perhaps it was part of my good fortune to have something up which I could begin the search right here, right now. I admit that without much information it was like groping in the dark. I didn't even have a date of his disappearance, just an estimated year. 1914. But without an exact location nothing was certain. Mami didn't understand much when I talked to her or asked her questions about him. However, I persisted, and so I made my first findings.

One morning, while I was concentrating on research on her computer, I was lucky enough to find a directory from that time period of a listing of cemeteries in New York. The list had about twenty locations and this filled me with hope. Then, to impress her, I was the one who called her over to the computer:

"Look, Mami...I found a directory with several cemeteries that were used in 1914."

She leaned over my shoulder to look at the monitor. I explained the words I used, how I found everything, and where I'd searched for it. Also, with the air of a bigshot scholar, I said to her,

"In case Isidoro died in New York, I also wrote to the City Health Offices...."

As I did with her jokes, she looked at me sideways, a bit dumbfounded. I realized that, once again in our lives, my mother and I did not understand each other. She didn't understand my fascination with the past and Isidoro's whereabouts. And I didn't understand why she didn't understand. *Why wasn't she intrigued to know where her grandfather had gone?*

"Only you would think of such things. Are you going to obsess over this now?"

I pushed back my chair to speak more directly to her:

"Mami, I don't know how you *don't* obsess over what might have happened your grandfather, and where he died. I don't know why you didn't ask your grandmother. You, the oldest of the cousins. Instead of saving tiny toads with Billy, you could have asked, "Grandma, where is my grandfather?"

"I was seven years old when my grandmother died!" she replied in annoyance.

Immediately, I felt bad for having spoken to her like that. I thought I was so blessed to have known all four of my grandparents growing up, to have heard the stories from their lips and to have kept their voices in my memory. While my mom, of all her grandparents, had only known her Babi. My oldest son was lucky enough to have met all four of his grandparents, but he was only seven years old when his first grandfather, my dad, died. He cried his eyes out! Now I was learning that my mom had been the same age when she lost her grandmother.

And this is where I came to my hasty conclusion. This story has two villains: time and oblivion. The former, time, was definitely not on my side as records were rotting away, more with each passing day. The air in New York and Italy was drier than in the Caribbean and this would probably keep them in better shape. In the tropics it is difficult to keep books safe. Bookworms are no laughing matter. If books get sick, the solution is to throw them away.

As for forgetting, modern psychology says to bring the past into the light of the present, acknowledge it, forgive it and let it go. However, in the old days, children were sent out of the room when adults were talking. This invites family secrets. And what is not told, is forgotten. I don't know if that's how it was with this story, but my curiosity demanded that I know everything. The good and the bad. Memories can be like shooting stars. You have to catch them in the moment. They can't be missed. I would've done anything to dig into Mami's mind and open the trunks of her memory.

I was using the computer for something important and even though I knew she wanted to read jokes she got from her cousins and friends, I wasn't going to let go of the subject so easily.

"I want to know more. It's not enough."

Looking at me for a moment, I think she finally understood. She moved to her nightstand to open a drawer and pulled out a small, antique key with a red tassel hanging from it. I knew what she was going to do. The key would open the enormous antique armoire that took up one entire side of the room. Seeing it there, tall and silent, I tried to imagine its history. It is a closet that can be completely disassembled to be taken on trips aboard ships. In the days when it was still faster and more pleasant to go from the capital to Puerto Plata by boat, it was dismantled, placed in the boat, and then reassembled at the destination house without the use of nails. Its design was magnificent. A true work of art. With the carved key, she opened its doors on each side and indicated to me, "Hand me that box."

She pointed to one at the top and motioned for me to reach it. It was a large book and was located under other boxes. It looked like a secret in plain sight. My chest filled with excitement because I knew it was a photo album.. Its pages were black, and each old photo was gripped by triangular corner brackets. All the pictures were duly labeled with a silver pen in Mami's beautiful handwriting. I had to reach down carefully and grab it with both hands to rescue it from oblivion. As I tugged on it, a photo slipped out. My reflex was to catch it in mid-air, trying to keep the box from falling on me at the same time. I tackled it. In fact, it seemed to have directed its fall toward me. I climbed down from the chair with the album and the photo pressed to it. Mami was sitting on the bed, waiting for me.

"This photo almost fell." I turned it over in my hand. On the back, there was a date. "1918." I passed it to Mami as I put the album on the bed.

"Oh, I didn't remember where I had that picture," she said, hinting that it was the only one that was loose.

It was a family portrait. In its center, Bianca was seated, dressed in black. Behind, a young boy smiling with his three sisters, all dressed in white. In front, three girls about six or seven years old. Their hair bows fell in cascades of soft curls.

Mami looked at the picture for a long time and then pointed her finger at each person.

"This is Isidorito...it's the only picture I have of him. Then Blanquita, Beatriz, Yolanda... The little ones are Chela, Mayú and Ana."

"Uncle Queco and Aunt Mafalda?"

"They were still living in Italy. They were the last ones to reunite in Puerto Plata."

She was still looking at the image of her grandmother. I went closer to see mine, my dear Mamma Chela. I told her about the position of the girls. The twins were at each end and Ana, who was the youngest, was next to Mayú. I pointed it out to Mami.

"Ana and Mayú, the blondes, are on one side and Chela, with darker hair, on the other. But they look like triplets!"

"Ana, although she was the youngest, was always the tallest. The age difference between the twins and herself was at most, I think, a year and a half. The three of them grew up very close."

In the photo, my mom explained why Chela was positioned where she was. It was because she was fully of energy, and my great-grandmother would always have to tackle her to get her to hold still.

"Look, notice that you can't see my grandmother's hand in the picture? That's because she had to hold Chela still while the photographer took the picture."

She described my grandmother as if she was hyperactive. But to me, she was just the liveliest of her sisters.

Then, she opened her album and looked for other pictures to show me.

"Here are Queco and Mafalda. They were still living in Bologna."

"Aunt Mafalda was very pretty, yes! But the men in this family, very handsome too! my uncles, Frank and Fernando, look so much like their father Queco."

"Isidoro was very handsome...that was part of the problem."

Mami handed me the album and I kept passing the pictures around. I was fascinated looking at each one carefully, thinking that these were Bianca and Isidoro's children. And when I saw the group of photos of Mami's cousins, that is, my uncles and aunts, it was inevitable for me to think that *these are Bianca and Isidoro's grandchildren.*

"There are no pictures of Isidoro," I commented aloud.

It was not a question. I already knew the answer. I looked up and realized I was alone in Mami's bed, holding the album open, alone.

Apparently, or rather, obviously, she had gotten up and settled herself in front of the computer. It had all been a ploy to get me out of my seat.

"Mami!"

I laughed at her ruse to get me to vacate my seat. She smiled back at me, holding the computer mouse and lifting her chin, triumphantly.

From that day forward, every morning, she waited for me to get up and fold the little bed we called *'the sandwich'* to sit at the computer and read her email inbox. She was having fun with her friends and elderly cousins, they sent each other jokes of all kinds. Silly ones like Pepito's and naughty ones that I won't describe. She was a giggling child in front of the monitor. Daily, her tray of incoming emails was full as her group of virtual friends grew. Her fingers, now inexperienced for this task, slowly, but enthusiastically, touched the keys on the desk, typing in capital letters so she didn't have to put accents on them. In her times, she said, capital letters in Spanish did not have a *tilde*. And I wasn't going to tell her that, in my day, capital letters had accents and that this meant a spelling mistake. In the end, I didn't want to stop or embarrass her. I hoped she would continue to enjoy herself. In the evenings, I had to wait for her to finish so I could go to bed. If it were up to her, she would be left reading them all again or poking around the internet to find others. On several occasions, I stood next to her as if I was the adult and she was the child: "*Ahem, ahem... Mami, please... time for bed....*" Then she would take that opportunity to read them all to me! Patiently, I'd listen to them while I pointed to the clock. But that didn't matter as her desire was to share the jokes with me.

On days when I didn't have plans and stayed home, she would

call out to me every now and then with my childhood nickname. "Lache, come... Hear this joke."

The most annoying part is that she wanted to see my reaction. If I didn't laugh, she would repeat the jokes back as if I didn't understand them. Sometimes, I would quickly run out of the room before she insisted.

"I ran out, *flash!* like Batgirl," I would joke to my sisters about the situation. To give them an example of how stupid they were, I would repeat a joke to them. They would laugh with me and shrug their shoulders. Soon, they began to welcome them, and they were fine with it. They laughed with Mami all the time about the jokes! It seemed that the only one who complained was me. There was nothing to do!

As she insisted on telling me the jokes, I insisted that she tell me about her grandparents. One day she convinced me to approach by saying, "This joke is really good," and laughing out loud. When I reluctantly went to read it, I was surprised to find that not only was it very funny, but it was also very naughty, one of those that we call "red jokes." Nevertheless, I couldn't hold my laughter, and I covered my mouth while blushing.

"Whaaaat??? Mami! And who sent you that joke?" I asked her, both horrified and amused at the same time.

I couldn't contain my curiosity and leaned over the monitor to see who the person was who had dared to make me laugh in spite of myself. When I read the name of the purveyor of such humor, I realized that the one who had sent it was Uncle Fernando.

"Is that Uncle Fernando Rainieri?" I pointed with my finger, more astonished than amused now.

HE WAS one of the most entertaining guys we had on my mom's side. Tall and handsome, he had straight brown hair and always wore a smile that was very special. He would smile by lifting the corner of his lips on one side in a half-smile, then the other. He was superb in entertaining conversation and talked by making gestures as if to lengthen the sentences he used. He could spin any situation into an anecdote or a witty comment.

"Yes, that *Colorao!*" she answered, calling him by his nickname. That's what all the cousins called him.

Fernando was the son of Queco and grandson of Bianca and Isidoro. Mami was from the "older cousins' group" and he was from the younger ones.

"But Mami, you have to ask him...."

I wanted to take the mouse out of her hands and write to Uncle Fernando with a thousand questions. I restrained myself because in the end, she had taught me good manners, although the truth is that I could hardly stop myself.

"You have to ask him!" I insisted.

"Ask him about what?"

I made my formal inquiry. "Mami, can I write him a note from your email?"

* * *

Dear Uncle Fernando:

How are you? This is Graciela, the fourth of Socorro's daughters, and I am writing to you through Mami's email to say hello to you but also for some information. I am visiting her with my children to celebrate the New Year, so...Happy New Year to you, Aunt Pilar and my cousins! Mami has told me about her grandparents and I am intrigued about Isidoro's where-abouts. Do you know what happened to him? Also, I want to know more information: when he was born, his parents' names, anything at all really. I've already heard a lot about your grandmother Babi, but I'm very curi-ous. Mami says that Isidoro and Bianca got married in Colombia, why there? How did they get there from Italy? I find the mystery fascinating. All this about our ancestors is a mystery and I love genealogy.

Cheers. Graciela

NOT EVEN HALF AN HOUR HAD PASSED WHEN he answered. I was in my pajamas drying my hair and Mami called me to come check it out. This is part of his reply:

* * *

Dear Graciela:

Yes, I know you are the fourth of Socorro's daughters. I am glad you are visiting your mom in the New Year and that you were interested in our family genealogy. They say genealogy is a science, but it is an art as well. It is the knowledge of our roots, the roots that bind us together. I have some information about my grandfather, but right now we are traveling, and I don't have it at hand. When I return home, I will look for it and I will send it to you and your mother.

What I can tell you is that the family comes from Castello d'Argile. There, my grandparents had a house where my dad was born and raised. He lived in Bologna until he finished school. Bianca's children grew up separated between Bologna and Puerto Plata. Isidorito, being the oldest, worked side by side with his mother until he passed away. Then my grandmother took over. She was a great woman, with mettle and determination. Exemplary. We love her very much. We admire her. Ask your mother about her.

As for dates and places, I'll send them to you as soon as I get home. What does your mother tell you about them eloping? They say they ran away, I don't know. I know they met on a boat. She was 17 and very young and Isidoro was more than a few years older.

I'm so glad you're interested in the family history. Check out the new Ellis Island web page and the new genealogy websites that are coming out now that may help you. With the dates I will send you, you will be able to do a more specific search. See how far you can get, to live life as an experiment, just to see what happens!

Greetings to your family,
Fernando

44

VIRGINIA

*V*irginia is a beautiful state. Country mansions, vineyards and horse ranches are scattered over rolling hills of green pines. I live in the northern part of the state, about forty-five minutes from the capital. The drive to my house is through grandiose trees and behind me is Great Falls Park. Our windows open onto the woods and we see families of squirrels jumping from branch to branch constantly.

That January, when I arrived back from the eternal tropics of Santo Domingo to the Virginian winter, the trees were already bare. Only the pines, pikes and spruces retained their ruddy greens, their morning dew freezing them to a brilliant emerald color. On the outside, my life had not changed at all since I had returned. However, in my mind, my life was different. From the mystery of the abandonment to the message from Uncle Fernando, everything had been transformed to an urging desire to meet my ancestors, to know more about them, especially to find Isidoro.

Since I had in my possession the directory with a list of period correct cemeteries in New York City, I decided to write to all of them, without sparing religion, from Jewish cemeteries to Masonic cemeteries. In all the letters, the text was the following: *Could you be so kind to tell me if you find among your graves, any with the name of Isidoro Rainieri... deceased in 1914?* To each inquisitive missive I added a pre-addressed stamped envelope so that they would not waste time buying or preparing letters and would send me the answers immediately. I didn't want fancy news but the truth. Every night, I checked my personal computer to see where else I could research. Every morning, I would wait for the square mail truck and run out to check the mailbox. Soon I realized that my strategy had worked, as I started receiving back the pre-stamped envelopes. Some replies were even written on top of the very letters I had mailed. However, the answers were the same: *"He is not buried here."*

Waiting is an art. One never knows what information will come back to them when they start on an endeavor such as this.. And although I knew the answer was going to change my life for better or worse, the tide of Mami's thoughts was that it was for the worse. But it pained me every time I thought that Isidoro had done something terrible, or that the reason for his departure could be anything dishonorable.

The only comfort was that Italy was opening up as a travelling option for me. My desire for adventure, along with the challenge of the quest, was a living flame. Just thinking about it set my heart on fire. Perhaps, in Italy I could find answers to my questions. Probably, genealogy documents could inform me about events or actions in the past that would give me an idea of what really happened. Not only about the reason for his death, but about his life decisions. Even, about some character flaw or some indication of his personality and the quality of his decisions.

And that is that, first of all, I have to tell the truth about myself. That there is an Italy inside me that was just waking up. It was waking up and clearing my emotional inheritance of fierce women and strong loves. I wondered what attributes I had inherited from my great-grandmother Bianca. I felt strangely proud of her. I felt that, thanks to her, a heroine lived in me. And not to mention Chela. I asked for the gift of being able to live her memories. I wished in my mind that my own grandmother would come to me in my dreams and tell me about her life. The alternative to this, of course, was obvious. My mom and Uncle Fernando would fill in those invisible spaces of family stories that exist about my ancestors.

I felt anxious, as if time was pressing in on me and I had to find Isidoro's whereabouts or signs of where his life had taken him as soon as possible. Why did he leave? How far did he go? She knew that the clock moved a needle, and it was one more miraculous day of life in the old records. Before the old sheets turned any more years, before their ink lost more clarity or turned to dust, I had to rescue all their information and my ancestor's story from anonymity.

I sent emails to Bologna asking for birth certificates or indications of residence there. When I saw that time went by and nobody answered, I decided to go back to the traditional way and send postal mail to the local civil offices.

I included five dollars in every envelope I sent out to Italy to cover the extra international stamp and to hopefully ensure a speedy return.

I told Mami about my plan, ending with, "So Abraham Lincoln is going on a trip to Italy."

She asked, "What are you putting five dollars in for?"

"This covers the cost of international shipping. Just as I put a stamped envelope in with the inquiries I sent to each of the cemeteries, and that's yielded me great results."

"And if they don't find anything, are they going to send the money back to you?"

I shrugged, thinking myself very smart, and answered. "It's a strategy. They will realize how important this is to me because it will get their attention. I'm sure it will stand out from any other correspondence they get every day. It will make them see that there is someone with a special request who is eagerly awaiting answers." (Perhaps at that time, in 2001, almost no one was looking at their Italian ancestors, so I didn't have competition, or just the lack of good internet technology didn't make it so easy...but I was determined).

Maybe it was like a good luck charm or maybe it was a practical way to do something more comprehensive than just asking a question. Either way, my inquiry about Isidoro in Bologna had flown out along with the image of the fifth president of the United States. So it was easy to think that when someone opened the envelope, I was going to inspire them to help me. I visualized an official from the local government office in Bologna having his *macchiato* with the five dollars, near his work. I imagined him as kind of nerdy, with glasses and short dark hair, inspired by the suspense of the question. Perhaps as he was sipping, he'd wonder: *Who was this Isidoro that this person is so eager to know about?* My inquiry would leave him pondering. The irresistible mystery would trap his thoughts as he sat in that street café under the shade of a tree. The letter asking for a certain Isidoro spoke of Italy, Colombia, Puerto Plata, the United States and...it was accompanied by Abraham Lincoln! Who could resist the magnetism of intrigue? Not him! Another sip of his *macchiato* and he would jump up decisively, rush into his office, take off his scarf and set to work. Among the archives of old registries from the mid-1800s, he would find something. He would make photocopies and address a package in my name...this is how the scene played out every day in my mind as I waited.

Meanwhile, back at home, I declared the red mailbox on the corner "the magic time machine" as I decided I had to use the power of positive thinking to receive positive news. My expectations were my soul candy. Soon, my children realized that their mother ran like a little girl to open the mailbox every time the postal service truck arrived. Together, we started racing to see who could get there first to get the letters. Alex, who was six years old at the time, enjoyed the game the most.

One day he shouted, "There's a package from Italy!"

And his little brother repeated with a big smile, "Italy! Italy!"

Just for that I would let them beat me to the mailbox every time.

Back in the kitchen, I opened the package with great care so as not to destroy the stamp, for I loved it and wanted to collect it for posterity.

But to my dismay, among the papers, I found a note apologizing for not having found my ancestor among his records.

Then, why so many papers? I thought as I checked the stapled photocopies. I turned my attention to the letter to continue reading. It explained that the surname Rainieri originated in Parma, and not from Bologna. To prove it, the photocopies were pages from a book entitled: *Guida alle origini dei congnomi parmigiani* by Roberta Roberti. A brief history of the last name was within its pages. He also added copies of another book with the names of illustrious gentlemen with the surname Rainieri. All diplomats.

"What else!" I reflected, "These are all politicians, or people working in the government!" I wanted to see if there were any masters of letters, writers, orators or even artists, to see if the blood would support my dreams of being a writer. I wanted to have a *Da Vinci* or *Michelangelo* among my distant relatives. And so far...nope!

As if to make me crack up with laughter, the officer enclosed Abraham Lincoln *as well*. By now, according to Mami, it was "the famous five traveling dollars".

He sent it back to me! I called Mami to tell her.

"This nice officer from Bologna sent me a very long letter and in it he asks how we got to *L'America?*"

"What did you answer him?" Mami asked.

"I'm going to write the whole story! I'm going to tell him that they even got married in Bogota...and that I'm the only one who lives in Virginia. And I'll give him back the five dollars so he can have a coffee in the name of Isidoro and Bianca and their descendants!" I applauded my great idea.

"That's the world's most traveled five dollars. You're going to lose it!" Mami said to me over the phone, enjoying my story.

The next document I got from the Italian official was about Bianca. Like the other one, it also brought a long, polite letter and the $5 traveling *pesos* back! I smiled when I saw the image of Lincoln again. Then I read his letter carefully.

"...I am enclosing a portion of the birth certificate of your great-grand-mother Bianca. She was born in Castello d'Argile which is in the jurisdiction of Bologna. If you write to the Commune offices, they can take a photocopy of the entire handwritten certificate. In our offices we also have a copy of her birth registry. But there is something very interesting on her page. In those days, any event with a contact date was noted in the margins. I would like to inform you that in the margin of this register in our Bologna office there is an inscribed annotation of a travel permit. This also indicates that she had residence in Bologna as she requested the exit permit from here. I have copied it for you in the attached document..."

Immediately, I turned the page over to see what it mentioned, and there it was! The annotations in the margins written with a clippers pen! It was the date of an exit permit issued on the date "21-2-1893" stating that "I had left Bologna with relatives."

I quickly called Mami back on the phone and explained everything.

I asked her, "Bianca asked local government for permission to leave at the age of seventeen. It says here that she traveled 'with relatives'. Who were her relatives? Her dad?"

"I don't know," she answered. Then surprised me by adding, "But it was repeated in the family because you left home when you were seventeen."

"Mmmh." I thought about it. "Precisely, and I traveled with my dad."

"I don't know who she traveled with outside of Italy. At one point I was told that Isidoro and Bianca had met and even married when she was only seventeen. That was one of the reasons why her family did not agree with it. That's why it's said they ran away together to get married."

"If she left Bologna at the age of seventeen and they met on a boat? Would that have been her first trip? After all, how many trips was she going to take at that age? The date is in February and she would have turned eighteen in June. That margin between her still being seventeen and them having met was only four months."

My head was already calculating the cold of Bologna in February, the departure on the boat, crossing the Atlantic and entering Colombia through the Caribbean.

Suddenly, in my imagination, scenes of my ancestors' meeting began to form. The ship crossing the ocean. The appearance of the cabins in those times. The gunwale with chairs where they sat to watch the sunset. The dining room...I imagined the two of them, seeing each other for the first time there, on a full moon night. Each one with their companions. Or perhaps, he was traveling alone, already a veteran of his voyages.

The scene I dreamed of was a dinner held in the captain's dining room. Isidoro was seated next to him having a lively conversation with some gentlemen. I imagined him, in appearance, looking like Uncle Fernando, and greatly enjoying the occasion. Likewise, I pictured him in elegant dress and seated at a long table laid with silverware in perfect formation. There were some empty chairs on the other side of the table; dinner had not yet begun because they were waiting for the other guests. Suddenly, the doors of the hall opened wide, and two ladies appeared on the threshold, corseted and wearing tall, feather-adorned hats. They were accompanied by a man and a boy of about twelve years old. Gallantly, Isidoro, along with all the gentlemen, rose and invited the new group to come in and be seated. They all offered customary bows and curtsies, then they took their seats.. Dinner chatter died down after a few minutes as the waiters began to serve. Among the young women who arrived, Isidoro noted the one he thought was the prettiest. She was Bianca, who, *accompanied by relatives*, had not looked up to meet his gaze. She hadn't even noticed him.

S.O.S

*W*ashington, D.C. is a planned city. It was laid out to be the seat of government in 1790. Some neighborhoods were designed in the likeness of a European city. Its monuments are grandiose and there is plenty of outdoor space to enjoy as well. I love to walkaround that beautiful city in the morning. More than once I have been caught up in the dawn as I crossed one of the bridges into the city a little earlier than usual in order to have time for a walk starting my work day. The parking garage I use is right next to my building on NW 14th Street. The parking lot attendant is very friendly. His name is Solomon, and he is Moroccan. He wears his uniform which is a navy-blue coat with gold buttons and his company insignia on the lapel. He always greets me with a big smile that shows off his very white teeth.

"You are Solomon, like the wise king, aren't you?"

"Yes, I am. Ask me anything you want," he said, holding my car door.

"When is the snow coming?"

"This afternoon. I hope they let you go home early because from the time the storm hits around three o'clock this afternoon, it will last all night. Tomorrow you shouldn't come to work because the roads will be very icy," he answered, puffing up with innate wisdom.

"So I will," I affirmed, bowing respectfully and taking the *ticket* he offered me to keep my car.

I decided not to walk long this morning then, so I could get to work right away in preparation of leaving early. I was dressed in my brown boots that ended just below my knees and protected me from the cold like armor on my legs. I wore a short skirt and a turtleneck sweater. My coat was camel colored with faint pink sparkles, and it had a fluffy neckline. The cold wind finished waking me up with a slap on my cheeks. Within minutes, I was sitting in my office doing my daily tasks.

At the time, in 2001, communication was not as easy as it is today. In those days, phones were not *smart,* and you didn't *text* like we do now. *Chats,* as they are known today, were done only through computers, at that time. Cell phones existed, but were not yet widely used, so for most people, telephones were used exclusively at home or work, and were connected by buried lines, not by satellites as they are today. ! Also, long distance calls were not free, so you would not make them all the time. One long distance call a week or every two weeks was a luxury.

However, since I returned home a month ago from my vacation, I had been calling Mami frequently to ask her questions about Isidoro and Bianca. And every now and then I would ask her if Uncle Fernando had told her anything as promised. She assured me that whatever information she received, she would email it to me. So when I saw an email from Mami, I would open it with great hope thinking that it would come with the desired information. But none of them came with what I wanted, they were just jokes and more jokes. I had given her my professional email address only for emergencies, although it seemed that she did not understand the word "emergency", because she sent the same jokes to both of my email accounts. The ones she sent me at work, I would read at work, and then that night at home I would read the same ones in my personal email account inbox. I suspected that having her computer and access to all the easy communication with her cousins was making her feel sassy. Or perhaps the word *"emergencies"* had been erased from her dictionary, since she not only sent jokes, but also wrote everything personal that came to her mind as well. Hadn't we agreed that waiting is an art? But this was more than an art, it was a virtue! I deserved a prize for patience. To top it off, Mami expected me not only to immediately read her famous jokes, but also to react to them right away. If I didn't get back to her quickly enough with a reply email giving her a comment on her jokes or something like that, she would call me on the phone to ask me if I liked them! I'd see "Caribbean Island" on the Caller ID display, know it was her, and then try to summon what little bits of patience I had left before answering.

"Mami, for God's sake! That's what emails are for! For me to read when I can, not right away!"

Bu then she'd just keep quiet. And I'd keep quiet too because I didn't know how to continue the conversation. And she remained silent. Then, I would be filled with guilt and pity and I felt sorry for her, and it made me feel bad! It was an emotional journey in 5 seconds! Finally, I would resign myself with a sigh and reply.

"Yes, yes, I got it... ha ha! It's great... Yeah. Ok... Send me more." And I would hand up the phone thinking, "Oh, my mother."

During one such call on that particular day, I took advantage of having her on the phone and attacked her with questions about her grandparents.

"Why did they run away?"

"Because he was twice her age."

"Wasn't that common? At that time?"

"He was from a different place than she was."

"But...wasn't he also Italian like her?"

"Yes, but Italy was just unified. Besides, Bianca grew up in a very close-knit community. Anyone outside her circle was a foreigner."

Mami seemed to know by heart details about her grandmother Bianca, like her birthday was June 7, 1875. She knew that her mother had passed away when Bianca was still a child. "Probably very young," she had said when I asked her how old she'd been. *Another child in the family who had grown up without a parent.* I imagined Bianca as a little girl, burying her tears in her pillow and crying for her mom. Then I reflected on her dad taking care of her. What had he been like? His name had been Franceschini. *Had he married a second time?*

54

I stopped to look out the window; I was very aware of the rapidly darkening clouds in the sky. I sighed as I watched the traffic below. The cars looked like toys. I wished it wasn't so congested. Normally, my commute from home to work and back took me an hour and a bit. If it rained, it turned into two hours. If it snowed, it would be three. Today it could quickly become three hours to get home!

I heard the *"ping!"* of an email going into my inbox and it snapped me out of my distraction. I turned to look at the monitor. I sighed hopefully, *would today be the day I would get the data I needed and not just jokes?* With Mami I always felt like I was playing a raffle game. Every time I opened an email, it was another ticket. Of the thousands of tickets in this raffle, not a single one had won!

I moved the cursor, selected the email and just as I suspected, it was another joke! *I'll read them in the evening and attend to my work issues,* I said to myself. Promising not to look at emails with her name, "Socorro," (which in Spanish hilariously means "Help") on them. It's the name based on the virgin of the perpetual help.

The "ping!" of a new email kept sounding on my computer as each new message came in. In the inbox, each one brought down the previous one making a list with my mom's name over and over again. Socorro, Socorro, Socorro. Soon, one whole side of the screen was filled with her name and yet still the sound kept tinkling. *Ping! Ping! "You've got mail."*

At that, the phone rang. The digital window read: *"Caribbean Island"* It was Mami! She was probably calling to ask me if I liked the jokes. I already knew that if I didn't respond to her email right away, she would call until she found me. I answered.

"Did you get my email?" A mischievous smile could be heard in her voice "Isn't it good?"

"Mami." Again I felt like the adult and she the teenager. When had we switched roles? "You don't have to call me every time you send me a joke. I may not read them right away, but I will as soon as I can."

She didn't even listen to me! She just asked me to read the last one she had sent. I obeyed, to appease her, and because, well, she's my mom. And I read it aloud to her.

Admittedly, it was a very funny joke. I laughed, to my disgrace, and exclaimed,

"Mami! That joke! Who sent it to you?" But I already suspected who it was and quickly gave the mouse a spin to see who had sent her the original "Uncle Fernando!"

"Colorao!" she said while chuckling, and before I could get over my amazement, she added, "Open the next one I sent you."

I felt foolish and started to protest. I thought I had made myself clear on what I wanted to receive. No more jokes! I only wanted the dates of my ancestors to follow the genealogy research with a little more direction. Why did she find it so difficult to understand me? I took the opportunity to remind her that she had promised to ask the very bearer of that joke, her dear cousin Colorao, for more information for me.

To which she replied, "But it's there. It's there!"

"Where?" I reacted immediately.

I clicked like crazy and started opening them all, one by one. I moved the *mouse* to see the sender. Quickly, I scanned the messages with my eyes from top to bottom, moving the mouse to look for the names "Isidoro" or "Bianca" in each one of them. I opened another and then another...until I hit the jackpot! Mami had, of course, written the email in capital letters so she didn't bother with accents.

* * *

I SPOKE WITH COLORAO AND HE SAYS THAT ISIDORO WAS BORN IN SAN SECONDO PARMENSE, ON JULY 17, 1857.

MY GRANDPARENTS WERE MARRIED IN THE CHURCH OF SAN PABLO DE BOGOTA, ON MARCH 23, 1896.

ALSO FERNANDO SAYS THAT HE WANTS TO SEE **HOW FAR YOU GO** IN THE GENEALOGY.

HE WANTS TO KNOW EVERYTHING AND SENDS YOU MANY GREETINGS.

HE HAS THINGS TO SHARE WITH YOU. BE SURE TO LET HIM KNOW WHEN YOU RETURN.

* * *

I thanked Mami. I was ecstatic with happiness at the information. Before hanging up, she said one of her favorite phrases: "I told you so." And this time I agreed with her. I was too to happy to refute her.

Not even half a minute had passed after receiving this treasure before my boss poked her head into the office. She was a tall, elegant, fun-loving Venezuelan...and a great friend.

"Snowstorm. Everybody needs to go home." She was going door to door.

"Look." I pointed to my computer screen before she left. "That's my mom's jokes."

She smiled because she already knew about my mom's jokes from all the times I had complained to her. This time she leaned over my shoulder and noticed the emails coming from "Socorro. Socorro. Socorro." Which meant, "Help. Help. Help."

"Who's asking you for help!"

"It's not a cry for help!" I explained with a chuckle. "It's my mom's name."

"Your mother is very colorful!" boss replied, laughing along with me while heading for the door. "Go home before you get caught in the snow."

"Right away!" I replied, jumping to my feet. I put on my coat and mysteriously added, "I have things to investigate!"

As I crossed the bridge that connects the District of Columbia to the state of Virginia, my mind wandered. I thought of San Secondo Parmense. *So that's the name of the town where Isidoro was born.* I savored the name just thinking about it. *Parmesan cheese, Prosciutto di Parma...* I remembered the river that borders it to the north territory was called Po and is near Parma. *That's why it's considered northern Italy...because of the Po river!*

But, above all, I loved to remember the message from Uncle Fernando: *"Go and see how far you go."* It was like a spell that augured adventures. I felt the confidence behind these words. In his own jovial way, he was giving me permission. More than that. He was inviting me to do this research and telling me to trust in myself. An unspoken support in the search for our ancestors. An incantation that came directly from Isidoro. *To live life as an experiment. To see how far one goes.* Why not?

Isidoro must have thought like this when he left Italy. "I'll see how far I can go." Or his mother must have blessed him before leaving. "Son, go.

Seek new horizons. Your mind is clear and your arms are strong. You can do it. Remember to love the work you do every day. Do everything with enthusiasm and be joyful you have the privilege of being able to work. Go a little further each day and follow on your path. Only then will you see how far you will go."

THE TWO ISIDOROS

*W*ith a renewed sense of purpose from Uncle Fernando, the next steps in my journey saw me knocking on the side door of a Mormon Temple. I was looking for a very special name. Since I knew Isidoro's name, I had a very particular idea. I had heard it among saints and street names, and of course ...with the faint whispers of an not-often-mentioned great-grandfather. When I began the search for Isidoro, still at Mami's house, I irreverently told Mami how easy it would be to find the birth certificate in his hometown."

"How easy it would be to find Isidoro's birth certificate!"

"How so?"

"With such an ugly name? Who would think of giving such a name to an innocent baby? When the officers receive my letter, they will say: "Ah, yes, the one and only Isidoro." Then they will go straight to the exact record book and find him!"

I really imagined it was going to be like that. But my mom didn't find my comment funny at all. She made fun of my impressions. She seemed to be angered by my attitude.

"What do you have against my grandfather's name?"

I stopped dead in my tracks, staring at her, and answered in a small voice,

"But Mami... really, to be honest... Isidoro is an ugly name."

I didn't want to offend her, but it was the truth. Or what seemed to me to be the truth.

Annoyed, she admonished me.

"Stop calling my grandfather's name ugly!"

She was really offended. I was aghast at her reaction because *she was defending him.* Even if it was just his name, she was defending him. Up until that moment, only I had spoken up for Isidoro!

"That name is no longer used. It must be very old. Is there a *reason?*" I asked, even though I was sure she could tell from my tone that I thought the reason was because it was a terrible name.

"My grandfather's name is not ugly at all! Besides, that was Moncho's name. Ramón Isidoro."

She lifted her chin in defiance, almost daring me to have the audacity to refute her. Uncle Moncho was a celebrity in the family and one of her most beloved cousins. He was the son of Yolanda, sister of my grandmother Chela. Moncho had suffered torture and been thrown in jail for a time in one of the most dangerous dictatorships in Latin America. His memory was unblemished. His name was not to be sullied. I did not know that Moncho was also Isidoro. Even if it was his middle name.

I had to shut up. I deliberated the name one more time and...maybe it wasn't as bad or as ugly a name after all. It even sounded elegant—I could reconsider. Admittedly, being the name of my dear Uncle Moncho, it suddenly took on an elevated value. It was worth investigating. I would research the etymology of that name to discover the virtues of its special meaning.

As this etymological research progressed, I was now faced with an enigma. I had thought the name was uncommon, however, I turned out to be very wrong. And my theory of its disuse fell apart in such a humorous way! One morning, a reply to my letter arrived from San Secondo and it informed me that they had found among their records two babies named "Isidoro."

"Two?" I accused the paper as if it were alive. "Really? Are you sure? Two babies named Isidoro?"

What must have happened in San Secondo at that time? Did they have shortages of names?

The letter in my hand seemed to mock me. The Archdiocese of Parma had definitely received my inquiry and was ready to answer me, but it was not going to be as easy as I had joked it would be. As it turned out, before they could send me the correct birth certificate, I had to provide the folio and registration number because (Surprise!) there was more than *one* baby with the same name and they couldn't determine which of the two my ancestor was. Two pairs of parents with the surname Rainieri, came up with the brilliant idea of naming their babies Isidoro. Apparently, Isidoro Rainieri was the most popular name in San Secondo Parmense within one week in July of 1857. I was shocked.

And now the ball was in my court, according to the archdioceses. Now it was up to *me* to specify to *them* which Isidoro was mine. I felt that someone was laughing at me. I looked up at the sky to see if any suspects were peeking out.

With my curiosity thoroughly piqued, I finally set out to investigate the etymology and meaning of Isidoro. When I found it, I absolutely changed my mind: *Isidoro is now the most beautiful name in the world!* It went from hated to being revered in my estimation. In fact, had I known beforehand how revealing its meaning is, I would have named one of my sons "Isidoro." It turns out that this ancient name has a very deep and divine meaning. It was used long before the first century of our era. In other words, it is older than Christianity. It was used, not for lack of imagination, but precisely because of its beautiful meaning. The name Isidoro represents a "gift of divinity." And that is what this great-grandfather turned out to be for me, a real gift.

Going back to the letter I received from the Archdiocese informing me of the two Isidoros, it also included all the necessary instructions to find baptismal records of these people in the United States. Not in Italy, but right at home.

What's more...in Virginia! The surprising thing is that I had requested the document from Italy and they had recommended for me to look for it in...Virginia! Before this happened, I thought that getting documents meant taking planes to Italy. Thinking about this possibility, I had been looking forward to going to the local government offices in Parma to go through the records page by page, like a detective. I'd pictured myself taking the utmost care, like a surgeon would with a patient, to make sure the pages of the old books didn't crumble under my fingers. I would have loved to recount some Indiana Jones-style adventures hunting for old documents more than 150 years old. But what I had learned by then was that our ancestors are out there trying to help us find their information, to find and learn about them. Also that every endeavor to research has its own mind...or rather, an angel. An angel assisting us, nudging us closer to our ancestors. My proof was that my research had taken me barely five miles away from home! I think the angel of this research had a great sense of humor.

And so I found myself, on a cold winter day, dry and not yet snowed in, standing in front of the back entrance of a religious temple in McLean. This was the chapel of the Church of Jesus Christ of Latter-Day Saints. In those chapels anyone can meet for church on Sunday and for various weekly activities. As it turns out, many of the chapels have Family History Centers where people research their genealogy. On this Friday, I parked next to a couple of cars in the large parking lot. The sky looked clear and cloudless, but it was extremely windy. I jumped out of my car and onto the steps, wanting to go inside immediately. The cold was chilling my bones. The sign announced that they did indeed have a Family History Center. It was embedded in the wall and below it was a doorbell. I rang and waited.

And I waited.

I waited, freezing.

I didn't want to knock again because the place looked so peaceful and heavenly that surely there were only saints here. Finally, I heard the creak of the doorknob turning. A man with glasses on his nose and a beatific smile opened the door. He was broad-framed, white-haired and wore a red sweater. In my head I started calling him "Santa Claus."

"What brings you here?" he asked, as he opened the door wider and made room for me to come in.

I found his questioning strange and, because I was confused, didn't immediately accept his invitation to cross the threshold. Wasn't it obvious that if I came to this The Family History Center, it must be for genealogy? The cold was bending my toes, but I didn't want to go in without explaining myself. I thought I had to be transparent and confess everything to him, tell him the whole story of Isidoro. I took his question very seriously. I speculated on how to tell it concisely from the beginning and did a little rehearsal in my mind before. *Look, Isidoro supposedly abandoned Bianca and I want to prove to my mother that it wasn't like that and I want to know more about him, you know...to know the reasons for his decisions, to find out if he had something hidden. Besides, now I have an insatiable curiosity. I can't stop anymore. I need to know everything about him.*

But then I thought, what if this saint thinks badly of Isidoro?

So I only dared to say, "Well look..."

His face seemed so angelic that my words froze in my throat. Luckily, a gust of artic-feeling wind decided to take matters into its own hands, and all but pushed me through the doorway. The gentleman took advantage and slammed the door shut behind me. I was trapped inside the place! Would I be made to confess everything? Santa and I looked at each other for a moment.

He seemed to notice my hesitation and asked again,

"How did you hear about us...about our Family History Center?"

If I told him the truth, that I had received a letter from Italy that sent me to his doorstep, I assumed he wasn't going to believe me. He'd think I was making up a story.

"This church...your church," I decided to start from the beginning, looking him in the eyes. "Your church has microfilmed all the record books of where my ancestors are registered."

My words were filled with immense gratitude. It felt very small next to the purpose which The Church of Jesus Christ of Latter-Day Saints have generously dedicated themselves to. Not only have they microfilmed as many old record books as they could, but they have also preserved them in order to keep their valuable information intact.

I immediately called Mami. "Do you know what happened? I have received news from Italy, and they are telling me to look in a Mormon ." I explained everything I had been told, ending with a sigh and adding, "What a beautiful intention!" This new knowledge had awakened the mystical side of me. "Can you imagine the idea of saving the ancestors? Doesn't it seem luminous to you that this can be done? The belief of this religion seems so inspiring to me. So visionary."

She answered me immediately. "I don't understand at all what you are telling me. And stop looking for things. Don't go changing anyone's religion in the family. Not even Isidoro. Not even your grandmother. And much less *my* grandmother!"

Mami had gone to the practical side of things. My grandmother and her sisters were famous for their devotion to the Catholic Church. But my grandmother, such an individual, always approached everything very personally and with an open mind. I remember when Mamma Chela lived with us, almost every day she would walk to St. Jude Thaddeus Church. On the way back to the house, she would pat her legs and knees and say, "These strong legs...do you see how wonderful these legs are?" That meant her independence and autonomy. It meant that she didn't need a car or to ask anyone's permission to go where she wanted to go. No one was stopping her. She was on a first-name basis with the priests and parish priests of the church. She volunteered for every activity that was organized. She came and went as if it were her second home. Once, she chased some children behind the church steps because they had taken the offering money without permission. I can imagine her running down the church steps and chasing two little boys! Her long skirt flapping in the wind and her skinny legs. While she walked almost every day, running was something else! She flew off after the little ones and made an unforgettable scream. When she came back empty-handed and told the priest, he replied with a smile. "Let them take it away, Chela, if they must. Don't run after naughty children because you'll fall down the stairs and then you'll really hurt yourself."

I remembered this anecdote and an uneasy feeling came over me. What if my grandmother, by some miracle, would be angry with me from the "beyond" and admonish me for what I was doing? Would she be angry from the beyond if she found out that I was visiting a church other than the Catholic Church in the hereafter? I thought my quest would justify it. I was trying to find her father after all. I imagined her in her wide, flowered dress, the kind that older people wear in our tropical countries, and in her Daisy Duck shoes. I loved feeling as if she was next to me. With my inner voice I told her, *"Don't worry, Mamma Chela, I'm not going to convert you to another religion. I promise. You stay Catholic forever, ok?"* I wished she really was next to me to have such a conversation! But next to me, in the passenger seat, there was only the green folder with the letter from the Archdiocese. I was still amazed that Italy sent me to Virginia.

Deciding on an answer, I looked at the Santa and spoke:

"I've come to get the birth certificate of all the children named Isidoro to determine which one is mine. Well, I am informed that there are two."

The gentleman nodded and with a hand gesture invited me to follow him down a hallway. There were several doors. I was astonished to hear another question in his low, echoing voice.

"Where are your ancestors from?" he asked as we moved forward. He looked over his shoulder.

Santa is asking the complicated questions! I'm sure he thought I could tell him only one country. Surprise! I am a mixture of many. As I had done with the previous questions, I took this one very seriously because I had not lost my desire to confess.

"Some are from France, others from Italy. Others from Africa and others from Spain... but not Spain-Spain, but Catalans."

I drew a map of that country in the air with my index finger and put a finger where Barcelona was supposed to be. Then, I felt a sense of guilt at leaving the Galicians undefined and added,

"And from Galicia!"

And in the space of my map in the air, I put a dot with my finger where Santiago de Compostela was supposed to be. For me, I had drawn in the air a perfect map of treasures. But Santa hadn't even noticed. He was still walking down the corridor and I, leaving me and my invisible world map floating behind. We approached the door of a room, which he opened and invited me to enter.

By way of farewell, I told him, "Today I come for one. Just one! An Italian. His name is Isidoro. Although he lived in Bologna, I recently learned that he was born in San Secondo Parmense. I wrote and they told me there were two Isidoros."

I made with my fingers the number two, but he did not flinch. He had stopped in front of the door only on one side of it and was looking at me with kind eyes. Apparently, he wanted me to come in so he could close it behind me and not hear me anymore. But I was still talking.

"Two babies named Isidoro. Do you know what that name

symbolized? It has a wonderful meaning. It is a name older than Christianity itself."

I stopped talking abruptly, thinking that I had gone too far in my exuberance. Perhaps Santa would take my enthusiasm for such an ancient and beautiful name as irreverent. I covered my mouth with the green file.

He leaned over and pushed the door open further to point to the registration table inside the room.

There, on one side, were about six chairs lined up next to the wall, and on the other there were long tables with computers and three chip machines. I understood his initial question when I saw the people already inside. Clearly, I was not the picture of a typical genealogist. There were three men sitting in chairs. The men were older, with white hair and one of them was bald, with white fuzz. One woman sat on the other side of the room, behind a desk and a computer.

I know that nowadays there are people of all ages looking for their genealogy, but in 2001, at least in that room, I seemed to be the only young woman interested in such matters.

The lady, who I guessed to be the clerk, offered me a broad smile and asked me to come closer. Continuing along in my North Pole theme, she looked like Mrs. Claus, Santa's wife. She kindly pointed to a line on the registration paper in front of her on the desk that indicated I was to write down a username and the last name of the inquiry.

I felt embarrassed. "I don't have a...username."

"Make one up!"

It was Santa's voice behind me. Apparently, he had stayed a moment longer, but then closed the door and left. I tried to concentrate on what name I would give him to honor all of my ancestors. I picked up the pen with unsteady fingers wondering what I was going to write. I decided to use my English name, which people use a lot and which I think is very beautiful: Grace. And in the second empty space where I had to write what family I came from, with a big sigh I wrote, "Spiritual Family." Then, I sat down nearby to wait, without moving, attentive only to her. I watched her search the shelves for microfiche cartridges. Then, she called each person according to what was written. The person would stand up to receive the black plastic object she handed them. As she named them, she would say, "John, of Becker Family" and give them a cartridge. Then, "James, from Smith Family" and handed him another. When it was my turn, she said, "Grace, from the Spiritual Family."

Everyone looked up to see who it was. And as I walked toward her, I thought to myself, *When I tell Mami that "her very own grace from the Spiritual Family" has arrived to look for her ancestors and that they are going to give them all of them to her in a cartridge, she will laugh too hard.*

When the clerk handed the cartridge to me, she leaned over and asked again, "Are you Grace from the Spiritual Family?"

"Yes, I am!" I smiled back even bigger.

Suddenly, I felt confident and self-assured, as if I had received a secret message.

I sat down in front of the last available microfilm reader and put my cartridge in as she instructed. This was one of San Secondo's extensive birth certificate registries. Names were arranged first by date of birth and then by surname. I turned a metal handle and scrolled until I found the part that read "1857", and then the letter "R". This made me feel that I was holding a key in my hand, the key to the time machine. Among documents in old Italian words, hand-written in beautiful calligraphy, at times with blotches of ink, I turned page by page. It was the first time I had seen these writings up close and through a screen looking for Isidoro. Page one, two, three, four....finally I found the first surname Rainieri. My heart was beating like a drum. "Rainieri Ana, Rainieri Etiene, Rainieri Jacome..." Then I found Isidoro's birth certificate. He was Stefano's son. There was only one Isidoro! I printed it as if it were the Magna Carta. And when I walked out the door, Santa was in the hallway. Not feeling self-conscious at all, I raised the copy in my hand, brandishing it like a divine trophy, and performed an excited little hop. With a smile, he bowed his head in a reverent farewell.

SANDRA AND HER NEPHEWS

$\mathcal{T}$he search for Isidoro and Bianca's marriage certificate then took me on a different adventure. This time, the help that came was unexpected and amazing because I didn't go out to look for it, nor did I have to go to any church or library or archive. I didn't even have to Google it. This time, it came directly to where I was...in my own office.

It started with a person I barely knew. Sandra owned a *desktop publishing* business and was my contact for formatting books and printing. I had never met her in person. We communicated by phone and email. Occasionally, she would insist on coming to meet me to put a face to my voice, but I was always short on time. Between kids, my employment, and now my big new genealogy project, I was very busy.

The day I finally agreed to her visit was a day full of work meetings. We agreed to meet an hour before lunch. Although as I checked my schedule that morning, I found it to be jam-packed and didn't know how I was going to get away to meet up with Sandra. Every moment it seemed like I was just moving from one meeting to the another. And as I entered each office for the next meeting, I couldn't help but check the names on the doors to see if any of them came from Colombia. I needed assistance with recovering the marriage certificate of Isidoro and Bianca from an old church located in downtown Bogota. I asked anyone I knew who would be traveling to that city and found one coworker, but he told me that going to downtown Bogota was highly dangerous, so I dropped him from my list of helpers.

I entered my office five minutes before the agreed meeting with Sandra and saw a young woman, about my age, sitting there waiting for me. Quickly, I excused myself thinking I had arrived a few minutes late and extended my hand to her in welcome. She said I wasn't late, but that she had arrived early. Playful freckles adorned her cheeks and nose and became prominent every time she smiled. I was pleased to note that this expression was frequent. For almost an hour, we talked about the ins and outs of our business. By the time the interview came to an end, we had grown to like each other so much that we decided to take advantage of our lunch hour and eat together. We walked down H Street until we found ourselves sitting across from each other at a table in a French bistro. That's how I learned that she was married to Bob, an American whom she had met in Bogota many years ago. She told me that she was fortunate that her parents still lived there and that they were in perfect health. She also told me that she was the youngest and only woman of eight siblings and that all of them had eight or more children.

"I don't even know how many nieces and nephews I have, I've already lost count!" she joked.

"Although I've never been to Colombia, I recently found out that I'm linked to that country in a very peculiar way."

"How so?" she invited me to explain.

I told her the story of my ancestors, ending with the fact that Isidoro and Bianca had been married in a church called San Pablo de Bogota between 1893 to 1899.

"I know all the churches downtown and I have never heard of San Pablo," she said, a little pensive.

She was not the first person who had conveyed to me this detail. No one who knew the city had heard of this church. I had researched the Catholic churches in Bogota in the 1890s, and when I couldn't find San Pablo Church on the list, I was disappointed. Until it occurred to me that maybe the church's name had changed. If that was the case, it could've been any of the ones listed on the directory. I set about the laborious process of making long distance calls to each of the churches. It was difficult because almost no one answered the phones. And if they did answer, communication had a lot of feedback, strange background noise, or the person couldn't hear well. And when I could finally get my question across, the person didn't understand why I was asking and wanted to know the whole story. And if they did understand, they wanted to know why I was looking for my great-grandparents' marriage certificate of 1896. All voices, of all ages and accents answered my phone calls without giving me a satisfactory answer until finally, one angelic, kind and intelligent soul came up with the solution.

"And why don't you call the archdiocese directly?" she asked boldly and sounded rather opinionated.

"and why not?" I answered back in the same tone but felt like my voice sounded waspish. I realized I should have done that in the first place and rolled my eyes at myself. *That's how someone sets me straight!*

Another angel appeared on the scene when I wrote to the Archdiocese. By chance, the archivist happened to be my namesake. The sympathy was mutual when she answered my next call to tell me that, indeed, the name of San Pablo had changed to Church of the Veracruz.

Sandra's eyes lit up when I told her this information. "De La Veracruz church, of course! I know where it is."

She smiled in relief and laughed at my story imitating the voice of the opinionated lady.

After that, I made the formal request for the document by email and I received back, from my namesake, the archivist, a reply. "Here I have your document, ready to be picked up."

And that was when I asked some of my colleagues to see if any of them going on a trip would be so kind as to pick up the document. Only one of them was available and able to go, but he was strongly cautious about it. .

"The church of La Veracruz at the center of a very dangerous area," he explained, "Three years ago, in 1998, that area was infested with narcos. If I were you, I would not dare to send anyone to fetch the document until the situation in Colombia settles down. There was an explosion around there." Following this warning, I received more macabre details; although the city's security problem seemed to have improved lately, every now and then they would find a corpse in the street in the morning. In other words, if I sent someone to pick up the document I could possibly be sending them to their death.

I explained all of this to Sandra. She was appalled and denied any knowledge of this, then looking at my scared face, started laughing and tried to calm my unease.

"Do you believe it? It's nothing like that! You have to be careful and don't go around there at night, that's all! Bogota is not so dangerous that anyone who goes downtown falls and dies. Don't worry, I'm going to help you! I will send one of my nephews to pick up the document."

"Dear Sandra..." I answered worriedly. "I know that you are one of, like, eleven brothers and sisters and that each one of you has about eleven children, giving you *hundreds* of nephews and nieces, but really!" I was half joking but I had forgotten the numbers.

Laughing her head off, Sandra protested. "It's nothing like that. Whoever told you that just didn't want to help you. I'll do it! I'll send one of my nephews. You'll see that nothing happens."

"I don't want to endanger anyone's life." I insisted. "How about I send the request to the priest at church, in a nicely written letter with stamp money included and extra for a donation?" She was still shaking her head. "Look! I've been doing that for letters of inquiries to Italy and it's a good solution. That way we don't endanger anyone's life."

"You'd be endangering the letter carrier's life!" She replied amused, her freckles jumping happily. "Let me do it my way! I'll take care of it!"

"But the last thing I need is to have it on my conscience that I endangered any of your brave nephews!" I noticed she wasn't afraid and thought this was a joke. "I'm serious, what if that day they go to pick up the document another bomb goes off?" I was fascinated with Sandra and her nephews' bravery.

"My nephews will survive!" She said amused, "You will see how determined and accommodating they are."

Jokingly, I asked her, "Will your nephews be part of a S.W.A.T. style team? I'm sure they are experts in capturing ancient documents! That's why you feel so confident that they will survive this mission!"

Sandra burst out laughing:

"If they are, they haven't told me. Maybe it's something secret," she replied, just following my lead.

While we enjoyed each delicious bite of our lunches, she was telling me about the streets surrounding the Archdiocese and the square in front of it. All her stories fed my admiration for her nephews' bravery and I imagined them on a secret mission.

First scenes: Sandra's nephews are dressed in S.W.A.T. uniform with helmet and bulletproof vest. Their figures are not noticeable in the moonless night and each one is located at strategic points in downtown Bogota. One of them, the bravest and most daring, hides in the corner of an old stone building. In his hand he carries a walkie-talkie, one of those big ones that looked like a brick. A green light comes on and a beep is heard! The nephew speaks in code:

"Four, tango, hare...done!"

On a deserted street in downtown Bogota, a black van is parked full of communication devices, cables and screens. There are two nephews sitting there listening to everything with headphones. They are also wearing their black uniforms and helmets. One of them answers from the walkie-talkie:

"Roger. Falcon. Tango. Eagle. Earth. Three-four." And other mumbled codes.

The nephew who's about to go into action with his gloved hands picks up the walkie-talkie to give a possible last message.

"If I should die on this mission, tell my mom that...that nothing is in vain...that everything has a reason for being...that things happen because they happen. And to Isidoro and Bianca's descendants that...(A hiccup chokes in his throat and he almost can't continue) all happens for the best."

They all know they are exposed to danger, but they are passionate about rescuing old documents. They were born for that. They are willing to die for it. One of them cannot contain himself, breaks the rule and says, "Brother, take care of yourself!"

And in the street, the young man closes his eyes for a second and takes a breath of air. When he opens them, his mind is made up —he breaks into a run!

Next scene:

He does several ninja-style somersaults, arrives in front of the church gate, kicks it open and splits it in two, amidst a great roar of bullets, crunching metal and the sound of bombs. Once inside the temple, slipping between columns, he arrives in front of the Christ on the altar. He takes off his helmet and makes the sign of the cross. From a side door appears the priest dressed in formal garment who goes behind the tabernacle. After giving him the blessing, he hands him the parchment. He points out the secret exit. The nephew puts his helmet back on and goes out like a black cat, running at great speed among the old and wet stones of the street. He disappears victoriously into the darkness, having accomplished his mission....

Suddenly, Sandra's voice interrupts my fantasy.

"I'm getting to know you, Graciela. You are a creative person in your tenacity. Nobody is going to die here, least of all not one of my nephews!" Her eyes shone with good humor.

While she was talking, a curious thing happened inside me. I resigned myself to trust Sandra's promise and remembered that earlier that morning I had asked heaven to find someone who could go get the document from the church in Colombia. I was indeed in front of that *someone*! Could it be possible that some angel had passed through the office hallway and heard me? Just like that? That fast?

Ancestors, you are good...you are really good!

Painted on the frescoed ceiling of the French bistro were three little angels, designed amidst clouds of light blue, and they were smiling down at us. I looked at them in amusement, thinking of the relationship between them inhabiting the sky and prayers fulfilled. In some magical way, I had positioned myself in the right place, at the right time, and the right person appeared. I was delighted that, with all the ups and downs of this investigation, life was beginning to be seen through a surreal lens. I felt a sense of *deja vu*; as if it was a dream come true. I felt like my ancestors were colluding to please me. Then I thought this looked like a movie. Who was the director? Maybe one of my ancestors! It wasn't the first time I felt that this research was being shaped by incomprehensible forces that I didn't even know existed before. For the first time, I felt certain that everything would flow as it should, in its own time. I would find Isidoro's whereabouts and much more. Many surprises and gifts probably awaited me. This was bigger than me. I had a feeling this was an extraordinary plan.

Even today, Sandra and I are great friends and every time I see her, I ask her how her hundreds of nieces and nephews are doing and if they have been lately employed for another crazy mission because of some passionate person looking for their ancestors.

SUNSET

*T*hanks to Sandra and her nephews, the information about the marriage of Bianca and Isidoro soon after arrived at my door. I cannot express the delight I felt as I held in my hands, between my fingers, the fine document of the marriage of two of my ancestors. I excitedly read their names written on the copy of the certificate. I imagined little angels sculpted in stone in each corner of the church as angelic witnesses of the sacrament of two of my dearest relatives. I imaginatively thanked the parish priest. *Thank you...thank you...thank you...*

Previously, I had estimated that Bianca arrived in Bogota in early 1893. That confirmed that she was seventeen years old. When I verified that her wedding had been in March 1896, I realized she was close to her twenty-first birthday, and this fact made the family history change. It gave me a strange satisfaction to learn that she had not married so young at seventeen, like the family history conveyed. It was as if I finally knew "the truth of the truth."

At this point, I had already collected Isidoro's birth certificate and Bianca's birth certificate. Now I had their marriage certificate as well. I still needed to find his death certificate or his grave. Where did he die? What year did that happen? Where was he buried? The answers may give an idea about the abandonment and whether it was on purpose or not. But the more I learned, the more I realized that the couple seemed inseparable. I'd also found ship manifests from Ellis Island that stated that they seemed to travel together more often than not. New York was the most logical place to look as the couple had lived in that city for a few months in 1905, precisely as part of a crew in a hotel, as it was stated in a special city census. Perhaps the was his destination when he left her... I decided to look harder for any clues to his death in that city.

In the local public library of the city of Fairfax in Virginia, I found a map of New York in 1910. I learned that New York is made up of boroughs: Manhattan, Brooklyn, Queens, The Bronx, and Staten Island. According to the instructions on the city health offices website, to correctly inquire after the death certificate I needed, I should indicate the borough where my great-grandfather Isidoro died. But I didn't know that. I didn't even know if he died there. Still, I felt drawn to instinctively chose Manhattan. I also didn't have the correct or approximate date. On my first inquiry the year 1914 was given. However, I needed something more specific as only a year was not enough to bring back results.

As I was pondering on this, I received a call from Mami.

"Yesterday I remembered something and immediately, I called Ana Felicita, my cousin who lives in Puerto Rico. She is Ana's daughter and confirmed the posthumous birth of Ana."

Again, Socorro to the rescue! I thought.

"Date, please!" I urged Mami.

"Aunt Anna was born on January 7, 1913."

"So, we're talking about two months earlier...like my cousin Josémaria."

The thought of Josémaria was the first thing that came to my mind because history had repeated itself in the family. My younger cousin, the son of Uncle Moncho and Aunt Teresa, had been born two months after his father died of cancer.

Mami didn't think about it for a second:

"That's right, just like your cousin Josémaria?"

"In this family stories have repeated themselves..." I muttered while my brain turned over doing a quick calculation on the possible date of Isidoro's death in New York City "With this piece of information I'm close to finding him. So, what...a month before, three months before?"

"She says about six or seven months before," she replied.

"Six months earlier is July 1912!"

This was consistent with a ship's manifest's date. *Was that the fateful voyage?*

I immediately sent a letter to the Health Department that had the date corrected with 1912, instead of 1914.

"Please search your records for death between July or August 1912 in the borough of Manhattan." I sent the envelope off with high hopes.

That night was the night I dreamt of his farewell I described at the beginning of this story. A lucid dream and so bittersweet... *How is it that my dreams are so vivid as if I had been present?* Like a little girls with my feet full of sand from the near by beach. Yes, I have a great imagination, but perhaps I had heard something as I was growing up. However, I suspected the answer could be more occult and esoteric. *Are ancestors dreams shared with their descendants? Would one of my great aunts have lent me that dream? Would one of the sisters have told it to my grandmother Chela and I inherited it from her? Just as DNA is inherited, are dreams inherited? Just as mannerisms are inherited, are joys and bitterness inherited? Are memories inherited?*

And so, I see them again standing on the threshold of the hotel, Bianca and Isidoro face each other. He tries to take her hands. She turns away without looking at him. Isidoro carries his small suitcase as a promise of a short trip. He adjusts his hat. He makes his way to the port. His silhouette passes me. He walks away into the mist and disappears. And I am left alone, standing on the sidewalk. The chill of the sea breeze on my ankles. I have the knowledge of the corner where I was standing. I know the shape of the street, the distance of the image. *Which one of the daughters woke up early and saw him leave? Who peeked out and watched his departure?* Someone heard his promise, that it would be a short trip, that he would never leave her. The promise of promises. I woke up.

All morning, his promise of return lingered in me.

If he *really* promised, then it was a promise that ended up broken. Broken like the blue butterfly in my yard fluttering among the red flowers. Butterflies represent the promises of the soul. I admired that butterfly for a couple of days for the indigo color of the center of its wings and the black border that looked like brocade. It cheered up my breakfast. I waited for it again as I sat writing. I picked up my pen and I waited for a minute, but I didn't see it! I decided to get up, go out to the balcony and look for it among the flowers. Suddenly, when I opened the door, I found the butterfly inert at my feet. A broken wing. As was a broken promise. How many more promises would we have to go through to find the reason about how it all began? "His broken promise," was the refrain passed around among the voices of this family. Girls whispering to their younger sisters, "He promised." Broken, as delicate hopes are broken. "He promised... but he abandoned."

And why dream as if it were in my present?

And why did it matter to me who went away and who did not return? What was the reason for my nostalgia, why I had to imagine them happy and dancing amongst the flowers of a grand salon? As I imagined the bliss of having met on a boat. The fantasy of marrying among sculpted angels. The fortune of finding a joyful port by a silver mountain where to settle a family. The satisfaction of working together, shoulder to shoulder, husband and wife, raising a family and a business, trusting each other... supporting each other in a new country.

If anyone had seen them say goodbye, by some divine grace, I had inherited that memory. I know because I found it within myself. I understood that, just as genes are inherited from our ancestors, as well as predispositions to certain diseases, other things are also genetically acquired. Gestures and mannerisms are inherited from grandparents to grandchildren. I say this because my son Victor inherited many of my father's attitudes, although he did not get to know him because he was born a year almost to the date after my father's death. However, when my little one places his hands together while laying down on the bed to watch TV, he looks just like my dad. And just as him, he'd place his knee on top of the other and his arms together behind his head. And he'd join his fingers exactly at chest level when listening at dinner...just like my dad. So, I'm sure there's something there that we don't know about such things.

And what about tastes? How can one thing be inherited and not the other? It's inherited beyond what we think, beyond what can be scientifically proven. Dreams too? Yes! Dreams, longings, memories and the memories of families. Even if they are cut into little pieces, among the descendants, like pink petals scattered at my feet on the green grass, under the cyclamen blooming in Virginia. I think that's what ancestral memories are like, like pink petals from a family tree that have drifted off their branches. Memories that fall to the ground. If I don't pick them up, the wind carries them to oblivion. So I do. I pick them up one by one. I bring them in my hands and place them on my desk. I sit down to write. I put down the pen and pick them up again. In an orderly fashion, I try to reconstruct them. I know they can't fit together exactly the same, but I still try.

"He was an absentee dad," Yolanda confirmed among the unseen remembrances of her family stories. "Always traveling. We're used to seeing him go."

"But where is he going?" I asked in my dreams to that little girl, daughter of Isidoro and Bianca, who was watching the scene with me back in Puerto Plata. She had gotten up early and we were both watching. Then, the scene repeats itself. "Why is he leaving?" I ask her as she stands next to me. The little girl doesn't answer me. We both watch the couple say goodbye again and I look around, wanting to give myself a chance to notice something else. I want to listen to the murmur of their words. "He travels a lot, he is always leaving," the girl by my side explains. Then, the scene dissipates.

I try to evoke other family voices I heard in my childhood. They come to me through time like whispers of the wind between two realities.

"To Santiago," say some whispers.

"To France," declare others.

I cannot recognize the voices.

I make out Isidoro in the haze of ports and ship arrivals. His figure appears, checking a watch. He is very well dressed, in a traveling suit. He is wearing a hat and carrying a small suitcase. I see him in constant motion, like in an old movie. He ascends and descends from the bow of the ship along with other people who are also traveling. He comes and goes. What does he do? Travel!

"To Colombia," other voices answer.

Isidoro climbs...comes down...adjusts his hat. It looks like a *film* passing in front of my eyes. Eternally moving, the fog serves to reflect the black and white image whose movement becomes faster and faster.

"To Italy."

Again, he carries his small luggage.

"To New York."

He descends and walks down a street, then he appears on the other side. The scenes pick up speed and repeat.

"But why was he traveling so much?" I insist on an answer. No one answers. The old images transpose. And from the opposite corner, under the Victorian houses, abruptly, I stop everything, "Stop!" And step out of the dream as if stepping out of a cloud.

The next day I am sitting at my desk, looking at my eyes in the reflection of a small mirror next to me. Today I am at home. The table is full of clippings, notes, and printouts. I try to reconstruct, paste, annotate, while the documents get confused with the petals, as the memories get confused with the annotations. Then, the breeze comes in through the window and lifts them up, making a little whirlwind. I don't move, I just watch them. I let them be. If I reach out my hands, I can catch some of them, but I can't catch all the petal-memories. Some fall to the ground and others scatter behind me. The only thing I know and can write is what tells the family story.

"Bianca and Isidoro had met aboard a ship. The scene takes place around March 1893, three months before she turned eighteen in June."

I concentrate and try to write the story with the help of family memories, some forgotten in the wind, others found within the heart. I have researched how long it takes a ship to cross the ocean. Its voyage from the port of Italy to Colombia would be approximately one month and one week, enough time for a love affair to begin on board the ship. That much is easy to infer and deduce. There are other details we don't know, but my heart tells me this is how it happened.

We don't know the name of the ship on which they coincided. We don't know who looked first at whom on the gunwale. We are not aware if it was Isidoro who distinguished her among the ladies dressed in corsets and feathered hats. Nor do we know which of the two more enjoyed watching sunsets. I speculated that they both loved to admire the sky and the sea in the twilight hour. After all, delight for those majestic colors, of course, runs in the family. I imagine her in her youth, wearing white gloves and a shawl over her shoulders. Her hands resting on the railing and her gaze to the west.

We don't know so we are left to wonder if Isidoro found her accompanied by another young woman or if Bianca was alone, admiring the sparkle on the horizon. We don't know if she, leaning on the rail of the boat, noticed his presence when he was amazed by her jovial countenance. Perhaps she was engrossed in the luminous colors dancing on the water.

I wanted details! Were they silk or brocade gloves? Her long skirt touched the floor. I wanted to know the color and shape of the soft hat that hid her face.

And...as he approached, was he dazzled at the first moment, or did it take him a bit to begin to admire her? I believe he would have advanced slowly so as not to frighten her. Perhaps he placed his hands next to hers, their pinkies almost touching. Perhaps she looked at him out of the corner of her eye. And I imagined, as the sublime hues of that sunset reflected on their faces, as he delicately leaned down to whisper as if to himself...

"Spectacular."

Did she then tilt her delicately young face to see him better? And did she wonder, as he was smiling with his eyes full of mischief, if he was talking about the sunset, or if he was implying she herself was "spectacular"? Perhaps Bianca blushed at this thought, and Isidoro, out of respect, would have turned his gaze towards the sea, to gaze at the wonderous colors again. Who knows if they remained silent or, although nervous, engaged in a conversation?

And if they did, what did they talk about for the first time? The sun's rays on the waves and the reflection of its light...or something more mundane?

I think there was no topic he couldn't contribute to or language that would stop him.

But...what did they say? Where were they going? Where did they come from? Maybe they even wondered about their dreams, about where they would meet when they got there or what they would find on the other side of the ocean. What would happen to them? Where would destiny take them?

I think Isidoro felt compelled to be close to her, to hear the timbre of her voice. And if Bianca remained modest and offered no reply, he would take it upon himself to share. Conversational, as only he knew how to be, he would recall an anecdote of another time on a voyage. On that occasion, the sunset was so spectacular that everyone went out to watch it and the boat tilted so dangerously on one side that the captain had to ask half the crew to go to the other side in order to avoid any risk.

"I usually get up early to watch the sunrise. There's hardly anyone here. Just the gunwale cleaners brushing the floor, and me. I get up to see the moon before dawn, brighter than ever, yet giving way to the sun. And with the first glimmer, suddenly the sea is calm and attentive, seeming to also bow to the sun."

We shall not know if she raised her eyes to him with a question in her young mind, "Who is this man that speaks to me like this?"

Fearlessly, she held his gaze for a moment. And then recognized him.

She would have recognized him because she'd seen him a few days before, a week before, we won't know how long before, but we could imagine. It was at that dinner in the captain's salon, when Bianca entered along with her relatives and the gentlemen rose gallantly to greet them. At that instant, she noticed his presence. Especially since he was a conversationalist and kept the captain and other men engrossed with his anecdotes. He had an enviable charisma and cheerfulness and loved to infect them all with his always positive mood. Perhaps Bianca, avoiding looking directly at him, had sharpened her ear to hear his husky voice when he conversed with another gentleman.

"Everyone in any language has the same longing. They want to eat well and sleep comfortably and peacefully. You have to offer what you have as a gift. You have to give generously what the traveler longs for, so far from home and after such long journeys, a safe place to replenish their energy. As far as possible, we must offer them the first welcome in a foreign and strange country. Provide rest in a comfortable bed that feels like a cloud made for the angels, where they sense they've arrived home, better than at home! They should feel that they have arrived in heaven! And choose everything that is going to be served to the newcomer for excellent quality...a warm dinner, a better breakfast, everything especially

clean and presented excellently. Please! When food is prepared and served elegantly, it tastes better!"

Bianca, shocked by his ease of speech, admired him? Of that I have no doubt! But did she love him when she saw him? I dare to suspect she did not. For if she had, she would have waited less time to marry. If she met him as a teenager, she would not have waited almost three years to do so. Still, this does not debunk the myth that her family disagreed with this union because she was only seventeen and he was thirty-four when they met on that boat. Double her age. And, if they disagreed for some other reason, that reason stayed right there, lost in the family's memory.

As for him, that glorious sunset was the opportunity to see her more closely and ask her name. Because he did admire her from the first time he saw her. Her youthfulness was a wonderful juxtaposition to her serious and upright countenance. She was small in stature, yet her presence dominated anyplace she stood. She was quiet and shy, but never timid. And though she had noticed he was gregarious and extroverted, she realized he also possessed the gift of knowing when to listen attentively and remain silent, as he stood next to her, also absorbed in that sunset and keeping a certain distance out of respect.

"There is a point at which sunset and sunrise are similar. So much so that one can forget, for an infinitesimal second, whether it is dawn or dusk. Thus, every second seems like a surprise. Like life itself, a beautiful and pleasant surprise."

For now, inside me, the questions are still as calm as water. Because at this moment, I have them both, Isidoro and Bianca...together, in the eternal, with their hands on the rail almost touching, together watching the mauve and golden sunset.

SURPRISE FROM NEW YORK CITY

$\mathcal{W}$hen I sent in the second inquiry with the correct date to the Department of Health in New York City to get the death certificate, I informed Mami. Understandably, she was mistrusting of any information I might be receiving and didn't want me to reveal any secrets. And I understood her, but I couldn't stop myself. By then, I fiercely loved that mythological great-grandmother I never knew. With the same love and admiration that Mami and Uncle Fernando did. Reciprocating the fierce love that I felt she radiated to her descendants. I was getting to know her or "knew" her through their stories but had also started knowing her through my being. That high forehead, her way of standing tall despite her short figure. So how could I leave things like that? An unresolved unknown next to her in the family tree. I couldn't believe that, if there was a family spirit, it would leave Bianca alone in eternity.

Weeks later, I received an envelope with a possible answer. It was a semi-sunny day. Nothing too important was happening. A few clouds were floating in the sky without misfortune. I was wearing jeans and a pullover shirt because if there was nothing else to do, I could at least go for a walk. I would admire my neighbors' meticulously manicured gardens. It was an ordinary day.

But when I opened the mailbox, everything became a whirlwind!

At the bottom, I spotted the white envelope. When I reached out to take it, I knew! My heart thundered. My fingers suddenly didn't work. A letter from the New York City health offices. Holding that envelope in my hands gave me a feeling of joy and sorrow. It was as if several ideas were embodied in a strange voice within me. First, I thought I heard: *A belated birthday present!* Then, a premonition with infinite nostalgia: *The search is over!* And then, doubts swirled in my mind killing all previous thoughts. *What...what if this is not my ancestor? And what if they are wrong?* And immediately, I corrected myself: *What if they are not wrong and this is the one?* The matter of the two Isidoros in Italy—that letter that made me visit the Temple of the Mormons, that was the only doubt I had regarding this. I needed to go to New York this time and examine the closely the information that this letter would provide.

As I opened it, my hands trembled.

Isidoro, I said to myself, *If this is you? If it is really you...all this time you have been in New York and I have been trying to find you.*

I read the letter. I sighed. I didn't stick to what it said. I didn't dare. I had to discuss it with Mami. The affair of the two Isidoros had marked me with caution. Before deciding that this was mine, I had to verify it, I had to corroborate it. Before I could believe this information to be true, I had to be absolutely sure and without doubt that this was my Isidoro. And, if this was him, was the search over? I realized that the investigation of my roots in general, but also of me, expanded me into the universe. The genealogical search for my roots had fit perfectly within me! I was born for this. My new life purpose filled me with love, its exploration had given me so much! I recaptured stories from my mother and grandmother. I had visions of the past and inspirations from dreams of ancestral loves. The search is something that belonged to me because I felt that I am the rescuer of family memories and lost memories...the keeper of stories. The translator of their love for us, their descendants.

This newly found inner world was vast and included everyone. When I say "everyone", I mean all ancestors. Those of a few years ago as well as those of a thousand years ago. In an ancestral consciousness of ages. The more I reached out to them in the past, it felt as they were reaching out for me. The more I stretched out my arm, the more they seemed to do the same, like a mirror.

It was like the scene painted by Michelangelo Buonarotti in the Sistine Chapel. Adam leaning, looking precious and vulnerable with his baby face and man's body. Naked, in full recognition by God. Adam reaching out to God, almost casually. And God, in a constant movement, in a bubble of time, with the gray hair of an old man, with the beard of a wise man, doing the same, with all the force and interest of his love. According to Michelangelo's painting, they each, in their own way, were trying to reach the other. Because love, which only emanates from the divine source, unites them. Thus I felt the protection of my ancestors. The naivety of my search with a pure heart gave me the feeling of never being alone even when there was no one around me. I felt that they accompanied me, and connected me with that source of love, support, and companionship.

However, it was true that, if I checked my heart, it was still broken. But it no longer throbbed or ached. It was no longer raw; it was healing. And the red, broken bits piled up? Somehow there seemed to be an invisible crane and it had begun to rebuild it again. Piece by piece. Part by part. With divine patience. Perhaps it was divinity itself, disguised as my ancestors. Perhaps they had set about the loving and naive task of rebuilding my heart for me. I don't think it succeeded in its entirety, at least not yet, although now I had new hope. I did not fully know, nor was I entirely certain, though there seemed to be a plan. And with that plan, a longing awakened. My heart wanted to be new, hoped to be born again. I just needed to trust. Something greater than me was holding me.

I had discovered an "outside of time and space" that seemed to me to be the dimension of spirit. I can explain it only as visual poetry. A metaphor. These dimensions resembled soap bubbles. In these bubbles we lived, in the faint colors of the rainbow when the light hit them. We'd float in them, connected by a stream of subtle love. We were all there...my family, the "living" and my ancestors, in various bubbles. We were all together, filling the mind of God. This knowledge of such a fragile, but joyful connection, was both familiar and unfamiliar. My soul, which is eternal, felt it. In the mind of God, we are all there, constantly elevated in His love. This sensation, or "knowing", was a wonderful feeling. But many times I'd blame it on my imagination. And when I exercised this incredulity, all the bubbles would burst.

That morning I called Mami; I told her all the information I had just received. I read the letter word for word. Letter by letter, scrutinizing every word, but there were problems with dates! The information was not lining up with what I had previously learned. Could this be accurate? I thought so, but it needed to be corroborated. The best way to do that would be to show up at the cemetery offices to examine the documents.

When I finished relating everything to Mami, she fell silent and, I found myself frozen, still holding the receiver in my hand. I let my breath release in a long sigh. It was an emotional moment, and my ear was still glued to the receiver, trying to feel what my mother was feeling. There was a minute of silence in which I waited for her understanding. Because after all, Isidoro is *my* great-grandfather, but he was *her* grandfather. The person who had supposedly abandoned her beloved grandmother Bianca. Her "Babi." The same one who received her in her loving arms every summer of her early childhood.

With her silence, I knew that her eyes, like mine, had turned to water.

"I will tell Fernando," she finally said, clearing her throat.

I refolded the paper in my hand with the return address of the New York offices. I heard her clear her throat again and I didn't like that. My mother never hesitated. I carefully placed the letter in the envelope as I listened to her. She began to speak, and my world began to turn a different color. The news she was giving me was unexpected. It squeezed my heart. Her words were medical terms like mammogram, biopsy, and prognosis.

"I need you to come down to Miami to meet me. I have to repeat the tests there. I've located some doctors in a hospital and a small house near there." At the end of her sentence a deep silence enfolded us.

I felt as if my heart was suddenly on the edge of a sword, and I was balancing to keep from slipping and being cut.

As I hung up the phone, my mind announced to my heart, *On*

our way to suffer again. And the latter replied, *I will do what I can to survive.*

In the coming months, I would dedicate my time, with my sisters, to assist my mother. The sisters would meet to make decisions, although we soon discovered that she made her own decisions. Still, all free time would be devoted to her and helping her. So, that summer of 2001 was entirely devoted to her: to wait for the results and for her to call me for whatever she needed. I put the genealogical research aside, planning to resume it later, when time was more propitious. I'd go in person to New York City when I could. I would verify if this Isidoro I was told about was indeed mine.

Then, at the end of the summer, fate manifested itself in an unusual way. On September 11, 2001, an inexplicable tragedy occurred in New York City. Foreign terrorists commandeered commercial airliners and crashed them into the Twin Towers, bringing them down and killing thousands of people. Another plane hit the Pentagon, in Washington DC. This tragedy occurred 20 miles from my home in Virginia. And as if that wasn't enough, a fourth aircraft that had been headed for the White House came crashing down in a field in Pennsylvania.

I was at work when that fatal day happened. My colleague had arrived with the information that she'd she seen something strange on the road. As she was driving down I-395 in morning traffic, she had spotted a plane that appeared to her to be flying very low. Strangely, she had leaned over the steering wheel thinking *Why is this plane flying so low?*

It was normal that, entering the city at that time of the morning, the congested traffic would prevent her from getting ahead of it. Therefore, she could not keep her eyes on the plane. It disappeared from sight behind the buildings on the side of the highway. Since Ronald Reagan National Airport is near that road, she concluded that it might be normal. A minute later, the unthinkable happened. Past the traffic jam, she spotted a large cloud of ominous smoke. Even seeing it with her own eyes, it seemed implausible that a plane would crash into a building and that it would be the Pentagon. Much less, that she would be a distant witness to such a tragic and iconic event. After that day, we would awaken to a new world.

But that morning, before the telephone connections became congested, I was called by the person who was caring for my 18-month-old baby Victor at the time. His name was Pavel, and he was taking care of him for a few hours in my home. He was the father of a friend of mine. He had retired from a math teacher position at a prestigious school in Peru. His daughter had a baby who was older than Victor by a few months. The arrangement was that Pavel would come to pick up my little boy in the mornings and then take him to his daughter's home so that our little babies could play together. My two older children who were at elementary school also liked him as he would help them with the homework. It was a great arrangement that suited us just fine. Since he started coming to our home, my children were getting good grades and my baby had a little friend.

"You'd better come," Pavel voice was grave over the phone. "I have a feeling it's going to get worse. I'll wait for you with Victor here." As soon as he hung up, all the phone lines became congested. It was a miracle that we could arrange for me to pick up my two sons, André and Alex, from elementary school. When I arrived at school, security was very tight. Mothers picking up children had to show our faces and an ID through a camera. At the time, we were a few mothers waiting outside the metal doors. Two of them commented that their husbands worked at the Pentagon. I didn't know what to say, but no one else did either. One by one, the children came out and I hugged them tightly. As we drove away, I turned to look at the red brick entrance and noticed other moms arriving to pick up their little ones. My children didn't know or understand anything. There was not much to say because not much was known yet. The news wasn't clear.

At home, we watched the television. The images we saw of New York were of an absurd and unreal situation. We watched the screen in horror. Again and again, the images of the planes crashing filled us with dread. Then, when the buildings came down, the white smoke seemed like a rain of chalk and ash covering all of Manhattan. Each image shook us to our souls. Our family, the neighborhood, the whole country was in shock.

I must admit that, as the days and weeks went by, I didn't think much about my ancestors. Not being able to go to New York to find the one I was looking for almost seemed ludicrous. Why would I even think to look for him after all these awful tragedies? Continuing genealogical research became an impossibility. The following month, a co-worker who went there told me that Manhattan still smelled of smoke and sorrow. Our nation was moving toward war. Verifying Isidoro's whereabouts was put on the back burner. I turned my attention to my children and family who needed me. At least, those were my plans. I resigned myself to the designs of time. This was definitely a pause. And it would be longer than I imagined. But there was nothing to be done.

However, now I know there was a greater force that was going to propel me equally in another direction. I would know that the wheel of history had picked up momentum and was coming to run over my plans with an ancient love. For there was a love that had gone and wanted to return. And there was no stopping it. Besides, the space between me and my ancestors had already narrowed. And even if I lowered my arms and let them go, I felt that they themselves would come closer to me. In some hidden way, their lives, their longings, their whole history were coming toward me. Fate, already unleashed, set me on the path to meet them. Soon, someone would bring me legendary stories and other adventures to be known. There was a greater force that was in control and this would cause the surprises of my life to come soon.

PART 2

MAGICAL TRAVELS IN ITALY

THE ACCIDENT

*I*n early 2002, I was involved in a car accident on the interstate while on my way home from work. I had left the building very late, and the rain delayed traffic enough that by the time I finished crossing the Roosevelt Bridge and entered Virginia, it was eight o'clock at night. On a curvy stretch of road, just before entering the freeway, my vehicle lost traction and spun out like a spinning top. It did not roll over or hit another car, but it did hit the walls on either side of the road.

While it was terrifying, something incredible also happened. As the car spun like a top, everything inside seemed to rise up. Time became eternal. I have no other way to describe it. My car, my body and all the objects around it were suspended in the air. For a second, my wallet, pens and small papers, including myself, were of the same weight and seemingly floating in the middle of a tornado.

It is usual for me to write ideas on small square papers. While driving, I listen to audiobooks, so I write a word or a sentence every time I stop at a red light. Things like, "Today, I will look at the world with love" or "call the endocrinologist" or "remember the pink sunrise behind the Lincoln Memorial." I write them so fast that sometimes I don't even understand my handwriting, which makes them difficult to transcribe later. I call them my "enlightened thoughts of the road." Yet, these thoughts often get lost in the space between my seat and the passenger seat.

In that eternal moment, all these colored papers appeared in front of me, suspended. As well as the tires in the air, without touching the road. My hair spread out like the branches of a tree. My hands on the steering wheel. It was as if we were flying towards the cosmic ocean. That second to the dark side of nowhere stayed in my memory as a fluctuation of linear time. A motionless movement of a clock. A silent second of infinity.

And then, everything fell.

The tires skidded on the wet pavement making a multi-decibel screech. The impact on the front wall..., another on the side..., metal crunching, spinning, hitting the opposite wall of the road. They were eerie crashing sounds in opposition to my emotions. I simply watched the performance, as if I was not involved or a part of it.

I remember as I was making a turn, cars were heading toward me, one managed to dodge me. In that momentary pause, I caught a glimpse of the driver's silhouette and ... his horrified expression! Finally, the car stopped with a thunderous crash against the wall. The only thing between the wall and my shoulder was the door, which had flattened and crumpled like cardboard. I thought, "I landed facing forward!" And the next thought was, "I broke the wall." It didn't occur to me at that moment that it might have been *me* that was broken and not the wall.

The silence was abrupt. My consciousness examined my body and resolved that I was unharmed but I perceived my backbone as a thin steel rod inside a spaghetti noodle. Strong and fragile at the same time. A feeling I can't describe came over me. It reminded me to breathe—I obeyed. I watched the heat of the steam from my engine against the timid raindrops on the windshield. My whole being was extremely sensitive, even sensing the tips of my hair. It was not pain, but the sensation of the space around me had taken on a new configuration. My knees had received countless blows, as if instead of human knees they belonged to a rag doll that had just been tossed around in a washing machine.. The next day they would look like two basketballs, but at that very moment I felt nothing.

And yet I was more alert than ever. My mind felt like that of a surveyor. It scanned from head to toe for something broken. A feeling of compassion came over me, but also of comforting detachment. The seatbelt squeezed me: it was the only thing my brain found *wrong* on its scan for every cell of my body. I didn't know it at the time, but I was clearly experiencing symptoms of shock.

Suddenly, I could see a policeman approaching. He came slowly toward me, as if he had seen this scene before. He examined the accordion hood for a second, then leaned in the passenger side window and lowered his head to look at me. His expression made me think I was trapped and buried in a smashed metal can.

"Are you all right, ma'am?"

I felt his concern.

"Y...yes." I stuttered.

I moved my toes inside my boots as if I had guessed his next question.

"Can you move your toes?"

"Yes," I nodded with relief.

"We'll call an ambulance."

I pointed to the thick smoke rising from the hood.

"Will the car explode?" I asked.

"No, ma'am."

"It's just that...isn't there a fire in there?"

I knew he was telling the truth, that there was no danger, but my mind returned to its usual nervousness. The previous feeling of compassionate connection without attachment had dissipated leaving an empty space. Terrified thoughts tried to take advantage and rushed in the void to invade me again. But I didn't want them! Taking a deep breath, I forced myself to return to that *other* state of observant peace. And I regained it.

The policeman asked his usual questions: my name, what day it was and others. I answered conscientiously. I told him it was Thursday, that I got off work late, that despite the rain, I had been driving in a hurry because I was going to see a movie with my husband. It was starting at nine o'clock and I was running late –by now, no matter how much of a hurry we were in, the movie would be more than started.

"What is your husband's phone number?" he asked.

I gave it to him.

The ambulance arrived with its red and blue lights reflecting on the wet pavement. Before I knew it, I was on a stretcher in the ambulance, rolling toward the hospital. However, I felt fine. I was unharmed and alive and nothing serious had happened other than the sensations in my mind and the convulsion my body had undergone. Then, a thought went through my head; in fact, more than one, until it formed a chain that would have lined up to parade in front of my imagination.

I had read somewhere that people who are in a state of shock, even when they have been on the verge of death, relate that their lives flash before their eyes. These people insist that it is like an inventory of all their good and bad deeds. The *good* appears in a deluge of love and fuzzy excitement; the bad is remembered with regret and pain. I don't know if this is true. I don't know if there is such an inner vision when one finds oneself in such a situation or worse. What I do know is what I experienced. I did see images in procession. And, yes, they were like a familiar movie making its way across the screen of my mind. But they were not images from the past. No, not at all. They were images of an unlived future, the film in order of my unfulfilled dreams passing by one by one like an accusing zoetrope. All the wishes and desires that had not materialized. A life not lived passed through my head.

Dressed in their most colorful clothes, these dreams appeared to me like a puppet show. People, documents, little stars, written pages, laughter, dances, trips, suitcases, ancestors. All those plans I had put off, weighing them as less important than my daily responsibilities. And yet, it was what my soul wanted. What I had systematically, with hellish logic, denied myself. They were the yearnings of my heart. I had chosen my duties, to do the *correct* thing instead of following my dreams. The latter I had judged and condemned to *waiting*. My dreams, my pure hopeful dreams, I had judged them *lesser* and sent them as punishment to the corner.

It was a profound judgment of myself. I contemplated it with horror. Until then, I had preferred to put aside my ideas and give what I had —my time and energy, my joy even—to everyone and everything else. Of course, who would tell me to do otherwise? I had done the right thing for my family, hadn't I? But I had forgotten my dreams! I forgot the reason for my existence by my first and last names. And that's what I saw in the vision on the way to the hospital! Not in outlandish fashion, not through divine grace. Not with celestial music or deep pain. No. It was just future dreams that were patiently waiting for me to bring them out of their cave, out of the attic of unconsciousness, and strive for them, to make them come true. And among them were the unfulfilled adventures with my ancestors.

Then, as if it were the most natural thing to do and in contrast to the events of the moment, I proceeded to make an inventory. While the ambulance was driving along, I lifted each finger as if counting them. Each finger was a different cherished dream that needed to be attended to, even the ones I considered the craziest, like going on trips to villages and cemeteries related to my Italian ancestors. I didn't judge anything as good or bad, practical or not, possible or impossible. Nor did I consider whether I had the resources to do them. I simply listened, watched, let them float pass by my imaginary eyes and took mental notes.

When the doors to the emergency entrance of the hospital opened with a loud roar, I wasn't even distracted. I counted each and every dream on my fingers and counted them again. Sometimes I would put them in order and go over them again: I would get to the last one and fear that the first one would escape me.

The medical staff placed me on a metal bed in a makeshift room with flickering lights. The doctors whispered questions to each other and speculated about my condition. But I wasn't interested in any of it. I had enough to attend to my own thoughts; I wasn't willing to be distracted by anything. At first it was a delicate, almost shy list. But also definitely a happy list. It came with the weight of inner wisdom telling me that I needed to slow down and focus my time on what I came into this life to do. I remembered Isidoro and his abandoned Bianca. I was consciously made aware of the catalytic thought that summoned me to face the mystery in my genealogical research. It had unleashed the discovery of an ancestral and divine love to my Italian ancestry.

"But there was more to my ancestor's life than that tragic moment, wasn't there?" Obviously in a life, any life, there is more than one act, and, although the story of the abandonment remained an enigma to me and I had not yet managed to learn the truth, I was convinced that more to the story than the obvious. My ancestors had traveled and lived, and had children, and had started a hotel business. They had laughed, cried, danced, kissed and hugged, and undertaken so many dreams. There was so much more to know about them, so much more to discover. And in my dreams they were all there, fascinating unknowns waiting for me to discover and bring to light the Italian in me. The Italy that came from them as a divine gift.

"I want to visit Italy...all parts of Italy. To find joy in all the places where my ancestors came from."

Even the hum of the machines helped me to concentrate and draw and drop my dreams into the ether in my mind. I would catch them in bits and pieces and put them in place. I wove some into an imaginary map. Others did not come to me clearly; they seemed more like little goldfish to be rescued from the depths of the sea of forgetfulness. I had to re-establish links to a soul that was asking me for a life not yet lived before it was too late.

"I begin today to walk in a figurative sense because I want to do it on the stones they stepped on and take the paths they took. To return to their starting points and walk the path with them."

It implied reaching Isidoro and Bianca's homeland. To breathe in the air of those places. To put my feet on the ground and take a walk on the cobblestones that they themselves had once stood upon. Then, I imagined their children's bare feet on stones polished by the passing of life. And I was honored by the opportunity to place my own on those same paths. I also thought of Isidoro and Bianca, holding hands with their young children, embarking onto new worlds. That made me focus on Bianca, to remember the photo of my great-grandmother with her children.

I will discover the strength I inherited from you. The woman I am because of you.

If there was anything inside me that was as formidable as she was, I had to find it and prove it to myself by practicing that strength wrapped in love.

A couple of nurses took me to my assigned room. I could hear the wheels of my gurney turning. I went on with my list that seemed more like a litany of images and words, like a gentle rain at dawn. Each drop, a wish. Each wish, a blessing. It was a shower of blessings.

I am the dreams of my ancestors come true. I will represent them in my life, every day. They live through me. They come through my eyes and through my heart.

I was amazed when I was overcome with the certainty that my grandmother Chela would approve with a smile, so I made a silent request to her for help and assistance with my dreams. But it was Isidoro to whom I spoke for the first time. I didn't even care if I thought of myself as crazy; I had just survived an accident that turned my car into a tin wreck, I well deserved a moment of delirium and I gave it to myself.

"Isidoro, see what you do....to take me there. Show me all that I want to see. Delight me with surprises!"

The doctors had tried to find something wrong or broken inside me, entering my body into every machine they found at their disposal, but to no avail. At two o'clock in the morning I was discharged. I insisted that I wanted to go home and rest in my own bed. I had kept among the feathers of my pillows more secret dreams that even I did not dare to confess for fear that they would not be fulfilled. Until this day! Fulfilled or not, I would give my longings a preferential place. I would treat them with honor, respect and gratitude. Even if I did not have the means or the time to travel to Italy, I would not fail to investigate their lives, nor would I postpone it any longer I told myself solemnly. I would also change my lifestyle to the Italian way to make sure I would include them and enjoy them on a daily basis.

My husband and André, my eldest son, came looking for me. Seeing me sitting on the bed, already dressed, André said to me, "Mami, you look so fragile sitting there that I'm afraid to hug you. I feel that if I do, I might hurt you." He just came closer and kissed me with exquisite gentleness on my forehead.

Altered by a strange feeling of ecstasy, I could not formulate words. I could barely manage to say, "I am more alive than ever."

My body might suffer, but nothing would break my soul. Because I am not only this physical body. I am more, much more. And there I was, standing in front of the rest of my life. Destiny was calling me with a limpid and transparent voice, and, with the path clear, I could see my dreams in the distance and open my arms to receive the divine gifts of my ancestors.

WILD DREAMS

"*I* missed you before I met you." That was what the spirit of my ancestors whispered to me in a dream. I woke up under a spring rain that pounded on the windowpanes, as if it wanted to warn me that it too was aware. The tinkling of the water and the rushing of the wind invited me to dream on. With my head on the pillow, the words floated in a kind of autonomous reality and made sentences. "Before I was born, I already knew you and I was waiting for you."

I opened my eyes, hugging my pillow and enjoying the sight of the colorful rattle I had bought that mimicked the one in my mom's room. I remembered the dream and the whisper of words. Were they in English? *"I missed you before I met you,"* they said. Ah, no! It was neither English nor Spanish. It was the language of dreams.

Dressed for work, I was sitting with my little ones at the breakfast table; in my hands, a tasty, steaming latte. Alex, six years-old, chattered happily while Victor, my two-year-old, took his cereal, catching it in his little fingers. The floating words made me wonder if these were the dreams of my ancestors, if they were dreams borrowed from them. So who was missing whom? *I was born after them, so it can't be that they supposedly miss me, right?* Before leaving, I looked at the boxes of genealogy documents that I had taken back out and placed on the living room table. "Which one of you is talking to me in my sleep?"

At that time, with such a demanding job and a young family, I thought going to Italy would take years to make happen. Besides, we were living paycheck to paycheck and had no extra resources to schedule a luxury trip. So, I decided to bring Italy home to me. Between food and genealogy I would make do until the opportunity came.

I had no idea what fate or perhaps my ancestors had in store for me! But I did feel a force encouraging me, sustaining me, and filling me with love. With this new focus, I systematically returned to my genealogy research. Isidoro's line had led me to his father's name: Stefano.

"This time it's your turn, Stefano." I said, organizing my papers and leaving the rectangle where his parents' names should have been on the tree empty.

At the Mormon's temple, I went back to the genealogy room to look for his birth certificate. I had done so with Isidoro and found it fruitful. I thought I was already an expert and that finding Stefano's document would also be relatively easy. But this time it would not be so. When I was able to sit down in front of the cold microfilm readers, I turned the reel, page by page through the San Secondo records, eagerly searching for Stefano. I didn't have an exact year, so I had to check several and many pages of the registry were out of place. No matter how many times I turned, I could not find his name. It seemed that my luck was changing in a hidden way.

Between working in the District of Columbia and living in Virginia, I was driving every day, and by the time I got home, I was exhausted. It was only on Saturdays that I was able to devote myself to it, I would go back and turn the spool looking for the document of his birth. Months later, I redoubled my efforts by sending a letter to the Archdiocese of Parma. I waited...and waited...and nothing.

One day, as I sat behind my office desk, the phone rang. It was a former co-worker. He told me that he had formed his own technology firm. A *dotcom*, no less. I congratulated him and he almost interrupted me, there was more! He had won a contract from a huge company and was now putting together a team to fulfill his obligations. He was calling people he felt could help him. "I want you to be part of my *dream team*," he told me. It included creative work for me, a short commute and flexible hours.

I accepted immediately! I said goodbye to driving almost three hours a day. Time cleared in my favor.

On the first day of my new job, I made my way to the red brick building in Fairfax at the address my friend had provided beforehand. The *lobby* was large and modern with electronic toys everywhere mimicking the offices of Google or Microsoft. A silver metal robot dog came out to greet me. It barked and wagged its tail and I thought it was a recording of a Pekingese puppy barking. Very funny and witty. A girl in an excellently cut office dress came over and handed me a note from my friend, the owner, which read, "As you may have noticed, the offices are under construction. Please excuse the boxes and dust. Follow the hallway and choose the one you want." Kindly, the young woman indicated which of the offices I could choose, and I chose one as far away from the noise as possible. Although it had no windows, it had a world of space. The freshly painted walls were blank canvases... ready for my imagination! I designed my place according to my longing. I christened it and put up a sign that read: "Italy. Land of my ancestors. *La dolce vita inizia qui.*" On one side, I hung a map of Italy. I marked in red San Secondo Parmense, northeast of Parma, Isidoro's hometown. I marked Castello d'Argile in Bologna, Bianca's hometown. From a calendar of photographs of this country, mainly Tuscany, I cut out images of its landscapes and pasted them on the wall. These would be my windows! So every time I was sitting at my desk, I could look up on each side and admire the Etruscan ruins, the painted frescoes, the fields of sunflowers and the tall, slender pines, typical of that geography I loved. I was inspired and I autographed one of the photos as if I were my ancestor: "For my great-granddaughter Graciela, from her *bisnonno* Isidoro."

"Are you going to gift me Italy, Isidoro?", I affectionately spoke aloud to the air, listening to the echo of my own voice and with an open smile in my heart. I didn't even have a picture of him, but I did have a picture of his precious land.

There is an Italy inside me! It's that of my ancestors. And all their dreams live in me. I imagined the day when I could visit the church where some of them had married to light a candle for the union of the family. I would whisper their names to the stones and tell them, "They came back...in me!"

On the road I would happily listen to audiobooks like Frances Mayes' *Under the Tuscan Sun* and Peter Mayle's *A Year in Provence*. Every day I would say, "I'm going to Italy!" and travel with the narration. And when pink cherry leaves sweetened the wind and petals danced on the undulating road of a track, I was transported to my Italy. At home, I decided to cultivate my bonds through cooking. I called Mami and told her I wanted to improve my culinary art and she promised to help me. "There's a culinary instinct. It will come out in you. You'll see." She was an excellent cook, like all the women in the family. But she accepted that even her mother and aunts were always better than her. "Each one had her specialty." And I couldn't wait to find out what mine would be.

The new routine in the house became lighter and more pleasant. Ancestral gastronomy was an esoteric alchemy that gladdened our hearts. With each thing, whether it was homemade or not, it made an incantation that delighted us. *Pizza*, for example, was not a simple matter anymore. Every Friday when the flatbread arrived, I would add extra oregano and even a drizzle of olive oil. My kids loved this topping. "There's an Italy in you too," I told them, and this induced them, André in the lead and even Victor copying him, to order food from me imitating the Italian accent, which gave us a lot of laughter.

At the beginning of the summer, Murat and I were at a party celebrating a friend who was receiving an award. Both he and his spouse were very funny, and he told us that he had asked his wife if she had dreamed of his success. Without missing a beat, she had jokingly replied, "I'm sorry, dear, but my dreams are dreams, and they don't have awards for you. My dreams are wild dreams, so you are hardly in them." We all laughed. It was a joke that Murat and I found funny, and quickly adopted, playing at saying to each other, "Darling, do my dreams match yours? Tell me from now on! What are you dreaming about? Am I in your wildest dreams?"

Mine were very clear. I wanted to go to Italy to see the land of my ancestors. But what was Murat's wildest dream? Surprise! Italy was not in any of them. Neither in the craziest nor in the most ordinary. I found out one day, after talking about dreams one more time.

"So, you mean Isidoro isn't in all of your dreams too?" I asked jokingly, pretending to be amazed.

"No...not really," he concluded after pretending to have given it a lot of thought.

We had enjoyed a dinner we had prepared together: *Spaghetti Bolognese* with *heirloom* tomatoes to which we had added a few sprigs of basil and thymus, the latter being one of my favorites. Our children had gobbled it up, leaving not a trace behind. Now we were watching a soccer game with popcorn that I prepared with coconut oil and salads. *Yummy.*

"How bad!" I replied, laughing and throwing a piece of popcorn at him.

He caught it with his mouth.

"Timbuktu is in my wildest dreams," he said, smiling.

"Oh no, we have to have the same dreams! Otherwise, they won't come true!"

"How so?"

"Don't you remember that the Bible says that if two join in prayer, what they ask for will be given?"

"Yes, but it refers to prayers, not dreams," he protested, catching more popcorn.

"Isn't that the same thing?"

All of a sudden, it was becoming imperative to compile at least the same goal: Italy. I explained it to him patiently.

"If two people or more together agree on something and pray for it, it is granted. Likewise, if two people agree in yearning for the same dream, it is granted to them."

Murat joked, "I have dreamed of pasta and *limoncello*. That's right! But Isidoro...in my dreams? Nah! Not so much!"

"And how are we going to get to Italy if we don't share the same dream, if you don't dream of Italy too?" I insisted.

"I have the impression that this is going to end up being my fault if I don't start dreaming about Italy right away. Let me think..." He closed his eyes and said, "When I was a kid, my dad used to take me to do archeology in Turkey, and what I liked most was to discover the ancient mosaics and put them back together again. When I think of Italy, I think of that art. The art of forming mosaics. In fact, those of Ravenna, and of Lucca. When I was young, I dreamed of taking a class there. Yes, I can dream about that."

I immediately set my imagination running. I spent the whole summer looking for art institutes that offered mosaic classes. When I got responses, I was horrified at how expensive they were! Plus, they had a demanding class schedule. Combining ancestry with mosaic art didn't seem to tie in, but then I thought, "And isn't it the same thing?" I changed tactics. I looked for a freelance teacher who taught workshops or an artist who wanted to teach. I visualized a free soul who would just teach a few classes for a couple of days. A kindred spirit who wanted to play art with us.

While that was taking its course, I was still researching Italian food to include in our lives, specifically from the Parma and Bologna area. I discovered that pumpkins were grown in Parma. When the season arrived, I experimented with pumpkins. That fall I scooped out the pulp and made a soup; another time, I added chunks to a *fusilli* pasta sauce. I toasted the seeds to combine with bread and olive oil. On the pumpkin shell, I drew cute little faces and put scented candles in the center.

I told Mami about all these adventures. I wanted her to give me family recipes, but I was astonished by what she told me:

"Actually, my grandmother cooked without recipes, but I have my own recipe book that I can send you."

As Italy is a vast country with a diverse climate, the cuisine depends on what is grown in the regions. I discovered that, although Isidoro and Bianca's towns were relatively close to each other, the cuisine in both parts was typically different according to the local ingredients. Mami gave me the example of one of Santo Domingo's cousins, who made variations on Italian recipes and they were exquisite."

"She makes *gnocchi* with sweet potato and yellow plantain, and when combined with the *Bolognese* sauce with meat it is a deadly delight!"

The latter sounded to me like permission to experiment according to the ingredients I found in Virginia.

As October rolled in, I continued to search for my ancestor

Stefano as well as a teacher willing to teach mosaic courses. To my husband, I insisted he should dream of Italy. Laughing, he agreed. "I'm already dreaming of it."

Something wonderful happened in late October. I received an email that looked promising. A freelance artist named Grazia wrote to offer me her services. "I am a mosaic teacher and can host you in my studio—what dates are you planning to come?"

I remember it was evening and my house was decorated and ready for *Halloween*. Murat was watching a soccer game in the living room; Galatasaray was playing against Tottenham. The kids were asleep in their rooms. My last action of the day was always to check my emails. Sitting in front of my computer, I clicked on the tray and read.

Grazia's message made me feel a strange premonition. Maybe because our names are similar. Myself, Graciela Maria and her, Grazia Maria. Or maybe because our last names are pronounced the same, forming the same initials. Believe it or not...there were more coincidences! We were the same age, married to foreigners and came from an island. In her case, Sicily. Moreover, our first children were born in October. Her son's name was Andreas and my son's was André. I was reading all this with great care, trying to calm my instincts that were screaming inside me. "This is it!"

The question she asked me put it all into perspective: "On what date are you coming?" I had to pause. In my previous search, it was the professors who imposed their dates, schedule, curriculum and payment in advance. None of them had made it so simple..., as if it was just up to us. She was the one who would accommodate our dates, our time and our desires. When I opened the photos of her artwork that she sent attached to her email, I saw that she had nothing to envy from what the other teachers had sent previously. Her work was amazing. And, to top it off, she offered to help us find accommodation.

I felt inspired and wrote to back that I wanted to visit the land of my ancestors, that San Secondo was in Parma and not Tuscany. In her response to my concern, she assured me that from Tuscany to Parma... it was only a three-hour drive! She made it sound so simple that, for an instant, I gave myself the opportunity to close my eyes and contemplate all that she had to offer. And the only question I asked was, "When are you going?"

I closed my eyes again and inhaled slowly, asking inwardly, *November? Impossible! Too soon... December? No way! With Christmas and my small children I was already busy. January? I don't feel it's appropriate!*

It was as if my heartbeat had an opinion of its own. As if I could find an answer inside me. And what surfaced was a clear logic: late February to early March would be the best time. But I hesitated. *Would it be the right date?* Then I calmed myself down, thinking that was enough time to see how things would unfold.

From my seat, I saw Murat in profile, cheering very enthusiastically for his team for a possible goal. I raised my voice a bit so he could hear me over the din of the television.

"If we go to Italy, would you mind if we went in winter?"

"No, not at all," he answered without turning around. He was still concentrating on his game: "It's cold here, it's cold there, it's the same climate. Only over there we would eat warm and delicious *tortellini.*"

As I wrote down the dates, my words took on confidence. "For a couple of weeks we will be visiting Italy between the end of February and the beginning of March.

It felt strangely true. Like a premonition.

Regarding her offer to help us find lodging, she replied that she knew of a couple of choices. One of them would be a little yellow house, next to her house. Grazia lived half an hour from town, in a house the color of the sun on the slopes of some Tuscan hills, near some Etruscan ruins. There, the cost would be minimal. Again, she made it sound so easy and uncomplicated. My heart began to beat happily in response. And I imagined myself living in a mountain cottage. But when I read the second offer, I got even more excited. "You also have the option to stay in an authentic Tuscan tower. Some friends are renting an apartment there. I'll ask for a discount and you can see it." Then I imagined myself living in the tower of a castle and seeing the whole *cittadina* at my feet.

"*Magnifico!*" I exclaimed, already dressed as a damsel in my imagination.

Now, it was my turn to ask her the key question: "What is the price of the course?"

I held back the possible mental shock at the cost. The answer came almost immediately. I was surprised given the time difference that she was also awake all the way over in the middle of Tuscany. When I read her price, my jaw dropped—totally doable! I jumped out of my seat and started dancing and singing

"We are going to Italy, we are going to Italyyyy...!"

At the same time, I heard the commentator on TV narrating a winning goal and Murat stood up shouting it as only Latin commentators can do, "Gooooal!" And he kept repeating, "Goooooal!"

We both ended up holding hands and dancing, stepping on each other's toes and running over each other with our joy! I sang, "We are going to Italy, we are going to Italyyyy...!"

As he was yelling, "Gooooooal!"

THANKSGIVING

"*L*et's change the Thanksgiving tradition a bit," I jokingly suggested to my husband. "Let's cook duck instead of turkey."

This was because I had read that during hunting season in Parma they prepared a dish of wild duck with rosemary and other herbs.

"No, ma'am," he replied with a laugh. "We'll stick with the turkey."

In previous years, I had added other side options to the dishes: yucca, fried yellow plantains, and even rice and beans. This had proved very popular with his family; my in-laws had loved it, especially the yucca! So I would prepare some more for them to take home with them. This Thanksgiving coming up, it warranted a much more extensive combination of preparations. I was going to add something Italian to the table, not pasta but rather antipasto dishes from the Emilia Romagna region. Because that is the region that encompassed both Isidoro's and Bianca's towns.

Also, taking advantage of the occasion, I made arrangements in the house. We hung oil paintings in the dining room depicting the Italian countryside with its ochre and orange tones combined with its red roofs. My kitchen, which was already painted in a canary yellow, looked great with light green and burnt autumn sienna accents, as did the dining table covered with a tablecloth in the same colors. With great enthusiasm and love, I cooked the turkey in orange juice as I usually did, with an addition of ginger that turned it sweet and sour. In the years I have been making these types of recipes, I have learned the trick of putting salt inside the turkey along with seasonings such as rosemary, thymus and many heads of garlic. After the turkey is cooked, I make a dressing with that garlic by pulling each clove and mashing it together with fresh herbs. All of this turns into a butter-style sauce... delicious! and served on the side for those diners who would like to add more with a spoon.

For the salad, I chopped dried figs in spicy honey, gorgonzola cheese, walnuts and placed everything on top of some tender spinach leaves. The marinade was balsamic vinegar with *fragola* or strawberry. I also tried cooking a tuber called Jerusalem Artichoke, which I discovered in Bologna is made with cheese. I mashed it and added it to the typical mashed potatoes served at this time of the year. In order not to leave the ham behind, I served it like prosciutto with bits of melon flavored with mint. Of course I didn't miss the sweet potato with marshmallow! Because...why not? The dessert was baked pears in syrup; I read that this is how they are made in Parma, with a vanilla ice cream to make it *a la mode* and even more delicious. The typical apple pie was also present. I was glad I put so much effort into this celebration because it was the last time we were all together. The dinner was a gastronomic success. My little kids and the grown-ups feasted all weekend on the leftovers. We celebrated with Christmas carols.

Unfortunately, after so much happiness, tragedy soon came knocking at our door. After such illusory dreamlike images in which I discovered Italy and felt her stronger in me, reality became a solemn nightmare. Every week, a new sadness. Real life. Most painful of all was that Pavel, who took care of my three children, the one who drove them to school in the mornings and picked them up in the afternoons, died of a heart attack. Every day, he would go out for a walk with Victor, the youngest, who was not quite three years old. By chance, that Monday they did not repeat the plan because he had not woken up. Undoubtedly, this fact miraculously prevented another tragedy. That of my little boy being in his car with him. This was one of the strangest and saddest days of our lives. Our children were grief-stricken for months. All of a sudden, we had lost a very dear person who cared for them so lovingly. This situation reminded us how delicate and fragile life is. The pain that the whole family felt cannot be explained here. A loss that we still carry and that has been irreparable.

After this event, in December, Murat's father informed us that he had been diagnosed with lung cancer. We were shocked by this news. His decision he was to let the disease take its normal course. He only asked for medicine to avoid pain and keep him comfortable. I admired his courage and fortitude.

Slightly less traumatic but also destabilizing was that at the end of December there was a change in my employment position. My friend's company where I was working was acquired by another company and my status changed from director to consultant. It came with the advantage of being able to work from home and even more flexible time, but also with the disadvantage of uncertainty. My contract would remain in place for a year, but I didn't know what would happen after that.

On December 31, as I was talking to Mami on the phone and she was trying to soothe my soul, she said, "Don't add me to your list of worries. For now, all is well with me and my health. The disease is in remission and I don't plan to die for now."

Because she was so strong, I believed her. However, I was not so sure about my husband's dad. I had taken my plans for the trip to Italy out of my sight as it seemed selfish.

As I had done so far, I turned my energies to the kitchen. In it I found a kind of solace. For New Year's Eve, I cooked polenta with sage. Actually, at home in Santo Domingo, polenta was fried in little square pieces, but this time I did not fry it, I put it in the oven. Cooking this recipe was my grandmother Chela's specialty, she made it delicious, soft and light, it almost felt whipped. Mami had instructed me in the steps over the phone. The result was a smooth and creamy mixture with tomato paste. For garnish, I included the extra sage on top, as I like to see the green among the red.

That first New Year's Day, as we cleaned up the kitchen, Murat and I commented,

"Oof! It's a good thing we didn't buy the tickets, we would have lost them!"

"Yes, we were lucky in that," he replied. "Have you informed Grazia yet that we're not going to Italy?"

"No, not yet. I wanted to feel Italy close to me. That's why I have delayed in informing her, because I thought that, by doing so, it would be like closing a door on those dreams."

"I actually was dreaming to have those adventures with your ancestors," he confessed.

"In the first week of the year I will inform her that there is no Italy happening for us," I added.

Inside, something was telling me to wait, *for what I did not know.*

Surprisingly, something happened that woke me up on the second morning of that new year. For inexplicable reasons, I woke up much earlier than usual. I opened my eyes and noticed the new wind chimes hanging in my window. They were made of stained glass suspended from a piece of wood. I had bought it to imitate the sound of the one in Mami's room. But they didn't sound the same! Hers were like little bells that produced a cheerful tinkle! while mine was almost a crazy *tinkle-tri-trinkle!* I woke up sensing it, or so I thought. Awakened, I jumped up quickly. Then I stood by the side of the bed thinking, *What now?* My husband was still sleeping peacefully. Like a zombie, I went downstairs looking for coffee. Instead of going to the kitchen, I continued straight ahead and wandered into what we called "the little office" to turn on my computer. As if directed, I sat down in my chair and calmly opened my email inbox. Maybe Mami had sent me one of her jokes. It wasn't that I needed them but, then again, maybe I did. If there weren't any new ones, I'd reread some that made me laugh. Cell phones at the time didn't yet have the technology to be able to check emails; you could only do it through a computer.

When I opened my inbox, I saw something that caught my attention −an unexpected email! What I read on the screen woke me up. I read and reread. I straightened up in my chair and went back to reading. My breath caught. Almost to convince myself, I repeated it out loud:

"Flight specials to Italy... Airline with new route to Rome offers the $199 per person fare."

I had run out of air. My brain was spinning, trying to understand.

Graciela, breathe, I commanded myself.

My heart kicked in and my lungs filled with oxygen. I made the necessary clicks. I saw the words "flexible dates" And that's what I chose. My mouth was still open in amazement. Suddenly, I got a calendar with the month of February and next to it, the month of March. Red squares indicated the unavailable days and in green, the available ones. With my right hand, I checked the days, and my left hand was busy moving the computer mouse, clicking on the outgoing flights because that was the only way to show the return ones. I didn't want to shout so as not to wake the children, but it was imperative that Murat came down and see this. The decision to buy a plane ticket for that price had to be made in less than five minutes. I could imagine how many people were waking up right now and starting to shop. There was no time to waste!

So, with my left arm crossed over my right, I picked up the house phone and called him on his cell phone. The computer desk was exactly below our room. It made me laugh to hear his cell phone ringing upstairs, through the ceiling. I imagined him in our bed, opening it a little confused. As soon as I heard his *"huh?"*, I didn't want to waste a millisecond. I blurted out the words like bullets fired:

"Tickets. Italy. Two hundred dollars."

"What?"

His voice on the other end of the line sounded like from beyond the grave. I had never called him from the inside our own house before.

"Tickets! Italy! $200!" I repeated and urged him to understand immediately. Although I knew he didn't understand in the least.

"But...where are you?"

"In the house, downstairs, in front of the computer!"

With my arms crossed, not wanting to let go of the mouse or the phone, I told him to come downstairs, but he didn't react. So, I told him that a few months ago I had put myself on a mailing list where the airline notified me when they put their tickets on sale. I had received other notifications in the past, but the prices were no less than $700. But today, the price was much lower, almost for free!

"A trip from here to Rome, can you imagine?"

No, he did not imagine. I ordered him to come down immediately and come and see. He was neither fully awake nor fully convinced. What if it was a trick or a scam? On that, he was right to doubt, we had to be careful. I was just focused on getting the operation done. I needed the final click. I needed him to agree.

"I understand." I said. "If, after I choose this, they come up with some outlandish charges, then I click where it says cancel and that's it!"

"But what if something happens to my dad? What if we buy them and we can't go because he gets sicker?"

I was trying to protect myself from possible disappointment. For a second, I thought he was right. But then I thought that a ticket at that price was already a miracle. A gift! And that it would even be irresponsible for us not to accept such a gift. My intuition was asking me to trust. I thought of Isidoro and Bianca.

"If something bad happens and we can't travel, that's a risk I'm willing to take. I'm willing to buy them at this miraculous price and lose them if that's their fate. It's like a metaphor. It would be like going forward towards our dreams. The first step to crazy dreaming!"

I knew this seemed like an absurdity among so many tragedies. But to my state of mind at the time it was like a lifeline. It was hope. What if the spirit of our ancestors simply trying to indulge us! It seemed like a plan. I just had to follow it.

In the end the term "wild dream" managed to motivate and fill him with enthusiasm. He ran down the stairs.

"What are the dates?" he asked.

He was standing behind me. We were both talking on the phone in the same room, and it was funny.

"I think the one for February 19 is open...."

Then, we started laughing because we were both looking at the screen, still with phones held to our ears and he was looking at the dates over my shoulder. I hung up so I could concentrate.

"Pick the dates you can...this is a miracle!" He agreed. Now awake and overjoyed, he went to the kitchen to make coffee.

"Awesome! The only dates available are almost the same ones I gave Grazia before." When I had the printed plane ticket in my hand... I couldn't believe it! I read all the little letters with the disclaimers. It looked valid. Two airline tickets...normal, ordinary, plane tickets. Feeling exuberant, I looked up to where the map of Italy was hanging. "I'm going to visit you, Italy. I'm coming to visit you, San Secondo. I'm on my way."

And that's how the ticket purchase happened. A true gift...from my ancestors? We celebrated that day with a delicious Italian meal.

Time went by and three weeks before our supposed departure and I had made the appointment with the Italian embassy in Washington D.C. to get a visa. I thought I would have it stamped in my passport, even if only as a decoration. I was not despairing, but I was aware that my father-in-law's health was deteriorating. One night we were told that he had a serious setback. Murat said to me:

"I don't think we can go to Italy."

His eyes had a grave expression, as if apologizing for my disappointment.

I answered him sincerely. "I have no problem in not going. In my mind, I have already traveled to Italy a thousand times. It's clear to me that my dreams are always better than reality."

But he was still crestfallen, there were so many things! So, I added, "Italy is not going to move from its place. It will always be there, waiting for us when the time is right. I don't want you to worry about me... not at all! A trip to Italy we can always do at any other time. Another year. That's fine."

He didn't answer, so, to ease the situation, I said jokingly, referring to Italy's shape, "What do you think is going to happen to the boot? Do you think he's going to pack his bags, pick them up and telling the rest of Europe' *'I'm moving, eh! Let's see what they do without me!?'* And then, as he jumps into the middle of the ocean, Italy will shout, *'Hold on, everybody, we're getting out of here!'*" I was already on my feet, doing the theater act, "The people will be grabbing and shouting, *begging him to stay.* But Italy is stubborn and will just keep repeating, *Let go, I said!*"

I raised my arms in proof that this was never going to happen. "No, Italy is not going to move from its place. It will always be there waiting for us when we are ready."

This was also my attempt of making him laugh before he could feel bad for me. He's used to seeing my little Hollywood productions with acting and everything. This time, he didn't laugh. He just watched me from his side of the bed.

Finally he replied, "No. I don't think the boot says it that way. It sounds more Dominican than Italian..."

Now, he was joking.

I lay back down on the bed and sighed.

"Everything will be fine." I knew it by a strange conviction. "Don't forget, at this moment, there's nothing waiting for us in Italy."

I wasn't being completely truthful, but I was trying to make Murat feel better. After searching in vain for Stefano's birth certificate in the genealogy offices, I had written to San Secondo inquiring about it and, recently, I had received an answer. An official of the commune had replied to me by email that he had found it. Romantically, I replied that he should not send it to me, that instead I would retrieve it from his own hands—that I'd go and visit San Secondo! I dreamed of appearing in the civil offices of that town and searching page by page in the old books. Perhaps, they would have a wilted scent, the stitching loose and the leather cover wonderfully cracked like furrows in their history. I would open them carefully so that their aged leaves would not disintegrate. Amongst the calligraphy, I would discover the hidden treasures which were the names of my ancestors; Stefano, and his parents' names *What were his parents' names?* And I'd finally, be able to fill in that little rectangle on the family tree!

Now, I was not so sure of this decision to wait until I arrived and receive it in my own hands. Maybe it hadn't been a good idea to tell them that.

Through the window, I saw the dark, moonless night. They had announced a storm, but there was still no snow or even rain to entertain the wind. The space between the house and the trees seemed empty. "Destination: Italy" was not something I could influence. There was nothing else to do. I surrendered everything and a curiosity blossomed in my being. *If so, how would it happen?* Logically, years would pass, though truly, I felt Italy was so close!

What are my ancestors and the angels of divinity up to? Will Italy be our destiny?

ITALIAN EMBASSY

*I*f there was even a small possibility of traveling to Italy, there were a few things to prepare, and I needed to figure them out in case it became a reality. To go, I had to have my passport stamped with an entry visa. Two days before my appointment with the Italian embassy it snowed heavily. In my yard, the snow had accumulated a foot high. That morning, from the kitchen window I could see the tips of the pine trees glistening with frost. The ice had stuck to the evergreen needles and bent the boughs almost to the ground. They were like this because on top of the snowfall, it had rained cats and dogs, so now everything was frozen solid. Sometimes, rain after a snowfall can be good because it sweeps away and melts the snow, but if the temperature drops, the roads become very dangerous because layers of ice form on them.

A few days before, we talked to my in-laws about the potential trip to Italy. We told them everything that had happened, how we had discovered Grazia, the price of the tickets and Stefano's certificate that was waiting for us. They were immediately supportive. "We want you to travel and come back with your anecdotes," they told us cheerfully.

So, that day after the snowstorm, I was driving alone on the interstate. The hum of my *Odyssey* van's engine broke the frozen silence of the early morning. My vehicle was heavy, and I knew I had to go at a steady speed. The "shish" sound of the wheels as they rolled down the road kept me very serious and focused. My eyes were like those of an eagle soaring over the prairie. .The flat snowy expanse of six-lane pavement was my immediate destination...the road to the Italian embassy to obtain the entry visa.

In a conversation with Mami the night before, she had given me her very philosophical take on the situation, with a *carpe diem*-style twist. "There are always going to be hard situations to deal with in life. There's never going to be a better time to do things."

I appreciated her words and remarked, "I have a couple of friends who have offered to stay home to watch the kids for those twelve days we'll be gone."

She added, "See, it all works out. We have to do everything we can. What we can't, we leave in God's hands."

Anything could happen in the week we had planned to take the plane. However, sitting in my car, I mentally encouraged myself: *I no longer care if I go or don't go, but I want to have my passport stamped with the Italian visa.*

I crossed the Key Bridge to enter the city. Soon I arrived at the embassy. With the care and precision of a juggler, I slowed down. My van behaved like a champion. If it had been a person, I would have rewarded her. "Nothing is going to stop us!" I mumbled to her. "My ancestors and my angels won't let anything stop us!"

But when I spotted the slope at the corner of the embassy, my heart deflated a little. The sidewalk was frozen. My hands clasped in prayer to the almighty, and I pleaded to the sky. I asked my ancestors to help me come out of this ordeal unharmed and without a bruise.

The only parking I could find was at the top of the hill. The entrance gate to the embassy was made of iron and was all the way at the bottom of the hill, at the corner of an intersection. I would have to come down all the way the frozen sidewalk. I turned off the car and calculated how to get out in the least dangerous way. I moved from my seat to get out through the passenger door. I pushed the passenger door from the inside and was amazed that, at the first attempt, I could not open it. It was stuck—frozen shut! With great effort, I managed to push it open and there was a loud creaking sound. Digging the heels of my boots into the snow, I got out. Closing the door with great momentum, I almost fell back-

wards. I managed to balance myself and let myself slide until I diag-
onally touched the opposite wall of the sidewalk. I stabilized
myself, and at the same time realized that I was not going to walk,
but rather slide down that hill until I reached the entrance. The
soles of my boots could not grip the surface; it felt like I was on ice
skates. I clung to the wall until I managed to grab hold of the
nearest tree. It was cold and hard as stone and as I held on to a
branch, it rained frost on my face. So, hugging my purse with my
precious passport inside, I let go of the tree and skidded downward
until I reached the rail to the side of the embassy wall. From there, I
swooped a little further down until I could grab the trunk of
another tree. I was zigzagging.

Ok. One tree down. Twenty more to go, I thought. There weren't
twenty of them, but it felt like it! I pushed myself again and kept
going like that. It must have looked like a dance: touch the wall,
push, hold on to a tree and then another... more frost on my face
and so on. *Tree...easy...easy...easy...don't move.* If this kept up, I was
going to have a fit of hysterical laughter.

As best I could, I managed to get close to the entrance. But
when I let myself go, calculating the moment when I would reach
the bars of the door, I couldn't grab it! I couldn't stop sliding, and I
saw to my dismay how I was moving away and almost to the
corner. I had passed it without being able to grab it! I was using my
arms to swing! I smoothly stopped at the lowest part of the sidewalk, managing not to fall. Now I had to pull myself up the hill! I
wasn't liking this game anymore.

"Enough with this!" I shouted to the sky. I was afraid I was
going to fall. I held on to the wall and climbed sideways. The
effort seemed superhuman. "All for Italy! Isidoro, please help me!"
I said. I think the cold was affecting my logic. Of course the ancestors couldn't help me. Or could they? Would it be possible for
them to help us if one asks them? *Stop dreaming, Graciela, and get
on with survival,* I told myself. When I finally reached the front
door, I clung to its bars like a life preserver. "Thank you, metal
door!"

I looked inside the guard's booth...there was no one there! Or
maybe there was, but the glass had a dark tint, so it was hard to see
in and the dim light of the day wasn't helping me either. At that

moment, I realized that I hadn't even checked if the embassies were open..

With the bars in my hands and my head almost between them, my voice became loud.

"*Ciao!*" I shouted, "Is it locked?"

Panic in my heart! I remembered the word "closed" in Italian.

"*Chiusa? Chiusa?*" I asked the air.

I wished I had X-ray vision to see clearly if there were people or not. If there was hope or not. As I began to despair, a shadow appeared, a movement inside. It was a guard who came to life and suddenly I heard a clacking, metal-like sound. The door opened a crack. I pushed it open further and entered.

"It is very cold!" he exclaimed in English as if we were in the middle of a storm.

"I was scared! I thought the embassy was closed," I replied in Spanish, thinking it was Italian. I didn't even know what language to speak anymore; my brain had frozen. And we both laughed without understanding each other.

He pointed out which way to go and finally, and when I entered, I heard Italian everywhere. Dressed as officers, people were walking back and forth, while rolling the X-ray security machine where I was to put my wallet. I did so immediately.

That's music to my frozen ears, I thought cheerfully about the Italian language. After I made it through security, they pointed to an elevator with Italian numbers! I laughed to myself at my little joke. And then I arrived in heaven! I mean, I arrived on the second floor, as instructed, then was directed toward the waiting room. On the other side of it was an anteroom. It was small and, in contrast to the modern offices I had seen, this one seemed to be from another, older time. It had a central tea table set on a round wine-colored rug and a green armchair with its back almost to the open entrance space. I couldn't help but notice a black-haired man with a mustache sitting there. I watched him from the side. Suddenly, he settled into the chair, picked up a newspaper and began to read. I was curious and wanted to go closer to check if there were more people dressed like that. It looked like the waiting room of a train station or something similar! I had the impression that I was watching an Agatha Christie *Orient Express* style movie. I could see him almost in profile and admired his clothes, they were so distinguished! I noticed his shoes shined as if he had just had them polished, like in the old days, when there were shoeshine boys at the entrances of buildings and stations. His long arm moved, turning the pages of the newspaper and then shaking it to keep them straight. The paper now covered part of his face. I noticed he was wearing a black bowler-style hat. Then, as he put the paper down to check the antique pocket watch on a chain, I saw his round, rosy cheeks. I thought it was a lovely scene. It was like watching an actor about to get on an old train and I thought, *Is this is what I'm going to see in Italy?* The picture made a mental feast, and I thought, *If I had a camera, I'd take a picture of it right now!*

Carry a camera at all times, was my next mental note.

With a sigh, I turned to the waiting room. My Italian dream visa awaited me and I didn't want it to slip away.

There were only a couple of people in line ahead of me. With the snowstorm, rain and ice, many had probably cancelled their appointments. When it was my turn, standing in front of the window, I took out my passport and all the documents pertinent to my application to complete the process, including the printed paper with the tickets as proof that I had already bought them. I gave them to the agent.

"*Parli italiano?*

"No. *Mi dispiace,*" I apologized.

"I thought you were Italian," she muttered without smiling, lowering her eyes to the documents.

I felt she was accusing me. After checking my passport, she looked at me again and, very seriously, asked me in English:

"What are you going to Italy for?"

I wanted to tell her the whole story of my ancestors in Italian, but it didn't come out. In my mind I rehearsed. *It's about my ancestors, Isidoro and Bianca...* But nothing came out of me. I was debating if she would think badly of my Isidoro if I told her the whole story.

Then I saw her face change to suspicious mingled with surprise. The clerk had been looking and reading at the sheet with the airplane tickets with great attention. With great energy, she exclaimed in a voice of alarm:

"Six hundred dollars for a plane ticket!"

I was shocked! I didn't understand what she was saying. "For *one* plane ticket?" I had bought *two*! For a moment, panic clouded my mind because I thought I had mistakenly bought only one airplane ticket. *But I checked a thousand times!* Maybe I had been tricked after all. Something was wrong. I felt as if all the blood was coming out of my face. The agent looked at me and noticing my pallor, added:

"That's a very good price. *Molto bene! Brava!*" She clapped her hands while still holding the papers in between them and a smile as she congratulated me.

"It's not $600 for one, *it's supposed to be two*. Let me make sure, please!" I held out my hand to point my finger at the paper. I was trembling until I saw that it was correct, "Yes, it says so." I pointed it out to her with relief. "One hundred and ninety-nine dollars for each ticket, one for my husband and one for myself. And the rest is taxes and fees..."

Now, *she* was the one who jumping up excitedly and showing her colleague, who was at the other window, my tickets.

"*Guarda! Guarda! Un biglietto aereo da duecento dollari per Roma!*"

Her colleague took it and read it carefully.

But now I got really scared as, for a moment, I thought they were going to confiscate it or something. The word "guarda" in Spanish means: "to put it away" like in a drawer or something. I thought they wanted to confiscate the ticket!

"No, don't keep it, please!" I begged her: "Give me back the ticket, please! Don't keep it!"

Calmly and smiling, she explained to me that "guarda" in Italian means "look" and not "keep." Now, she was smiling in amusement. She had her kind eyes on me, and a spark of admiration shone through. She seemed to be seeing me for the first time.

"And how did you get it?" asked the companion who now stood beside her, looking at me in the same way.

These two beautiful women were watching me from the other side of the window and waiting for me to give them the secret formula as if there was a potion or a magic spell. I calmly explained that I had put my email on an airline list to receive ticket offers. And one day, they sent me a notification. That was it.

"*Che bella! Bravissima!*" They both applauded, enthusiastically.

With joy, the officer who was serving me stamped all the documents and upon returning them to me, she leaned further over the window and in a whisper, said slowly in English so that I would understand well,

"Someone up there." And he pointed to the sky with his index finger: "Must really love you."

Suddenly, my heart lifted

"Moi? I mean, *io?* Me?"

It was as if she had told me the formula of love.

"It's a gift! It's like finding a treasure!" added her companion, who noticed that I was stunned and not moving, as if I didn't understand.

She repeated, pointing upwards,

"Someone, up there in heaven, must really love you... very much."

With my eyes moist with emotion, I nodded and did pirouettes of joy in my mind. Now in my imagination, I saw many little hearts floating all over the place.

I said goodbye to my new friends, who, in unison, said goodbye to me with an *"arriverderci."*

And as I left the room, waiting for the elevator, I instantly remembered the old-fashioned gentleman I had seen before. I craned my neck looking for the armchair in the corner where he was sitting. If I saw him, I would dare to strike up a conversation. If he was a movie actor, I wanted to ask for his autograph. I was going to tell him the whole story of Bianca and Isidoro. I was sure he would want to know. And I longed for a celebration. I felt invincible.

But he was gone. Even the chair was gone.

I reaffirmed my mental note to carry a camera with me at all times in the future so this would never happen to me again. I didn't want to miss a moment's opportunity to talk and take pictures with someone dressed like they were from another era!

When I got out and looked at the frozen climb that awaited me, I thought I had everything ready. If I died in the attempt to get to my vehicle, I would do so with infinite joy. Perhaps tomorrow it would be on the front page of the newspapers: "Woman dies of happiness while pirouetting on the ice as she leaves the Italian embassy."

And so, remembering Tarzan, I climbed the hill. From branch to branch...from tree to tree...from near-slip to near-slip...holding on to the wall, the rails, the trunks...whatever! Alive, unharmed and with my passport stamped with my Italian visa, I made it back to the car.

And of course, wearing my Italian smile under a loving Italian sky!

DESTINATION ITALY

"*Y*es," I confirmed the sad reality to my husband. "We are in Rome and without a Ferrari."

We were at Leonardo da Vinci International Airport in Rome. We were looking for the car I had rented online. And I was teasing Murat because it wasn't the famed Italian sports car.

After we landed we were incredibly happy at first because we found a coffee bar right there at the exit gate. This is how Italy welcomed us, with the delicious aroma of freshly roasted coffee! We read the extensive menu as if it were poetry. Between the café *lungo* and the *corto* coffee...which one should we get? Murat ordered a *doppio espresso* with *panna*. I went back and forth between the café *macchiato* and a *latte macchiato*, finally choosing the latter, but when I finished it, I ordered the former. After that amount of caffeine, my whole being was ecstatic in bliss that only Italian coffee can provide. I was thrilled, because we were in Italy!

After this sublime stop, we made our way to the airport parking lot where the rental cars were located. Just as I suspected, the car I chose was not the one Murat had in his dreams. It was not a Ferrari! My poor husband was looking for one that looked like the one he wanted.

I joked again, by way of consolation for his immense sacrifice. "My Italian ancestors have been great! Almost free tickets to Rome...a more than perfect place to stay in Tuscany that's only three hours from San Secondo Parmense, the village where Isidoro was born. And a wonderful hostess was waiting for us. What more do we want! A luxury car? Sorry, my love. Next time *you* can ask *your ancestors* for whatever you want."

Murat compared the number he had on the rental contract with the number on the floor of the parking lot indicating that we were the proud renters of a tiny purple Fiat. I confess that I ordered the cheapest car. I didn't even notice its brand name or what year it was. I did! But I made sure it had four wheels at least!

I felt at ease walking behind him. Our one suitcase was rolling along beside me, while he kept saying "I can't believe it!" He repeated that phrase as he passed every Italian car he had dreamt of. And when he stood in front of our little ugly duckling, "Noooooo!" But he was laughing as he said it.

I realized that his crazy plan was not to study art in Italy. Now I knew it was to drive a Ferrari! Had he confessed earlier, who knows what the ancestors would have done to please him? As for me, I was satisfied, I was in Italy! This issue was between him and his ancestors.

The purple Fiat was waiting for us: ready, innocent and cheerful. When we opened the trunk, the suitcase didn't fit.

"See? It doesn't fit!" he declared, ready to run out to the rental office and change it for another vehicle.

I'm a very practical person and I didn't want to waste a minute in a discussion, so I came up with the best idea.

"Let's put it in the back seat," I suggested.

With a little pushing and shoving, we threw the suitcase in there. It was perfect! Clapping my hands, I looked at him with success glowing on my face. And him? *Discombobulated!* To soothe him, I said,

"How lucky we brought only one! Can you imagine if we had brought two?"

I had convinced him to share luggage. I took advantage of his dumbfounded face to put it between my hands and give him a thunderous kiss of consolation. *Smack!*

"My adventurous man," I celebrated his still-not-quite-good-humor.

As I settled into the passenger seat with the door still open, something on the floor caught my eye. I noticed that a rectangular postcard style cardboard with red and gold colors was stuck to the toe of my boot. It looked like a ballot or coupon. Above the image of a costumed Venetian mask, it read *"Carnevale di Venezia."* I picked it up, passed it to him, putting it in his hand briefly as I buckled my belt. Murat began to read it:

"Carnevale di Venezia...."

Then he handed it to me so that I could continue reading while he started the car. "Come and enjoy a free drink on hotel." It had a date, looked valid, and was a hotel whose name I don't remember.

"I think we just got an invitation. Look!" I showed him the word 'free'. "I didn't even remember it was carnival time."

"I did!" He smiled at me, put the car into gear (he always preferred to drive a stick shift), and followed the arrows out of the parking lot.

"How many hours is Venice from here? Or, rather, from Tuscany," I asked him.

He glanced over at me and said conspiratorially,

"Let's get to our first destination and from there we'll see, ok?" Then, as though suddenly remembering something important, he said,

"Tell me again about where it is that we are going to stay." I think after the surprise of the car, now he was suspicious on what else might be awaiting him.

I repeated the options that Grazia had offered, reading her message from my notes: "There are two. The first one is a yellow cottage with two rooms in the splendorous Tuscan mountains, from where you can see the small valley and the forest full of serene pines that adorn the peaks. By car, it would be half an hour from the center of Colle di Val d'Elsa which is the city or *cittadina.*"

I looked up at him, "It must be beautiful!" I fantasized that if it was near the home of my favorite author, Frances Mayes, maybe we could go visit her. Then I wondered how many surprises the hubby could take and seeing that he had assented while driving, I continued my reading. "The second option, if you don't mind ghosts, is in the cellar of the only tall tower in the *cittadina*. It is the same as the famous ones in San Gimignano. Inside, they have renovated it and made a series of apartments. One for each floor."

Colle di Val d'Elsa has a single tower. In medieval times, these buildings were like an expression of power and pride of the owner. The higher the tower, the more powerful the feudal lords, owners of the town, felt. Personally, if I am going to stay overnight in a castle-style tower, then I would prefer to stay in the dungeon. Just to tell the anecdote to my children! Then I would brag to them, "We stayed in a dungeon—a real one!"

I asked Murat, "What do you think, would you choose to stay in a nice little house? One where the vineyards sleep, the forest of long pines rises on either side of the road and the winter grass is the glow of yellow ochre. Or... Would you prefer a castle with ghosts?"

"In a real castle...right?"

"Well, it's the tower of the *cittadina*. It's a medieval idea. We won't understand until we see it. It may be tiny. I don't know. We'll know when we get there. Ah! And there might be ghosts, but that could be fun!"

"We'll know when we get there," he concluded.

I was convinced that, for him, the idea of staying in a castle would be more fun, as well as the idea of a Ferrari. It would even be a better idea for him to arrive at a castle in a Ferrari! But I don't have those dreams. I trust that what happens to me is the best thing for me. Besides, I'm always in the clouds and life in the clouds is better.

"And on which floor would we stay in the tower?"

"In the cellar."

"Where the wine is kept," he said, nodding with interest. "Isn't the cellar the lowest floor of a castle? Without windows?"

"Grazia says that the cellar is not the lowest part of the castle. It's on the second floor but the tower is so high that you can see the hills with their pine-filled slopes. The dungeon would be below us. This seems optimistic."

"It sounds good to me," he nodded.

"Would you mind if we found ghosts?"

"Boo!" he replied.

And I laughed because it came out so bad.

He continued. "I don't believe in ghosts. If they existed, first your dad and now Isidoro would have appeared to us years ago!"

"That's my husband, the bravest! You're absolutely right. Ghosts don't exist."

Ha! I thought with delight. *What if they* do *exist in Italy?* Without further discussion, we had chosen from the beginning the wine cellar.

On the passenger seat, I opened the huge map book I had brought. It wasn't just one map, it was a whole manual that, when I opened it, covered my knees. Under *Road Maps of Italy,* I found the northbound highway that would take us to Colle di Val d'Elsa. With my finger, I marked the *autoestrada*. As we went along, my finger moved to the edge of the page to turn to the next. On the square of the page, I'd turn the page for the next square on the new page. And so, I'd run my hand along the same path we were following to our destination. Such was the way of things before GPS existed and before cell phones could be used anywhere! It's a miracle we ever got anywhere or got anything done!

By this time, I had put the Venice carnival ticket on top of the dashboard of the car. And it was sliding from left to right depending on the curves. I was a bit amused by this movement.

A little over three hours later we arrived at the skirt of the *cittadina*, which stood walled in with beautiful tall golden rocks. We parked in front of the square. From down there, we could see an imposing tower. We suspected it was the place where we would stay.

"Do you think so?"

"Well, it's the only one we can see."

Grazia had mentioned the bar across the square. When we walked in, we saw a woman with short black hair and big dark eyes. She was wearing a green silk scarf over a wonderfully colored sweater in the same shade. She was having a lively conversation with the bartender, but when she saw us enter, she called my name out in Italian:

"Graziella." She seemed to be singing it.

"Grazia," I answered in the same way, as I had already picked up the accent.

We hugged like two old Italian friends.

"*Ciao*, how was the trip? Was it easy to get here?"

From here on, Grazia had a plan. We surrendered to it and

followed her. The first thing to do was to settle into our dungeon, I mean cellar, er I mean, our apartment in the unique and imposing tower that existed in front of us. In the walled city, only the cars of the residents were allowed to enter, and only in certain areas. The rest was pedestrian. Noticing the large suitcase in the back seat, she didn't even try to get into the car.

"It doesn't matter! Behind the wall you will find the parking lot. I'll wait for you on the other side, at the entrance. In the meantime, I'll cross the town here."

She pointed his finger at a diagonal stone ramp that I hadn't seen.

"I hadn't even noticed that ramp!"

"It's a secret of the *Cittadini*. I'll wait for you at the entrance!"

And with that, she disappeared.

Soon, we found ourselves at the entrance to the fenced city. We saw that Grazia was talking animatedly with a very dressed up gentleman.

"*Benvenuti!*" he exclaimed.

We walked uphill, dragging, thanks to inspiration, our only *one* suitcase. Admiring the cobblestones, the colors of the windows, and the built-in lanterns, we reached the highest part of the town. From any point and almost as if in a dream, we could see the tower in the distance.

Excited, I pointed at it and said, "Look! That's where we are going to stay!" At the same time, Murat yelled,

"Do you see it? That's where we're going to stay."

Grazia pointed with her finger to the places we would soon get to know.

"My studio is on that street, it's that emerald green door. That's where Estefania's restaurant is. It's that indigo painted door where we'll have lunch every day we can. In the morning, the coffee is the best in Italy! This one here, it's one of the most famous restaurants. It's very expensive but very good! You have to book months in advance, but there is a trick to get in...I'll tell you..."

In the last alley she stopped in front of the door of our tower. She placed in Murat's palm a huge old metal object.

"Here is the key."

It was one of those bronze ones, old and whose rust painted it with colors.

"Now, this is a key!" Murat exclaimed, like *Crocodile Dundee* over a knife.

Grazia smiled

"It's just that! And it's never been lost!" This was in reference to its size.

The wood from which the door was made looked like it came off a pirate ship because of the veins and the age it showed. It gave us the impression that at any moment it would fall apart. However, when we opened it, it was so thick that we consoled ourselves with the thought that, if it had not crumbled in a millennium, it was not going to disappear this very day. And it was unlikely that the stainless-steel hinges with which it was gripped were going to give way and come loose either.

I expected that, upon entering, we would be greeted by ominous, dark stairs and that we would have to grab a torch from the wall to go down and down forever until we reached the cellar. Not so! I was surprised to immediately find a totally modern and spacious apartment. The only original thing was the very old brick floor that sunk in the center. When I opened the windows, the golden light of the sunset filled and painted the walls with life and color. What amazed me most was that by now, they all resembled the pictures I had posted in my office. The landscapes framed a panorama similar to the one I had assembled on my walls as a blueprint for my first piece of Italy. My eyes lit up as I realized those hopes had come to fruition.

"I'll see you tomorrow in the studio," Grazia said as she waved goodbye.

As soon as she left us alone, I started to dance across the room. The floor was fantastic, and as I crossed it, it seemed as if I was descending into a valley. I said to Murat,

"Now you see me, now you don't!" I walked from one end to the other, exaggerating the slope.

We took the suitcase to the bedroom. The antique iron bed was huge. There was also a sturdy closet, made of precious wood, I'm not sure what kind. For a moment, I suspected that all the ghosts I didn't believe in were hiding in there. So I bravely opened its doors very slowly and found it empty. No ghosts!

Before going for a walk, I leaned out of one of the windows to sigh and enjoy the natural spectacle of the rising moon which seemed larger than usual. Downstairs, the lights of the town came on and we noticed the tavern where we had first seen Grazia. I thought to myself, *The purple Fiat has been forgiven!*

TUSCANY

*I*n order to have breakfast we had to wait in line for almost two hours. Early, at 8AM, the whole town was there for the best coffee in Italy. Thus, the cold was abated by the human warmth. We literally talked to everyone! I realized that the breakfast was an excuse for the people to start the day with a party. The funniest thing is that everything we said was repeated by the row of villagers. Hadn't Grazia told me it would be like this?

"She says she is looking for her ancestors." they were saying to each other.

"She says their names are Isidoro and Bianca." They followed the line.

It was a word game while some of us shivered, wrapped in our coats, hats, and scarfs under the clear Tuscan sky.

Apparently, since it was winter, there was not much tourism. Being the only ones, we were undoubtedly a novelty. Previously, another American couple had occupied this post until today—we had removed them. They had now happily settled in the area to stay. Moreover, they too were in the line, as curious as the others to know the reason of this trip and also enjoying the word game. Part of the reason for the interrogation was that they were curious to know if we had discovered the ghosts in the tower—so cute that they thought they could scare me! What they didn't expect was that I am Chela's granddaughter and I answered them like any good smart-aleck would, pretending to be slightly interested but with a tone of boredom. I felt Chela would have been proud.

"I'm a little disappointed in the tower, eh? Because no ghost appeared. I was ready, you know, pen in hand, to take their ghost stories. You have to understand. I am a veteran at this, and I think I scared them off. Plus, my ancestry is full of strong women so... they'd probably kick ghosts off should they venture close. You see, they want their stories to go first!"

I spoke this way jokingly with the suspicion that none of them would understand my meaning. At least, that's what I thought. One of Grazia's friends, the one called Loreno, who was a famous artist with his studio next to hers, seemed fascinated by us. He didn't know English and that was the language I had spoken. I found his interest adorable and so I changed a few words when I referred to my ancestors. I used the word *antinati* and repeated some phrases in Italian—trying to have him follow at least the gist of the story. He seemed amused, even delighted, listening to my stories. He was dressed much like Grazia had been the previous day. A colorful scarf contrasted with and was tucked into a dove gray coat. It was cold, yes, but his enthusiasm and that of those present was palpable and made us forget the cold weather. Soon enough, we had in our hands the *pasticcini* buns, *ripieni di cioccolatini e frangolle,* that is, filled with chocolates and strawberries. Then someone passed me a croissant filled with chocolate and hazelnuts. And I thought I could die happily at that moment!

I mean, no! I mean, I take it back. Not yet! I still had to find my ancestors.

So it was that by the first hour, all the people in line already knew we were Grazia's art students. And we hadn't even made it to the second hour, when they knew who Isidoro and Bianca, my ancestors, were and the reason for this trip. Only the rumors had distorted the story a bit and my Italian was not helping to clarify it. Grazia did what she could.

"But how is she not Italian?" Loreno asked, "If her ancestors are, she must be."

"She lives in Virginia, in the United States," Grazia apologized.

"But...how did she get to Virginia?" insisted Loreno.

I was delighted to see that he had already been bitten by the story of my ancestors.

"They first arrived in Puerto Plata," explained Grazia, she already knew.

"Well, first to Bogota," I put in, to be more explicit.

"How is it that, from Italy to Puerto Plata, from Bogota to Virginia?" Loreno had the order of the places chronologically all wrong, but before I could fix this, Grazia said something that made me laugh.

"You don't understand, Loreno. Isidoro and Bianca were a *fuga di amore*." Her string of Italian words sounded so cute and romantic that I left it at that, just enjoying how the phrase *fuga di amore* made it down the line of people. They commented to each other that Isidoro and Bianca had eloped on a ship and arrived in Colombia because the family was against their love because he was from Parma and she was from Bologna. That he doubled her age and was an adventurous entrepreneur and she was of some kind of nobility. I recorded all this in my mind to tell Mami, and Uncle Fernando, because I knew he would enjoy it most. To fuel imagination, I added to the group some things that my mother had alluded to.

"Bianca came from a community with very close ties. Families who had taken care of her since she was a little girl. I'm sure they had thought of another beau for her, one from inside her community in Castello d'Argile. But, no! She wouldn't have it. At seventeen, she also had a heart for adventure. Plus, my Isidoro was irresistibly handsome and *wham*, he took her! Do you think that those Italians, the ones from San Secondo, are all that fresh? I've known descendants from Bologna, but not those from Parma, so..." I shrugged. "I imagine they must be. But do you think all of them, really? Or just Isidoro?" I asked the air.

"Oh, it's like Romeo and Juliet!" said the American lady standing behind me, who listened to me and passed it on to others who wanted to know. What a curious town!

In the days following this first morning, the Tuscan *cittadina* seemed to us to be part of a fairy tale. In the morning, as we walked towards breakfast, we enjoyed the stones radiating the pink apricot of the sun's first rays. The *alba*—they call it. And in the evening, the stones would tinge in an ocher color as if the sun itself was reflected on each wall. The hills that we could see from almost every street were dressed with pine trees and bordered by yellow grass. They looked like an expressionist painting that changed color as the light and shade changed between sun and clouds.

Grazia's workshop was in front of the square. Immediately, we got to work with her art. We began by learning how to cut Venetian glass that came in the shape of an oval. First the glass was placed on a trunk that served as a table. Then with a special axe, small but very fine and lethal, we cut this glass and the colored stones we needed for our works into squares. She showed us how to glue them with the type of cement used. As we were in winter, drying was going to take time so, we stuck to simple designs that only took about two days to create in order to give them time to dry for the rest of the week. We worked listening to Italian music and, from time to time, admiring the people passing by and the Tuscan landscape through the windows.

It became routine for us to receive Grazia's lessons in the mornings and then we made visits to the neighboring villages in the afternoons. Once, we took the bus to Florence, although most of the time, we drove in our Fiat. We visited San Gimignano to admire towers even taller than ours. In the few days we had been there, we devoured the delicacies of the restaurants that were recommended to us. At one restaurant in particular we ate *agnolotti* stuffed with a spicy gorgonzola cheese, delicately bathed in a white sauce with bits of green pears and walnuts and nutmeg, and it that left us...overtaken by the flavor! Of course, I researched the recipe and I got it!

The truth is, if we could've, we would have gone to Stefania's restaurant for lunch every day because we loved the idea of being in her presence while she was cooking. Besides, it was where the whole town went. Just like in the morning, when the people would line up for coffee; they would line up for Stefania at lunchtime. It was a very casual affair in front of the square. Stefania cooked whatever she wanted. I mean, whatever the heck she wanted! After all, it was her house, and no one told her what to cook! The living room was small, but there was still space for about four tables and one of them, a long one, was placed to one side. Loreno, Grazia, and their other friends sat with us at the long table. Sometimes, there were 10 of us and we were very crowded, but it didn't matter. The most particular thing about the place was that the owner was so young, it seemed that she was not even thirty, and yet she had so much strength of character. The restaurant had no sign, and you only knew it was open after Stefania had placed a basket full of plastic sunflowers on a chair out front. She only received a certain number of people, which I think was as many as she could feed that day and no more. When she opened the door, she would choose who would enter. She would hold out her hand and since she didn't like tourists, village locals would get preferential treatment. We felt like special guests because, thank God, she always chose us. Or maybe that was thanks to Grazia Basically we had Grazia to thank for just about all the amazing aspects of our trip, which I did not take for granted. Many times a day I found myself clasping my hands together, bowing my head slightly and saying to her, "Grazie, Grazia."

Stefania wore her straight black hair in a ponytail and wore a white apron over jeans and a sweater. Despite looking so delicate, I got the impression that her hands were stronger than a man's. She was not tall in stature but when she spoke, everyone listened, and followed her instructions, as her voice was very energetic. She had character and this caused me to imagine Bianca in her. From her kitchen we ate the best pasta stuffed with spinach and ricotta or vegetables in balsamic vinegar reductions with green beans or fava beans. She said she chose all her ingredients from local suppliers who came to bring them to her.

But I didn't always eat without asking! The first time there I was served a somewhat unfamiliar dish. I was told it was *ribolita* but I didn't know what that was.

"What is it?" I asked Grazia slyly when I saw what looked like just a piece of oddly shaped dough on my plate. There was never a menu, Stefania basically served whatever came to her mind. When I saw that ribolita on my plate, needless to say, it didn't look the prettiest! Rather, it resembled a dry dough filled with colorful pasta. I noticed that it had carrots and something green that looked like pigeon peas or something similar.

"It's a soup with all the leftovers from the week."

"But it doesn't look like soup," I mumbled.

136

Because of Stefania's reputation, I had prepared myself to eat well, and I didn't know if this would be the first, or only course, so I was going to try it no matter what it looked like. However, when I tasted it, I couldn't help but murmur, "It's sooo good!" It really was very tasty, and the wine was wonderful too! She served it without asking if we wanted it or not.

"My dad makes it," she explained as she tipped the unlabeled bottle into our glasses. "It's a young wine. This means it hasn't fermented much."

"It's like a juice," said Grazia.

"It's not juice!" Stefania protested.

"Well, I love it," I said to soothe the possibly upcoming hot temper. "It doesn't have much alcohol in it; I like that. It's delicious and aromatic. I can't stop drinking it. *Salute!*" I couldn't believe it was artisanal wine. I wonder if Bianca or Isidoro knew how to make something like this—*I'm sure they did!*

At one of the lunches Stefania sat with us, making room for herself to sit next to me. I was happy, shoulder to shoulder to such a great woman who served as a model for my great-grandmother Bianca. I took the opportunity to tell her that she was named after one of my ancestors. The one I was hoping to meet in San Secondo when we left on Friday.

"On this trip, I'm taking the opportunity to look directly in the records of San Secondo for one I haven't found... And his name is like yours: Stefano."

Stefania was not impressed and looked at me with her big dark eyes. She was waiting, I think for the punch line. But I didn't say more. The next thing she said was something that sounded like a challenge, but I took it as a joke.

"The name is one thing, but I hope your family taught you how to find mushrooms in the forest to eat. I get people to supply me with the best! They bring them to me to choose...well, I have my people!"

"That's right, they're great!" I celebrated because the truth is that there was nothing more delicious than her food. "The *tagliatelle* with the *funghi-poscini* sauce was like ambrosia from the gods! Although my ancestors' food prowess comes from Bologna." I kept my eyes on her expression in case I needed to retreat after I said what I was about to say. "In fact, my grandmother used to say that the best cooks came from Bologna." Seeing her laugh, I dared to add, "Because of the way pasta is made."

Immediately, this sparked a standoff over how to make the dough for the pasta. She called her helper and asked him to bring some flour. Since the boy did not understand and the first time he brought her very little, she got up herself to fetch it. She returned with flour, egg and water. This time she sat down in front of me to teach me.

"In Bologna, they are made with egg and in the south, with water. But the flour is different," she explained.

She threw the flour on the table where we had just finished eating, and adding water left from a glass, began to knead quickly. She gestured me to throw the flour on my space of the table in front of me so that I would do the same. So, I threw flour in front of me, imitating her, and cracked an egg on top of it, like people from Bologna would do. First I kneaded with my hands and then, when my fingers were getting hopelessly sticky, I used a fork. I dare to say, eventually I became Bianca's great-granddaughter and kneaded with some vigor. Of course, mine was a mess and Stefania's was well formed. With a lot of humor, she put them both together, incorporating my mess into her work and managed to make sense out of the goo. It ended up looking like real dough ready to be made into pasta. I was enchanted with this new kind of magic I had been taught, mixing it on a table and shaping it with my hands.

Then, she said, "It's acceptable to do it both ways! Now...whether that gives the women of Bologna an advantage, I doubt it!"

I wasn't going to argue with her about that in case it influenced her daily invitation to enter her culinary abode next time. But I had also told her that Isidoro and Bianca had a restaurant in the hotel in Puerto Plata and that it was considered the best cuisine of that time. I explained that the children of this couple learned how to cook at an early age and that each of them had a specialty. They knew how to make spaghetti by hand! I remembered my grandmother and told Stefania, while bursting with pride and love, that my grandmother, daughter of this couple, was known for a specialty which was *gnocchi*. As I spoke, a memory came to me of her teaching me how to make it. It was like an *instant* memory. I must have been six or seven years old, the kitchen counter was high for me and Mamma Chela looked imposing. She was petite, but to me, I was little girl next to an imposing woman. Granddaughter and grandmother together in the kitchen. A delightful memory that uncovered my Chela's talent. And the best thing about it, is that it was neither a borrowed memory nor something someone told me —but totally mine.

"The women of Bologna are the best cooks in Italy!" My grandmother had said that to me as she put flour on top of the counter and took great pains to teach me how to knead the dough. She spoke of the women of Bologna with great vigor as she energetically, yet very precisely grated potatoes, cracked an egg and heated water. I stood on tiptoe watching her clever hands and her fine, strong fingers move expertly over the dough. She told me, "At the hotel, we each had a specialty. Mayú made spaghetti by hand, like my mother, and *tagliatelle*! Yolanda made the dough so thin that it would feel like melting butter in the tongue, Blanquita and Beatriz... well, they were the oldest, they knew everything! But we all learned from very early... and in the kitchen we were allowed to choose what we like to do best and when a customer would ask for one of our dishes, we would be called to the kitchen, even if it wasn't our day working in it...just because we only served the best and everything was handmade from scratch. Not like today's restaurants. I loved to make *gnocchis*."

As she spoke my dear Chela elongated the dough with rotating movements. Then, she cut it into little pieces that looked like miniature pillows. With a fork in her hand, imitating a magic wand, she acrobatically turned them around, making them fall already turned into tiny seashells. The fork drew a texture of stripes that curved into themselves in a spiral curve. I was so amazed I couldn't close my mouth! All the original cut dough that looked like "pillows" were suddenly and flawlessly shaped like seashells, plump in the middle and tapered at the tips. My grandmother was a wizard sculptor of miniature flour doughs. She passed me the fork and I was stunned. *Did she want me to do this?* It was as if she had passed me her magic wand. *How could I try to imitate her magic act?* The spiral snails she had created were now, in perfect line, resting on the counter as examples to follow. But my clumsy fingers didn't make them the same. I wanted instead to grab the spiral shells she had made and hold them to my ear to listen to the waves of the sea. Although tiny, they seemed so real, and being as young as I was, I thought to myself, *Oh! That's how God makes nature, and that's how you make seashells, like my grandmother...with a fork!*

"You do it, now. Try. Yes you can! You can do it!" my grandmother encouraged me. Very slowly and hopelessly, I picked up the fork with my clumsy childish fingers. I tried, but only succeeded in crushing the little pieces. I tried to convince her that that I liked it that way. "They look pretty, like little pillows. I'd better leave them like that," I told her, trying to cover up my ineptitude. She replied that she had learned from her sister Beatriz when she was my age. Poor Chela with a granddaughter like me!

Nowadays, *gnocchi* are made by machine. I doubt if anyone knows how to make them by hand like in the days of the Hotel Europa restaurant! Luckily, I am a witness that once, in my family, I saw women artists, magicians, miniature sculptors really, who could turn a piece of flour dough and make it fly. And let it fall, having turned into tiny seashells.

When we went back to the square, with our bellies full and our hearts happy, Grazia said to me,

"This is the first time I've seen Stefania share with someone like she did today. I think she loved that you tried to share how your grandmother made *gnocchi* in Italian."

"It's because she's a strong woman, like the ones in my family! But the truth is that I was the one who was fascinated because I had forgotten a memory of my grandmother teaching me how to make them and now, it is a memory that I will treasure in my heart. Someday I will write it down!" Then I thought about it more and said, "The things Italy has given me. Perhaps it is the land of memories."

The night before we left for San Secondo, the hubby and I were feeling energetic and sleepless. We decided to go out. We carefully locked the front door with the eternal key, admiring with relief that the lock had not yet disintegrated. Holding hands, we went for a walk.

We entered a place that had a neon-colored Open sign contrasting with the old windows of the place. The bartender was a girl with long black curls like her eyes, which were huge and beautiful.

"We don't serve food here. Only drinks. Come back after dinner. This bar will be full, and I'll have a surprise for you. I'll be waiting for you!"

We promised her to come back. In the meantime, we decided to try our luck with the restaurant that Grazia had said was "the best in Tuscany." She gave us the guidance to say we didn't have a reservation because we weren't from there and to be served whatever they had available or whatever the chef wanted us to try. Quickly, we were placed at a small table against the wall outside the kitchen on an open space. There, still snuggled in our coats to keep warm, we waited contentedly for the chef's surprise. We ate like the gods! I will only mention one dish the chef sent that was like a taste of glory. They were lentil meatballs, but served as a meatloaf in rectangular slices. It seemed that, after preparing them, they were fried. I can't find words to describe how delicious it was and, since then, I have been looking for a similar recipe. I found several about lentil patties, but I don't think it's that simple and nothing more than that. I think it was a gift from the angels.

After having dinner under the stars, we returned to the bar of the girl from Sardinia, who was accompanied by a handsome, muscular guy with his hair slicked back. Both greeted us with a big smile. Natali put two small glasses in front of us, which she filled with a pink liquor. Immediately, we were treated like old friends. We marveled at our luck. We were in the middle of Tuscany, in February, in winter, in a bar built on a high rock with a beautiful couple who made us laugh and served us a delicious drink without even asking us if we wanted more.

"It's *grappa*. It's a typical drink of the island where I come from. It's the official drink of sailing ships in the Mediterranean. Throughout the summer, those who sail on these boats drink it like water."

We asked her to tell us more about Sardinia.

"We, the people of *Sardignia*, do not feel completely Italian; we have our own culture, our own language, our own food. Our history is arduous and foreign to all this."

She raised her arm in an expansive movement to gesture around her, while with the other she tilted the bottle to serve us again. Her *grappa* was a delightful elixir! She told us the brand name a thousand times; she showed us the bottle a thousand more, but I knew I would forget. If I don't write it down in my research notebook, I forget everything, and at that moment, I didn't have it at hand.

"Sardinia has great wonders like an emerald sea," said Carlos, the Cuban who accompanied her. "A unique gastronomy based on the sea."

"Why don't my ancestors come from Sardinia too?" I lamented, drinking more *grappa* to console myself.

It's funny that, light years later, when I did my genetic study for genealogy reasons, I found Sardinia among the geography of my ancestors and I remembered this beautiful girl with black almond-shaped eyes, who served us this magic potion called *grappa*.

And if you find yourself wondering whether or not I mentioned Isidoro during this talk, fear not! Because, to the astonishment of few, I told the whole of my family history and genealogical research to anyone who would listen!

"Poor Bianca!" said Natali in reference to my great-grand-mother. "Abandoned pregnant, and with so many children. How did she make it!"

"But...what a woman, that Bianca!" exclaimed Carlos, inflating my own pride over my great-grandmother. Or was it the drink?

"The one who was born in San Secondo is your grandfather?" Asked Natali.

"Yes, Bianca's husband is, of course, my great-grandfather Isidoro. This trip was designed with him in mind. I want to keep on with my genealogy so now it's my turn to find his father, Stefano. But no matter how hard I search my resources, I can't find his birth certificate. However, according to a source at the local government office, someone was kind enough to find it and this person will be waiting for us with it."

"And when do you plan to go to San Secondo?" asked the fascinated girl.

"Tomorrow," Mufat answered.

"I am anxious to get my hands on that missing document. This way I will know the name of Stefano's parents to follow the line of my family tree. With it, I will have a party in San Secondo!"

As we were leaving, the beautiful girl bartender raised the bottle to give it to us.

"Take the bottle of *grappa*, it's my gift."

It was her answer to our question, "How much do we owe you?" We insisted we wanted to pay something. But Natali would not be swayed.

"It's not from the bar. It's mine! My own bottle I brought from *Sardigna*. It's my gift." She added that she probably wouldn't be up to send us off the next day at breakfast.

We accepted it with effusive gratitude, left her a good tip and went to sleep in our cellar.

I'd like to report that every night, although I sharpened my ears, I never heard a ghost. While I knew the dungeon was below us, no soul in pain could be heard. Still, in the mornings, I always searched my memory to see if in my dreams I had caught a glimpse of some lost spirit somewhere in the tower who wanted to give me news from beyond. I was always looking for a good story! But there was nothing! I never managed to find any vision among my memories of dreams in the golden dawns. When I woke up, I would ask my husband if he had received a sign from the beyond. And I would ask him to rummage in his memory, reminding him that we were in Italy and that, if we were ever going to dream of a relative of mine, there wasn't a better place.

"So, did you hear anything last night? Did you hear...anything strange?"

"Not yet," he said to me. "But maybe tomorrow night!"

"Oh, what a pity! I was hoping..." I joked.

"Don't worry." And smiling, he added, "If Isidoro comes out to tell me something like where he's buried, I'll let you know right away. Okay?"

FINALLY, SAN SECONDO

*E*arly in the morning, we met our small-town friends and breakfast companions. They had helped us carefully mark all the streets and exits to take on the printed map. We announced that we were leaving for San Secondo Parmense. Everyone was very happy because we were leaving in search of my ancestors. As I noticed that Grazia was the most excited about the journey that was beginning, I asked her if that was how she felt about Sicily.

"It never occurred to me that I could find such fun stories in my family—I doubt it!"

"I'm sure you have fun ancestors. You just don't know them well. If you go out and look for them, you'll see how they'll come back to you!"

I said it as a joke, but I meant it. She laughed and then I remembered what Natali had said about Sardinia.

"Last night, Natali told me that Sardinia has a very ancient style of its own and she feels a little different because of it. Is that how you Sicilians feel?"

"Bah," she replied, waving her hand, "Since time immemorial, we have been Greeks, Africans, Romans, Phoenicians. Sicily has passed from command to command. Can't you see that we are in the middle of the Mediterranean? These things are like the wind. One wind comes, brings a Turk, another brings a Tunisian. In the end, it's like a dress. The essence is the same, only the dress changes. After it all, we are the same as we wish to be."

"See? You answered me like a poet! Surely there is one among your ancestors who is one…if you search, you will find charming stories like that."

Excited, she took me by the shoulders and gave me a very personal blessing.

"I hope you find everything you want to find about your ancestors. I hope that when you find them, they will shower you with blessings. What's more—I know they are there, waiting for you. They will welcome you with surprises and joy." And as we were walking away, it seemed that she was filled with a sigh of inspiration, because as she waved goodbye, she shouted again to us, "Your ancestors are waiting for you, Graciela! They are waiting for you there."

I was delighted that she told me this, although something inside me, squeezed my heart with inaudible words: *We are always with you.* I sighed with nostalgia because I thought that if they were traveling with me and in me, they must be eager to return to the place from where they left. For me, it was a way to meet them; but for them, it was a way to return. We might get lost on the road there, but they would always find us on the path towards them. I came from a place they chose to go to, a place where they planned and planted new roots, and now they would return in me.

Two hours later, our Fiat was rolling merrily down the *autostrada*, curious as we were in search of the original land where my ancestors were born. At each stretch, Murat was drooling over a fast, red-colored, Italian-designed racecar that was speeding past us. Jokingly, I told him that this made my "ugly duckling" Fiat look bad. To distract him, I began to read him my ancestors' notes in trivia form.

"What were the names of Isidoro's parents?"

He was trying to maneuver out of the middle of two huge tour buses and change lanes. However, every time he put on his turn signals, a speeding Italian car would make him dive back in and eat dust.

"Darn!"

"No! Stefano! And his middle name, Antonio. He was married to Maria Benedetta Carrara, affectionately known as Betty."

"She was called Betty?" my husband asked innocently, knowing full well that I often gave nicknames to my ancestors as I studied them.

"No. That's what I call her." I thought it was a funny nickname, but not so much for him.

"I like Benedetta."

"Well, Benedetta, it stays."

"How many generations of your family have been in San Secondo?"

I still didn't know the answer to that question. But at least since the early eighteenth century, when Parma was occupied by the French, the way records were kept had been changed. The French code was implemented. Another innovation of this time of French influence was the fact that people were buried outside churches and that all subjects, whatever their social class, were given the same treatment and recorded in the same civil book. This is the book I was expecting to see when we arrived in San Secondo.

I was musing what the calligraphy would look like in this book when Murat's voice brought me out of my reverie; he wanted to get there quickly, and I was distracted by my own thoughts. I wondered about every hill or tree I saw and checked my whole being to see if I would feel it familiar.

"What's the next exit?"

I checked the map. I told him the number written down. Then I reminded him:

"Waiting for us is one of the officers from the *anagrafe* with Stefano's information. Apparently, he was indeed born in San Secondo, but I could not find him myself. The gentleman will be waiting with the document if we arrive on time."

Listening to Italian music on the radio, we turned off the *autostrada* and drove along beautiful curvy country roads. We had passed from Tuscany to Parma, seeing from afar some mountainous trails that the map said went to Bologna. We were not going to pass through there just yet but rather on our way back. So I just said, "Goodbye Bologna. Bianca's descendants send their regards. Let me tell you that in Puerto Plata they called her Doña Blanca and she, one of your daughters, became a legend."

"On the way back we will stop there," Murat promised.

We enjoyed the Apennine Mountains with a blue-gray background against the green pines of the flat terrain. I was so distracted by the scenery that when I looked down at my map book, I realized I didn't recognize any streets. The finger that followed the path was on some other road. Technically, we were lost. Getting to San Secondo Parmense was becoming quite epic. Breakfast was more than digested and my stomach was rumbling for food.

"Very nice!" Murat had been amused at my stories, but his stomach was also making noises. "I'm starving!"

"Oh, look at that old house in ruins! What character! The color of its stones. How beautiful!"

"Please take me where there's food," he begged.

Worried about this hungry man and my stomach that was also growling, I tried to make sense of the lines on the map. I suspected, well, I knew we were lost but didn't want to tell the whole crew yet. My secret weapon was to stop on the road and ask anyone which way was the road to San Secondo. We were supposed to be close enough. The problem was that we saw no one and the path became so narrow that we didn't even have the space to turn back should we have to! Not even a rodeo juggler could have helped. Some Roman god would have to come with his giant hand to turn our car around. At the most desperate moment, we spotted a man walking down the road in front of us. He had tall black boots like those of a river fisherman. We stopped to ask him where we could eat and where San Secondo was. To these simple questions, he recited Italian that sounded like poetry to me. My ears were fascinated, listening to the language of my ancestors. Then fascination became alarm when, between his tenor accent and his hand-dancing gestures, I realized I understood absolutely nothing!

"What did he say?" Murat asked me when he noticed my square smile of distress.

Nonchalantly, from the open window and leaning against it, the Italian man observed our interaction.

"He says this is the road to San Secondo..." I hesitated and looked between my husband and the man.

"*Si, si.*" The gentleman supported me with his bushy eyebrows and singing accent. "*San Secondo...é vero.*"

I smiled at him and looked at Murat again.

"But he also says that this is the way to Venice. And that in Venice we will find a restaurant."

I was ashamed of my explanation because it didn't even make sense to me.

"*Si, si.*" The gentleman supported me again. "*Certo.*"

"Are we near Venice?" Murat asked confused but then answered himself. "No, we are not near Venice."

"*Si, si.*" The gentleman nodded vehemently and pointed with his hand to the road in front of us. He urged us to follow. "*Vicino, vicino.*"

I looked at Murat. "He says San Secondo is near here and this is the way to Venice as well. *Vicino* means 'near to.'"

"*É piú vicino, vicino,*" repeated the gentleman, wagging his heavy gray eyebrows. He kept motioning for us to go on, to move forward, and to tell the truth, I already wanted to obey and go on because the cold was chilling me to the bone.

"Well, thank him and let's move on," Murat said after I insisted to keep going.

I said *grazie*, the kind man kept talking to us as we moved slowly ahead. I could see him through the rearview mirror: "*Avanti, avanti.*"

We moved forward, as it seemed to be our only option, and the hubby said,.

"Why did you ask him about Venice?"

"I didn't ask him about Venice! He was the one who mentioned Venice. I only asked him about a restaurant and San Secondo." I raised my hands innocently.

"Of course there are restaurants in Venice, but why did he think of mentioning it? Did he see the ticket that says Venice?" Murat asked, confused and pointing to the invitation to the Venice Carnival still on the dashboard of the car, "Because, honestly, we are nowhere near Venice."

When we reached the end of the road, to our amazement, we saw a restaurant in front of us. And if this restaurant had been a person, he would've been making fun of us! The street we were on happened to end at a restaurant whose name was *Ristorante Venezia*. The man was *certo, certo* and Venezia was *vicino, vicino*!

Quickly, we jumped out of the car, climbed the two steps to the entrance and pushed the door open. "It's that all roads lead to Venice." I laughed as we entered.

The laughter stopped abruptly when we realized the place was empty. The tables were without tablecloths and the chairs were turned over. Not a soul was to be seen! We looked at each other in despair.

"Go to the kitchen and ask for food," said Murat.

"I don't dare! Are you crazy? They'll think Isidoro's descendants are a bunch of jerks"

I was joking, as hunger had already taken away my shame. Plus, I was already walking toward the kitchen door. Before I could push it, it opened and out came a boy dressed in black pants and a white shirt who was talking very rapidly. He shook his head and with a myriad of exaggerated hand gestures, he informed us in Italian, "Closed! The restaurant is closed, we have nothing left to eat!"

"Please, whatever there is! Anything!" We begged him.

He kept shaking his head and trying to speak in a language we understood.

"Whatever you are going to throw out for the cat!" I exclaimed. Murat looked at me suspiciously, he wasn't sure what kind of food I'd accept. But I know Italians are proud of their food and would not bring me something disgusting.

The young man sighed mercifully. After pondering for a second, he began to lower two chairs and spread out a tablecloth.

"I'm going to rummage," he replied with an exaggerated sigh of resignation and disappeared through the same door by which he came out.

In a minute, he returned with two plates of lasagna and apologizing, he explained:

"That's all I have. *Mi dispiace*. There's only *lasagna* left."

Well, it was the most delicious lasagna we had ever tasted in our entire lives! Even today, more than a decade later, whenever we talk about lasagna, we always award the imaginary prize to that masterpiece, the best in the world. The tomato sauce was painted delicately over each pasta rectangle and the cheese was...well, I have no words. The cheese was king! It was smooth as if it had been whipped, and so light that it felt just enough liquefied as a sauce—that made it unique!

When we finished eating, the boy appeared with a dessert. And a little later, with coffee.

"And this is when there's nothing? I wonder what it's like when there's *something*. Let's come back then!" I was thoroughly satisfied.

"Ask where San Secondo is?"

So we asked him.

"Vicino," he answered.

We looked at each other and shrugged our shoulders. Apparently, everything was *vicino*.

"Well, at least I took you to Venice," he said romantically.

"No, no, no," I said with my index finger up, "It doesn't count."

When we got back on the road, we continued along the path until the view cleared and the horizon opened up. Ahead of us, the sun glinted off the vast expanse of dry grass like gold. On the flat terrain stone buildings interrupted by rough trees and pines gave way to other little stone houses half-destroyed by time—a masterpiece of ochre and reddish tones that the daylight made luminous. The play of the light within the clouds made the light on the rocks glow like beating hearts.

In the distance, we saw horses covered with thick winter blankets. One of the steeds raised his head to see us pass. I imagine the purple color of our car looked funny to him on this almost empty road.

"I am in love with this land," I declared ecstatically. "I think it is an ancestral love."

We arrived at the intersection of three narrow roads and some cars full of families joined us in the same direction: San Secondo Parmense.

"Why are there so many cars going in the direction of San Secondo? Is there really a festival? And how beautiful this entrance is with those tall trees that meet in the sky! Look at that little church! Small and beautiful...it looks like it's thousands of years old!"

We were closer to San Secondo than we realized. And this road lined with trees on each side, as the tops of the trees joined together to form a tunnel, typically Italian, we didn't know at the time that this was called Ronchetti and Isidoro had been born there. Or that the small church I liked so much, with that round central window (which we tried to take pictures of from the Fiat with an old camera, but they came out blurry), was precisely the church where he was baptized. Or maybe I knew by the knowledge of my heart, because my heart was glad to sense it!

THE CASTLE OF SAN SECONDO

*W*hen we entered San Secondo, we noticed that in the center of town the houses were all close to each other, their doorways were wide, and the windows had balconies. The purple Fiat was the perfect size to roll along the cobblestone streets. We stopped in front of the castle park, planted with tall oak trees and with little paths between them where people strolled.

"Let's hurry! Park anywhere. We have to find the man who is waiting for us in the *anagrafe* building with Stefano's information."

The local government building, adjacent to the park and the entrance to the castle, was a modest little one-story house. I tried to open the door but could not.

"I hope the officer hadn't left and is waiting for us inside."

I knocked hopelessly. A few seconds later, a man with thick black hair, glasses and a mustache greeted us and opened the door wide.

"Graciela?"

After introducing ourselves, we apologized because we had arrived almost at closing time.

"We got lost..."

"No, it doesn't matter," he answered kindly. "Here it is."

Without much fuss, he put an envelope in my hands and smiled with understanding at the expression I made when I opened the package. I exclaimed, "Etienne?!"

That was Stefano's name in French; it dawned on me why I hadn't found it in the record books. Stefano was as registered as *Etienne*, the French version of his name.

"Because of the French occupation," the gentleman began to explain.

"Of course! I was looking for a Stefano and not an Etienne. That's why I didn't find him!" I almost jumped with happiness and relief.

He continued. "The French changed the way of recording to a much more orderly one. What changed the most is that the books are written in the French language, so I translated it."

He presented each document and detailed what the package he had given me was about. The first was a copy of Stefano's birth certificate. The second was a photocopy of the registry book in the wonderful handwriting of the early nineteenth century. It was written in French with the name Étienne, due to the French occupation of Parma by Napoleonic forces, as the man had said. The third was the translated transcription, typed in Italian by the kindly officer. He himself had gone to the trouble of finding it, photocopying it and translating it. All for me—so that I would have it, and he didn't even know me! Now I couldn't believe that I had in my hands a copy of the original in the book, a translation and the certificate itself. My heart swelled with gratitude.

"I don't know Spanish and I speak very little English; that's why I translated it from French into Italian," he apologized.

For me, his English was perfect enough to explain everything, and I told him so. I told him about my research in the genealogy room, where I went on Saturdays during the summer:

"You don't know how long I was checking and checking, as I was looking for Stefano. It never occurred to me that they were going to register him with his French name. All this time I thought I was reading old Italian!"

I wanted to apologize for my ignorance, but he just bowed his head gracefully. He understood.

A little history on the French occupation: the Duchy of Parma and Plasencia had a common government under a Spanish duke. First there was Alexander Farnese, and then, his son, Antonio Farnese. During the birth of the ancestors, Stefano's predecessors, the Duchy of Parma and Plasencia was ruled by the House of Bourbon. However, by a legal land transfer agreement between Spain (Charles IV) and France (Napoleon Bonaparte), this territory, in addition to the state of Louisiana in the United States, became part of France. The agreement was in dispute until it was ratified in 1808. By becoming part of France, both states, Parma and Plasencia, were organized separately, each adopting its own form of government. I will add that it is interesting to know that the state of Louisiana was part of this transfer. Stefano came into the world at that time of unrest and perhaps something had happened to the records. I had estimated Stefano and Benedetta to be born in 1810 and 1820 respectively and under this occupation—those were the dates I checked in my research. And when, finally, I wrote to the civil offices asking for the data, this kind officer in charge found them without any problem. Stefano was there, just with his name in French. I would never have imagined that it could be Étienne. Without meaning to, I was bursting with admiration for this government official who, in my eyes, had become an eminent scholar. Only genealogists and historians or those passionate about their family legend can understand this.

So, with the widest smile in the world, I read aloud:

"Stefano Antonio. Born October 22, 1811. Son of Giuseppe Rainieri and Domenica Gonzaga."

And I saw something that caught my attention.

"Wait, please," I urgently asked him. "Am I related to the bride who is getting married now?"

On the wall and also at the entrance, there was a poster of the feast that was being celebrated in the castle: a wedding celebration that was also commemorating the wedding of the town's progenitors centuries before. The groom's name was Rossi, and the bride's, Gonzaga. I pointed out the announcement.

"The bride's surname is Gonzaga, the same as Stefano's mother! Could it be that a current relative is getting married now? Is that the wedding the town of San Secondo is attending in the castle?"

Smiling, he shook his head.

"There is no relation. Domenica, the mother of your ancestor Stefano, was born here, in San Secondo, as was Antonio, his father. There is no relation because apart from the fact that there are two hundred years of difference, they are not from the same Gonzaga family. But anyway, don't miss the celebration. In my case, I'm going home away from this hubbub."

Among the documents, there was a note from Stefano's parents. The good man had also written me a note of his nuptials, officiated in 1792. On the photocopy, one could read scrawled handwriting.

"Wait!" I begged him, "What is written there?" And again I showed him the documents.

Leaning over and reading, he said, "The wedding celebration of his ancestors, Giuseppe Rainieri and Domenica Gonzaga, lasted for three days of festivities. Those are notes in the margin."

"Three days!" I shouted dazedly, with the images of the medieval-inspired festivities settling in my mind's eye.

"Any excuse to celebrate longer—typical in this family!" Murat mentioned.

The gentleman was gathering his things and, when he finished placing his things in his briefcase, he leaned over to show us out. We understood that he had to close up. As he put on his scarf and winter hat, he added,

"Today Signore Rossi is getting married to Camilla Gonzaga. They are not your ancestors, but...don't miss the wedding. Enjoy the celebration." The clerk locked the door, bowed and hurriedly said goodbye.

I was left there, enchanted, thinking I had a treasure in my hands: my Stefano; and after so much searching for him. And better yet! It was as if my ancestors wanted to delight me further, by dangling the Gonzaga surname in front of me. I daydreamt that she was a cousin, distant probably,, but maybe not! It was the same surname, and she was getting married today in the castle. Maybe there were cousins of mine in this town!

Murat, enjoying my reverie immensely, whispered in my ear,

"Well, not this one." He was referring to the official who had just left. "Otherwise, he wouldn't miss a party."

"Ha! But he did something better. He waited for me to gift this to me. Tell me that's not ancestral intervention!"

I knew it was because since I had arrived, I could only think of Stefano. Because the officer waited for me and was kind enough not only to photocopy this data, but to translate it into a language I could understand, and to give me a certified copy free of charge without having been asked for it. An extra gift! It gave me more than I thought I needed. If this was not intervention from my ancestors, what else could it be? If this was not illumination from Stefano, what other explanation was there? There were too many coincidences in this investigation! It was as if my ancestors wanted to show me and transport me to the time in which they lived. As if they wanted to give me an idea or show me something of their lives. *"Look where we come from. In this town that was waiting for you and welcomes you with more than you asked for, it all began."*

"He invited us to the wedding!" I said to my husband, showing him Stefano's mother's surname and comparing it to the name on the poster on the tree. As I spoke, dreamlike images of the bride and groom parading down the aisle of a church filled my imagination.

As we walked through the park, I clutched the envelope I'd just received tightly in my hands. The thickness of the trees showed their age, and it was as if the whole town had gathered there. On one side there were parents strolling with their children; on the other, teenagers in love holding hands. Paper cones filled with roasted walnuts gave off a delicious aroma. Suddenly, a horse-drawn carriage arrived, decorated in the style of the medieval royal era; at least, that's what I assumed. It was the bridal retinue and it meant that the festivities inside the castle were about to begin. People got out of carriages and onlookers stepped aside to let them pass. A group of musicians came forward to play violins while actors in period costumes paraded in front of us. They took their time as they moved toward the castle waving to the spectators who crowded in to see them. *"Salve! Salve!"* some would say.

"It's the celebration of the Rossi's wedding to Gonzaga," I said to Murat in his ear.

"He said she's not related to you? But I think he's wrong!"

"Uh! Why?"

"Well, this well-dressed group came to celebrate, and they're going to eat, drink and, for sure, dance..." he answered when he saw the last couple enter. "And that's just like your family—a normal affair at one of their parties!"

Suddenly, everything became more personal.

"I think you're right—why not? Let's go in! Some cousins of my ancestors are getting married."

So, when they opened the gates to the initial garden, we went inside for a brief tour that included a visit to the wedding of this illustrious family, the Rossis.

"What a coincidence!" I exclaimed, although I was convinced that it was *no coincidence* and that wherever my ancestors were, I knew there would be a party. My ancestors were in charge to make me laugh and delight me.

The members of the act, dressed in Renaissance costumes, with feathered hats and elegant suits, stood in the middle and acted out their lines. We stood in the doorway until the act was over. We were informed that our group could stay if they wanted to, as there was still more of the performance, but we decided to leave. Although the celebration was very beautiful, I was relieved to get out of there while there was still a remnant of clarity left in the evening.

I wanted to walk the streets of the village of San Secondo. And so, we made our way back to the park and enjoyed the moment. We were in San Secondo Parmense, the land of my ancestors.

We were absorbed, watching some children playing when I noticed a little boy of about four or five years old approaching us. He came running towards me, his golden-brown curls bouncing in the breeze, and his eyes of the same color staring intently at me. He seemed to want to give me a hug, so I knelt down to greet him. He was so small and skinny that I only managed to take him gently by the shoulders.

"Hello, are you my little cousin?" I asked him.

He didn't understand me, turned around, and turned to his father who was approaching us. The boy was a replica of him.

"You scared him," Murat joked.

"Ciao!" I said to the boy who was now coming back holding his father's hand, walking towards me and pointing at me: *"Come si chiama?"* I pointed to the boy and bent down to greet him again and greet him by name.

"Marcelo," the father answered me.

"Ciao, Marcelo, did you know you're adorable? I have a little friend your age in my home back in Virginia!"

I spoke softly because I knew he didn't understand me. Soon, Marcelo had found a stick and was raking the grass with it while talking incessantly, clearly believing we understood everything he said. With the little stick as chalk, he would make imaginary stripes while I pretended to understand him, saying "Ooooh!" and "Wow!" and looking at the invisible shapes he traced. I was fascinated by the color of his eyes, that beautiful golden-brown . In the middle of our conversation, he insisted that I answer a question.

"*Me dispiace. Non parlo l'italiano.* (I'm sorry. I don't speak Italian)" I apologized.

Had I known I was going to meet little Marcelo, I would have learned it back home in a heartbeat. "Adorable little one!" I kept repeating. Marcelo was busy telling me an epic story, and I just nodded and said, "Yes, yes, *certo.*"

"*Che lingua parli?*" Marcelo's father asked us.

"Spanish, English," I replied.

"English, Turkish," said Murat laughing because he was not going to find anyone around with that combination.

"Italian, French," Marcelo's father added.

Despite him not claiming it among his known languages, the man pulled some English out of some mental drawer because he correctly explained everything to us about the wedding.

"My wife is part of the cast of performers. Maybe you saw her. She is dressed like..." and then he described her, but we didn't particularly remember anyone. We proposed to wait for her so that when the show was over, we could take a picture with her. However, Marcelo's father told us that very soon he would have to take his son home to have dinner, take a bath and rest, since they had not agreed with his wife that they would wait for her. As the little boy was still not sleepy and wanted to continue playing, he stayed in the park.

"Are you of Italian descent? Foreigners hardly ever come to this town."

"I'm doing some research on my family's genealogy and their surnames are Gonzaga and Rainieri. Do you know anyone with those surnames?"

"Well, the only thing I know about the surname Gonzaga is that they are from the adjacent region, where the castle of Soragna is located. Here, I know of several people with the surname Rainieri. It is very common here."

Murat warned him, "Don't tell her that because she thinks she's going to find cousins. She'd dare knock on the doors of every house and ask everyone to come out with their family trees!"

We laughed and, chuckling, I agreed that I probably would go out into the street and run around knocking on doors. Or better yet, to be more effective, I'd use a loudspeaker and shout, "To all possible relatives, a call: come out of your houses! Tell me the names of your parents, your grandparents, your great-grandparents, your great-great-grandparents? And if there is anyone named Isidoro or Stefano, you will get special attention. I want to know everything! Come out!" *Can you imagine if I ever found the house of Stefano Rainieri here in Italy?*

"Well, if you want to come to the innkeepers, maybe we'll find a relative of yours."

So, we set off toward one of the stone buildings. Soon we found ourselves inside a restaurant with a central garden. There were tables with cheese, *prosciutto*, wine and other delicacies. To one side and very casually, someone was playing a little music. Behind the table, a plump gentleman welcomed us. He was also dressed in medieval costume, and had a beard framing a broad smile.

"Come. Taste the wine!"

They served it in aluminum cups.

"What a delicious wine!" I melted when I tasted it.

"It's wine from the Taro River."

"The Taro River!" I made a note of it. I was fascinated by this town…and now, the wine.

We said yes to all the cold meats and antipasti they offered us. *Salamini* with *amarene, copa, capichola* with arugula leaves, *culatelo caldo* and *pancetta*, made from pork belly meat. A delight. And all accompanied by fried bread in a triangular shape.

A lady hugged little Marcelo on her lap. The child seemed to be sleepy, and the father started to say goodbye. When I brought my face close to kiss his little head in farewell, he clung tightly to my neck. I welcomed him into my arms, carrying him.

"I still don't want to leave him," I said to Murat. "If it's not too far, let's take him home."

"It is not far. We live behind the church," Marcelo's father replied.

"Perfect! This way we can see the place where my ancestors were married."

As we started walking, the boy woke up and we walked hand in hand through the stone streets. My little Italian chatterbox made me think about how talkative my ancestors could have been. Isidoro? Yes! Stefano? For sure!

The church of San Secondo was painted yellow. The artificial lights on the floor made the color look much brighter. Marcelo's dad pushed open the door. He and Murat went to look at some statues while the little boy, holding my hand, jumped over the floor with its black and white geometric details and together, hand in hand, we reached the altar.

MY ANCESTORS' WEDDING

*E*ntering the church was for me like entering another world. In retrospect, I can say with certainty that I was aware it was a sacred moment. I was crossing the threshold of the church where my ancestors had been married. And with that idea, a picture of an oil painting that I once found and cut out to put on the wall came to my mind. It was of a 19th century couple kissing passionately. The painting is called *The Bacio*, or *The Kiss*, it dates from 1867 and was painted by Francesco Hayez. I was fascinated when I saw it at that time back home, so I stuck it on my "Piece of Italy" wall. "Good heavens," I joked to myself. "I bet they are my ancestors!" And now entering the church, that image came to my mind.

Based on my ancestors, I had created a little story of the maiden and the handsome beau wearing a little Peter Pan-style hat. In the image it seemed that the groom had stopped her and taking her in his arms, kissed her in broad daylight, in the square and in front of everyone. For this reason, I projected the story of my ancestors into the painting. I gave them names: he was Giuseppe Rainieri, and she was Domenica Gonzaga. I imagined that in a few days they were going to get married and that they were in the preliminary preparations, enjoying their engagement. In the old days, parents decided for their children. They would say to each other, *"I have a son of such and such an age, and you have a daughter of such and such an age. What do you think?"* And if their offspring would be willing, they'd tell each other, *"Don't you see they like each other! Okay, then—let's get on with it!"*

This time, however, it wasn't like that. This time, they loved each other from the first time they met *and* chose each other. It was fortunate that their parents had approved of them immediately. Likewise, with their blessing or not, they fell in love with passion, just as the eternal kiss crystallized on the canvas for eternity. In this painting, in this story, there were no adults involved...just the two of them kissing; locked together in an eternal embrace.

It did not escape me, nor did I believe that it was pure coincidence that, on the same day I visited San Secondo, a wedding was being celebrated in the castle and enjoyed by the whole village. And, although it had not been the wedding of my ancestors, Giuseppe and Domenica, I was here in the same church where my ancestors had been married, and it was more than enough to get a little emotional.

In my dreamlike story, motivated by the memory of the image of the kiss, I still imagined a little more. The couple, madly in love and just a few days before the wedding, were anxiously finalizing so many preparations for a party that would last three days. The groom, very handsome, would be dressed very elegantly for the ceremony. And she, being a Gonzaga, would have worn the regalia of her house lineage, colorful silk and velvet brocades. Why not? Excuse me, but I allowed myself to imagine her beautiful like that! And since we have no photos of the event, here I share my mental reconstruction. As for the groom, if I used as a reference the Rainieri males I know, I'd describe him with a unique mischievousness.

As the oil painting in my mind came to life around me , the uninhabited church seemed to fill now with the shadow silhouettes of illustrious guests. It had been a few days since Domenica, in her light blue evening dress, had been walking carefree through the streets of the village, just outside the market. And the charming Giuseppe, had spotted her in the distance. In a fit of rapture, he ran to embrace her. Why? Because she was *his* fiancée! And he was beside himself with happiness. Right there, in the middle of the street, he kissed her lovingly. Together, they stole a moment for each other, even if only for a second. Their lips passionately touching. Giuseppe and Domenica, those love birds that were the protagonists of my fantasy. In the future, they would be the parents of Stefano, who together with Benedetta, would be the parents of my dear Isidoro. Without suspecting it, this grandfather of Isidoro, who did not know his future, could not even imagine that his descendants would inherit that mischievousness smile. His only desire, at that moment, was to take his future bride in his arms.

Soon, at the reception celebration, he would dance and drink with her, sharing the moment with family and friends. Stretching out his arms to exaggerate every gesture, he would tell stories, amusing everyone with his special and contagious smile. And in the church, in this *very* church where I found myself in the present day, the doors would open and she'd appear in a halo of light, illuminating the gloomy atmosphere of the church as she walked down the aisle to the altar. Even the candles in the windows would tilt their fire toward her as she passed. The bride may not be shy, but rather determined. With her big brown eyes, she'd look for the intense gaze of her beloved, who, dazzled, would be waiting for her at the altar. The maidens, alongside, would sigh in awe as they witnessed this scene. As the soft red and blue of their silk dresses falling in folds are lifted by the beam of light that follows the bride's footsteps, her beloved would say quietly, "The most beautiful among the flowers of a bouquet."

And as the parish priest would continue to drone on in solemn Latin, the bridesmaids would cover up their giggles by hiding behind their bouquets as they watched the groom throwing kisses to his bride as she advanced to meet him.

When they faced each other at last, the groom would whisper to his fiancée,

"I waited for you, I waited for you, I was waiting for you and I would wait for you all my life."

And she, with trembling lips, would answer,

"We will repeat this moment in hundreds of years for our descendants..."

And that's what I think happened. Because, thinking about it, it could have been something jocular, worthy of his descendants. Maybe, after kissing her at the market, he would have said, "Run away with me!" And she could have replied, "After my father prepared this party for three days—have you gone crazy?"

Proof of this was what my parents told me they said to each other on their wedding day. My mother, rushing him, exclaimed, "Let's go, the car is waiting for us!" And my father, who also loved to party, replied, "Do you want to go on your honeymoon already? But let me dance and drink until dawn!"

In the encroaching darkness of the chapel, the row of empty armchairs and the carpet that reached the altar took on an extraordinary glow. I very clearly saw the flowers and heard the laughter of the two lovers, and felt filled by their light, even more than I felt the light streaming in from the sun setting outside. It was a moment in which I thought, *While I reach out to my ancestors in images, I feel that they reach out to me by giving me what I ask for.*

It's that feeling of connection. All I want is to find their stories in me. I convince myself that I could get to know what they were really like. No one can deny that I have the impression they are listening to me, that they bring me their images, their dreams, their loving, funny and beautiful experiences.

Marcelo's hand tried to pull me into play jumping from the altar's stairs, and the noise of the echo brought me back to reality. I wanted to share with him a part of my story. I told him,

"This is where Stefano and Benedetta got married. Also Stefano's parents, who were Giuseppe and Domenica. My Isidoro and my Bianca did not get married here, but in Bogota."

He laughed at the word Bogota. When he started to want to jump again, his father came, and we thought it was time to leave. On the way out, we said goodbye with a big hug.

"*Ciao,* Marcelo, *Buona notte.*"

Murat and I returned the way we had come, admiring the streets. In front of us, the castle was once again unveiled. The party was still in full swing with the last of twilight shining down upon it.

"Wait for me here, please, I'm going to take some pictures before it gets dark. This is the best light of the afternoon."

While Murat photographed the celebration, I leaned back against the building in front of the park and returned to my daydream., I had stopped at this precise corner where the trail of one of my own remained—I suspected as much. I felt that Stefano must have stood there once, contemplating the castle in front of him. Perhaps without being able to enter, as I did. But that was not what he came to do. He was here, a little less than two hundred years ago, saying goodbye to this place, to these lands where he had picked grapes to make wine and ears of corn to make meals. Here, he honored his experiences—both sad and joyful. In a respectful farewell, he offered those remembrances of his heart breaking, as when his first wife and his first son, only two years-old, had passed away. And then, the joyful, when he met Benedetta, and with her, he was able to reassemble a new hope, a new love.

I wonder if they had any idea what they were saying goodbye to when they emigrated from this town and broke the chains of tradition. Could it have been the family angel who inspired them to get up one day, grab what little they had and leave? From where I am, it's easy to say. I have to thank them for unmooring a destiny, giving their descendants the chance to be born in other lands and continue the legacy. Perhaps they wished to please my grandmother's own soul and put down roots in Puerto Plata. I think her soul wanted to be born where the sun and the sea meet on the same horizon and where the waves undulate incessantly, whispering love words to each other. My grandmother Chela, proud to be *puerto-plateña*, would have wanted it. For the blood of the family, embracing new lands was their destiny; and part of mine was to represent this return. I was back with them, stepping on the stones they stepped on, touching with my hand the corner of the wall, and at the same time thinking, *Where will it all take us? This destiny of ours —how far will we go?* And thinking of the words that my uncle Fernando had said to me about trying to get very far down our genealogy, I thought of Stefano and Benedetta. *If they only knew how far their descendants went!"*

Stefano and Benedetta, who were my grandmother Chela's grandparents, attracted new destinies with the desires of their souls. In short, a better life for their children, and for their children's children; their destinies flowing towards an unthinkable future. For them, here I was, being whole with the free and adventurous spirit of those who preceded me. Because I felt that a part of their heart stayed there; I felt it when I placed the palm of my hand on the peach-colored wall. At this corner, my predecessors returned in me. I brought them in my blood, and the deepest part of my being danced and rejoiced. Perhaps I would regain this feeling when I visited the places of my other elders, like Galicia, and touched the church where another other ancestor was baptized. Or perhaps I would feel equally moved when I got to Bogota and said a prayer in the church that united them forever. Wherever my ancestors were, I'd feel it. I know. But this was the first time they ran through my veins in this intimate way. I realized wherever I moved and wherever they had been, my cells would rejoice, would be filled with life and recognition because I carried them within me—all of them.

"Today it's your turn, Stefano."

I felt very grateful in that moment. Because they migrated and moved and each one was born where their soul ordered or was inspired to happen. Thousands of places, thousands of lives and thousands of loves within me—my heart rejoiced in this knowledge. I was invaded by nostalgia, very conscious of the stones that treasured these memories and that, when I touched them with my hand, they transmitted them to me.

Murat was beckoning me to come closer. I crossed the street to meet him and told him proudly,

"I feel that I have returned. Somehow, they have returned inside me."

I wanted to say more, but my emotions constricted my throat. I would have liked to say goodbye to San Secondo with more eloquent words, but none came out. Only that feeling of return, of coming back, that I was the daughter who had returned. The person inside me who represented all those sorrows and joys they experienced. Inside me, my lineage is my eternal companion, my joyful heart. I was overcome with a radical feeling of belonging and of knowing that I am always blessed by them. I knew that they had encouraged, and given me permission, even expected me to achieve more than them. If they could have, they would have given us the world—I had come to Italy and meet that expansive clarity.

Murat and I continued in the direction of the parking lot, passing through the park. Suddenly, I remembered the purple and crimson paper ticket offering a free drink in Venice that we had left in the car.

"How long is it from here to Venice?" I asked, innocently.

"Six hours."

I smiled mischievously.

"I'll buy you a drink in a hotel in Venice?"

"Oh, yeah?" He laughed. "Wasn't I inviting *you* to a drink in a hotel in Venice?"

"I invited you first," I said laughing. "But I accept!"

"Shall we?" He broke into a run.

"We shall!" I ran after him.

Competing like children, we ran and crossed the park full of trees; we jumped over the bushes, dodging bicycles, cars and passers-by, we played to see who would get there first to take the ticket and invite the other one.

On this unexpected escape to the Venice carnival, we didn't want to waste time stopping for dinner. It was after six in the evening, and we would arrive at twelve midnight. If we didn't get lost!

Before we took the *autostrata*, we stopped at the first sandwich store we saw. It turned out to be a wholesale Parmesan cheese shop, that mainly dealt in restaurant sales. The funny thing is that we had never seen anything like this before. The cheese was sold in giant wheels, and the clerks would happily roll them on top of the counter.

"Can we have the smallest piece, please?"

Turning over itself, came the *smallest* cheese—which was the size of the wheel of our Fiat!

"I'm sorry. *Me dispiace.* Isn't there a smaller piece? *Per favore.* I mean, like this..." I formed a triangle with my hands imitating a normal piece of cheese. "*Piccolo, piccolo... piccolino, per due.*"

I pointed to Murat, who was waiting for me outside in the car. The clerks, dressed in white with chef's jackets and coiffures, were showing me another one just as big.

"*E'un chin que quiero, na'ma'! A chinininin!*" I spoke to them in Dominican because I was giving up, they weren't understanding anything, anyway.

As they looked at me, blinking and still on bringing out their cartwheels made of cheese, I almost turned and left, but I saw Murat sticking his head out of the car's window and looking at me in dismay. I called to him from the store entrance, as though he knew what was going on:

"The cheese wouldn't have fit in the Ferrari either!"

And I went back inside.

Behind the counter, my onlookers observed me, curious and smiling as if waiting to see what I was going to say next. I pointed to our car, which was visible through the window. Our purple carriage looked smaller than usual. Maybe this time I could make myself understood.

"Look! That's the car and the piece you're offering will not fit. We just want a little piece..." I made the triangle with my fingers again. "It's just to hold our hunger for the road." I touched my belly, "So we don't have to stop on the way to Venice."

In the end, I think we looked pitiful enough, or they thought we were crazy and just wanted us to leave because, finally, one of them came out of the kitchen with a triangular piece, which, although it was the size of my arm, was not as big as the previous one. Smiling, another chef set a *baguette* on the side of the counter. They wrapped it in a long piece of paper and said to me in Italian, "Five dollars, please."

I bowed about ten times to thank them. *"Grazie. Grazie. Grazie,"* I kept repeating to them as I walked out the door without turning my back to them, as if I had just spoken to the queen. That was our dinner on the way to Venice.

"What would it be like to live on bread and Parmesan cheese alone? What made your ancestors complain so much about that they wanted to get out of here?"

"I don't think it was a complaint. Just that Mamma Chela would have told you that this Parmesan needed a crunchy salami, Puerto Plata style."

What else can I say about this first trip to San Secondo, land of my ancestors? The most delicious surprise was that this was the best Parmesan cheese we had ever tasted! It wasn't dry or salty or anything like what we commonly have in the supermarkets. Oh, no! It was spongy, juicy and even had a sweet taste. And there were tiny, crystallized pieces of salt that added a crunchy surprise with every bite. A real treat! And we had enough to take some as a gift to Grazia when we went back to Tuscany!

THE RETURN

$\mathcal{T}$he sky was changing color. Twilight had enlivened the golden color of the stones on the walls. Even the shadows seemed to hold a thousand colors. We were back in Tuscany regaling Grazia with our adventure in San Secondo Parmense. She couldn't believe everything we had done. She laughed when we told her we had headed to Venice without having planned a hotel to stay in—she wanted to know how we found one during such a busy time for Venice.

Remember that at this time, there were no smart phones that could search out accommodations for us. We had to look the old-fashioned way. The first hotel we found was near the ferry and was an American chain. I went down to ask the price. I came back with shock all over my face, and my eyes widened.

"Three hundred and fifty dollars," I announced.

"More than the plane ticket? Impossible!"

I came up with the great idea:

"Let's sleep in the car, like when we were young and went to New York after parties."

Murat looked at me frightened, "I can't fit in this car!"

"Oh, that's right. Small detail."

We arrived at the Lido, where there were some *boutique* hotels. At the first one we stopped at, I asked the price, then returned to

Murat with a smile from ear to ear. The price was so low that it was a gift!

"You have to come and see inside how nice the hotel is. Breakfast is included and they told me about parking. It's all taken care of!"

Before leaving to take the ferry to the center of Venice, I called Mami. There, at home, it was seven o'clock in the morning.

"I'm in Venice! Tomorrow, on the way back, we will pass through Bologna."

We quickly took the *vaporetto* to attend the carnival adventure at midnight. It was three in the morning when we finally came back to the hotel. Although the room was tiny, the pillows made up for it —they were very comfortable. At eight o'clock we were awakened by the aroma of baked bread. Hunger got us out of bed as if impelled by a spring. Quickly, we showered, dressed and went down to the *lobby*, a charming space with *Art Nouveau* woodwork and hanging lamps with red, blue and yellow lights, very much in the Venetian style.

"I don't think we're out of last night's fairy tale yet," I said to Murat after we checked out and were on the road back to our tower in Tuscany.

Although we made every effort to look for Castello d'Argile, we never found it on our map. In the future, I would visit it with my sister and discover that it is much smaller than we expected and it is listed as a small gated neighborhood. The truth is that, if we had had something like Google Maps, I would have put in the address of Queco's house that Uncle Fernando had given me.

In Bologna, we imagined Isidoro and Bianca walking the streets and eating at some of the old restaurants we saw. We toured the town with the car and drove around the outskirts. We found it to be a very diverse town full of young people who we presumed were university students, as Bologna has one of the oldest universities in the western hemisphere. It was a much larger expanse than I had expected and much nicer than in my dreams, and that was my impression—although we didn't stop too long. If I had seen the ancient libraries with the paintings of ancient frescoes on its walls, I would have stayed forever!

On the outskirts of Bologna we had lunch at the oldest place we came across—a restaurant that caught our attention with the promise of the best *Tortellini al brodo*. We bought some *mortadella*, a typical local sausage that I like so much. It's made with pepper and pistachio—a deadly-delicious combination. We bought them as gift for Grazia, which we hand-delivered to her along with the big piece of Parmesan cheese, as if they were spoils of a war we had fought.

The night before our departure, Grazia organized a farewell party in our honor at her home. Loreno came as well. The plan was to arrive early to watch the sunset from the mountain and then walk with us along the pine-lined paths. Stefania brought the artisanal wine she'd served us before, and we drank as if it were an elixir of friendship. From the window of Grazia's house, we admired the entrance of night breaking through the big stars. We were delighted to have a sight of the little yellow house we could have chosen for our lodging.

"I don't regret staying in the cellar. The cottage is nice, but our spooky, yet wonderful place made the story better."

I shared with them how we had decided on taking our trip. I told them about all the tragedies that had befallen us in the previous months before we made our plan and added that the only ones who always seemed to be on our side were our ancestors.

"Grazia, what a blessing to have met you! How lucky we were to find you!"

"One day came an email from a beautiful person who was looking to come and see the land of her great-grandparents and said she had a crazy dream, and the rest is history," she answered.

Murat and I laughed, remembering the summer we had talked about dreams.

"Yes, but seriously." I looked at her and in response, she placed her hand on mine. I continued, "This world that you have created and that you have invited us into for these almost two weeks has been a balm for us. You don't know the impediments we had, and in the end, it seems that everything turned out well. And it's thanks to you. Thanks to the fact that you solved so many things for us, like where to stay and what to do each day. In short, it was like...I don't know...."

I couldn't find a way to put it into words. I didn't want to say *magic*, but the stars twinkling in the sky whispered that word to me.

"Magic," Grazia then said for me.

"That's right," I agreed. "Only, I would like to offer you a more concrete explanation; to be able to explain it in some other way. Not as if you had cast a spell."

"Do you know who Marconi was?" She asked, but before waiting for an answer she continued. "He discovered radio waves. Unsuspected, perhaps, at the time. Radio waves are vibrations that can only be received with an apparatus. So how did he discover them? And, to understand that those waves could cross the ocean—what creativity! He discovered that voice could be transmitted through a device—how did he know how to do that?"

"Easy. Because Marconi was Italian and Italians believe that everything can be done," I said, inventing an answer.

"Could he be related to someone around here?" Murat looked at me slyly.

Grazia smiled and continued. "I think that each person has a specific vibration, like the waves emitted by a radio, something that cannot be seen or defined. We only know that it works. Each of us has something like that. There are people who emit a vibration on the same frequency, and it doesn't matter how far away or close they are; if there is another of the same vibration, there is a good chance that they will find each other. I am sure. You had a longing and because we are on the same frequency, the great mystery brought us together at this point in time and space," she concluded.

"A wonderful alchemy!" I clapped my hands.

"A good kind of crazy!" We applauded enthusiastically.

"Believe me. I've had a wonderful time too! Being with you has been like being on vacation at the same time as working! The best combination for me. Thanks to you, my business has stayed open during the winter. You have also entertained me, taken me for walks and invited me to share. And when you came back from your trips, you told me your wonderful anecdotes!"

"The way you each think is not so different," said Murat.

"I just believe that things happen according to one's belief. The limits of your belief are the limits of each one," explained Grazia.

"Okay! My belief is that my ancestors have given me this journey, otherwise, who else could have conspired it but the divinity itself, perhaps disguised as them?"

I began this genealogical research with a pure heart...and also was wounded by a loss. I realize how the search for my roots has filled my days with meaning. Now I know that trusting the mystery and learning to let go of preconceived ideas has brought me to that epiphany.

I am now more convinced than ever of the following: I reaffirm that all my elders are part of me. All those to whom I belong and all those who belong to me are in me. I've inherited dreams. I've inherited loves. The love of my ancestors lives in me. And...so many untold stories! Today I want to tell them all. Their movement throughout this world, the swaying on the train, the rocking of the sea, all while they were traveling. The charm of a voyage to fulfill their dreams! They, on the way here, and me, on the way back. The charm is in everything we do and in the details; it's in a glass of wine and in a jar of delectable jam; it's between the new and the old, the sublime and the mundane. I have enjoyed it all! They had given me Italy, and in her, all that I had done and all that I have become and continue to evolve into. I am *everything* that they were...and they are *everything* in me!

Even as I sat on the plane watching us lift off and the grounds of *my favorite place* disappear, I felt these ancestral sensations and murmurs. My mind doesn't rest from thinking, so I started to write in my little notebook.

* * *

I have spent the happiest hours alone with my ancestors. Getting to know them...writing down my ideas about what happened to them. To put this on paper would be to put myself on paper. It is a task to translate my heart into words. I want to hear only what they want to say. Their memories are my memories. Their love radiates through this magic ink. The paper carries it; makes it a portable love. Suddenly, my dear heart rises, and I realize that, long ago, I had thought it broken and yet now I feel it getting strong. What is the plan other than to express my being and describe as fables the stories that were theirs and now mine?

* * *

I think of Isidoro. I thank all those who brought me here. Love is the vehicle. It comes from all those who came before me. Because it is a deep love. It is a love that transcends generations...

* * *

I was surprised when I discovered in me that I was never alone. All the time they were pushing me, lifting me up...and I owe that to them.

On my next trip to reconnect with Mami, I brought her the first sketch of the family tree, documents and photos. She thought it was an eclectically fun experience, especially when I told her that I had gotten my husband to drive the Flintstones car in Italy. She burst out laughing when we ordered a cheese sandwich and they brought us what looked like a car tire rolling out. She was amazed to know that we had stayed in the cellar of a medieval tower (I confess that I described it creepier than it really was). But when I told her about my visit to the embassy, what fascinated her most was the part where the clerk had said to me, while pointing up at the sky, "Someone up there must really love you"

And when I finished all the stories, that part was what she asked me to repeat again.

"Really? Did she really tell you that?" That day, her eyes were a wonderfully pale olive color. I only nodded vehemently. Silently and thoughtfully, we both looked up at the sky.

PARTE 3

THE MOST BEAUTIFUL WORD

THE MOST BEAUTIFUL WORD

or me, the most beautiful word in the world is *Mami*. It's the one I used for my mother and the one my children use with me. I love it.

My mother's eyes were classically Italian in shape. Her eyebrows were long and tapered, subtle like Leonardo da Vinci's pencil drawings. Her chubby cheeks were like those of baby dolls. Her nose with its straight septum and triangular tip looked like it had been sculpted by an artist from another time. From which of her ancestors did she inherit that perfect nose? I don't think from the Italians! My mother had five daughters and from oldest to youngest our names are: Cristina, Adelaide, Georgina (Gina), Graciela and Victoria. But of all these females, it was Laila, her only granddaughter, who inherited the genetics of her nose. After having five girls , ten out of eleven grandchildren were boys. The one and only girl was our dear *Laila*, who I was very proud to call my godchild.

My mother and I had two out-of-tune personalities, a mismatch between mother and daughter, an inheritance that went back generations as it also existed between her and Chela, and, as I understand it, between Chela and Bianca. My mother had a measured manner and reserved her musical laughter only for my father; and even for him she rarely laughed. She was especially generous with the sick: she even paid for the medicines that could cure them, and she had a soft spot for cancer patients, even before she herself suffered from the disease. After the loss of my dad, she became a volunteer at the cancer hospital in the city. She went twice a week, until the disease touched her, and she moved to Miami. We, the Thomen sisters, in her name and as an intimate tribute to her, continued her legacy.

I am like her in some ways, I share her love of reading, gardens, nature and tranquility. Growing up, I naturally adapted meditation and yoga into my daily life. At first, Mami found this inclination of mine to be strange. I guess it was a dichotomy of the ability I have had since I was a child to disappear into reading and writing for a whole day and yet also have the courage to lose myself in the hustle and bustle of a party. I could just as easily be a social butterfly and laugh uproariously. And I love dancing! This range of intellectual introspection combined with a loose cheerfulness confused her, I suppose. For my part I saw my mom as unnecessarily pedagogical and even stern. The difference in personalities made us impatient with each other. These differences do not make us unique as mother and daughter, even today. I'm sure it is repeated in many families.

And we would have continued this habit of looking at each other with narrowed eyes if the unexpected had not occurred. Cancer took over her life and forced us to change our respective attitudes. From the moment Mami was diagnosed with breast cancer, my sisters and I were in the battle. We learned about medicine and nursing; we used any free time we had to spend with her— to be of service to her. As for me, I used all my vacation time to travel, to be by her side, to help her. Between my sisters and I, we would arrange to take turns in pairs and thus have the opportunity to keep each other company. As a team, we assisted Mami in whatever was necessary, although she, despite her illness, maintained a clear control in her decisions. She interviewed, informed herself, and meticulously chose her doctors. She discussed her treatments, processes and timelines with a cool head; at no time did she behave like a victim. I admired the way she faced everything, right to the end, with a unique stoic equanimity—just as Bianca's granddaughter would.

Before, but also especially during her convalescence, I used

177

genealogy as a unifying theme between the two of us. If there was one thing we had in common, it was our love for our ancestors. In her case, a fierce love for her grandmother Bianca, and, in my case, for my grandmother Chela. We had differences in our approach to certain situations; she thought Bianca had been abandoned while I swore Isidoro was innocent. But even these differences invited us to have conversations about deep issues and to delve into and weigh the importance of family stories.

In early 2002, my mom got a house in the city of Miami to be close to Mount Sinai Hospital, where she decided to undergo treatment. It was a nice little house in a gated and landscaped community in Kendall County. I loved it from the first time I went to visit. She had added flowers to the garden from the beginning, such was her passion. That new home had a front garden that she filled with buds and blossoms, and it seemed perfect to me, as if it had been purposely created for her recovery. The little walk to the front door was like walking through a tiny but eternal spring. On the sides, lilacs adorned the path, and the jasmine bower scented each night.

"Welcome!"

Mami opened the door, smiling and holding before my eyes a set of keys dangling from her fingers. She handed them to me immediately for my convenience to come and go. She looked happy. As we walked through the house together, she showed me the spaces she had decorated with great care and modern freshness. For her living room, she had chosen wide white furniture. On the tables, glass ornaments reflected the light coming in through the glass doors that opened onto the patio. There were white candles and sprigs of bamboo that reached up, dropping their pointed green leaves. Picture frames displayed smiling family faces and pictures of my mom and dad, their daughters and grandchildren were scattered throughout the house. It was a zen space. The kitchen had a sign that read, "Socorro's Kitchen," and on the counter she placed a pair of ceramic roosters that I had given her. She said that these birds would bring good fortune.

"The backyard is very cool. Come and see it!"

She was happy; in fact, I had never seen her so excited. I helped her open the glass doors. That night, we would have a barbecue under a tall, thin-trunked oak tree whose branches spread out in intermittent, cheerful shade. During the week, I spotted with delight some visiting larks and a bluebird that seemed to be passing through and nestled in the beautiful branches for a while. What I liked best was the gray-violet lizard scurrying along the walls; all mosquito-eating animals are friends of mine, so please don't chase them away!

In this little house in Kendall she seemed content. Geographically, it was closer to Virginia than where she had lived before, which gave me the opportunity to visit her often and to bring my children to her when they were on vacation. She was a loving and enthusiastic grandmother to her grandchildren, just as her grandmother Bianca had been—as I knew it.

When we sat down after dinner, I opened my folder full of documents and photos. I tackled it with my notes from the trip to Italy, along with photos, the map of San Secondo, and all the documents I'd collected so far. I would fulfill my role and duty of accompanying her for tests, monitoring her treatment and keeping her comfortable in her convalescence. Our time together would be spent in an endless conversation punctuated with questions. As always, I would share something with her and, in return, I wanted to know what she thought about everything and dig deeper into her memories. Or, let's say, fishing for his memories.

"I thought it was great that you got to know San Secondo, but why didn't you go to my grandmother's house in Bologna?"

I knew she was going to ask me that question after I showed her the photos of my trip to Italy. She knew well my preference for Isidoro.

"Because your cousins Fernando and Frank know everything about Bianca, but not so much about Isidoro." To appease her, I showed her a document that, when I returned from Italy, I had received from the *Comune di Castello d'Argile*, where her favorite had been born.

"It's the birth certificate of your grandmother in Italy."

I told her that a lady named Galli was kind enough to photocopy the page from the registry. It was a large photocopy with calligraphy letters of the time.

The description on Bianca's certificate went like this:

* * *

On June 7, 1875, was born the daughter of Francesco Franceschini, transporter, domiciled in this community, who informed me that at the fifth hour before the meridian, today, of the current month, in this castello, and Mrs. Raffaellina Galletti, cohabiting wife, weaver, was born a girl named Bianca.

* * *

"I thought my grandmother's mother's name was Angelina...."

"Oh, no," I said, throwing up my hands in mock horror, "It's another family mystery!" One that I would definitely explore at another time.

I pointed out the definition of the professions. "Bianca's mother was a knitter," I added, pointing to the wool buns and yarn that accompanied her on this journey.

I later learned in my research that weaving garments was not the same as weaving other types of items. In Castello they wove ropes. And it is likely that this was what Raffaellina's family was referring to and that they were engaged in the trade of this type of articles. Their merchandise would be *carried* by Francesco to Bologna.

I told Mami that Castello d'Argile is a very small town located in the north, fifteen minutes by car from Bologna. From its name, I thought *castello* referred to a castle and, of course, I imagined Bianca, the grand damsel, in the highest tower, but that was not the case at all. The word comes from the Latin *castrum*, which refers to a soldiers' nursery that had a wall built around it. Over time, Castello d'Argile ended up being a small walled village, funny was the coincidence that it was described much like this gated community where she lived now. It was the old-fashioned way of living behind closed and private doors. Bianca had a very close family bond, we already knew that from inherited history. Her neighbors were her cousins and they were also her companions to school and church each Sunday. She trusted all of them since she had grown up with them, and that gave her peace of mind. And with them she left her children to go on trips with Isidoro. And that's why her children were separated on two continents when he departed.

Sitting under the oak tree and enjoying the breeze in the yard, I sighed happily to bring Mami new stories of Bianca. At that time, we had so little affinity that genealogy represented an open door. I was pleased with the pleasure and interest in her eyes as I eagerly read her the documents and asked her questions. Our lineage united us. Our strong women fueled the love in us.

But I noticed something else, the inner strength that showed itself at the mention of my great-grandmother. The embroidered stories of our ancestors somehow spun with our own. It was as if our experiences were a bit similar. The coincidence of where she now lived—this gated community. The weavings, too, similar to her love for knitting. The trust and warmth with their cousins—same thing she had with Fernando and Frank. Besides, the documents brought their own spark with meaningful and interesting details that stirred the imagination. On one hand, these documents gave us information about baptism, marriage, and changes in residence, but the other side of the story was their opinions, their words, their thoughts…those could only be reanimated in present coincidences. Could they also inform us of the quality of their decisions? The documents enlivened visual imagines in me, gave voice to thoughts, and cleared some feelings that my heart had. But all of those were subjective, while documents can be objective. How can we draw more knowledge about our ancestors from them? How can we draw knowledge about sentiments, emotions, or opinions from them? Could, instead, our hearts sense and thus be like a vehicle for a communication with the ancestors? Could love be the current that flows from heart to heart, as is electricity through the metal of wires? And if so, how is love passed from generation to generation? I suspect that some of the habitat of souls is also transmitted with DNA.

"She grew up with her cousins nearby," Mami repeated back to me. I smiled in satisfaction because she also had a special idea about her cousins. Close bonds that resembled the one Bianca had with her, as she entrusted her children to them—a trust and affection beyond questioning.

As I introduced and talked about each document, she watched me with new eyes. I didn't need to look at her to feel that. In the weeks that followed, she came out with comments regarding my fascination with this mystery as a singularity of mine. I understood that, deep down, it made her happy. Perhaps she also wanted to know more, but loyalty to inherited stories would not let her. For me, on the other hand, it was impossible to dwell on what I had received as absolute truths. I wanted to know about the other stories—those not told and try to see if my heart already knew them. I wanted to know if time was elastic, as Einstein had inferred; if it was possible to reach into the mists of the past and rescue more stories.

She could not even imagine the nights I had spent raving about the research. She discerned my preference for Isidoro, but she couldn't understand what I sensed: that the story of his abandonment of his family was poorly received, poorly told. For her, Isidoro abandoned Bianca and there was nothing more to look for or discover. Her grandmother Bianca's life proved it. Hadn't she started the business practically on her own? Wasn't it Bianca herself who had raised her children and put them to hard work every day of their lives? She had single-handedly put them on track and made them good men and women. The family history supported her. The anecdotes praised her. And my heart and my logic didn't disagree. It's just I felt that something had been overlooked. And that sensation pushed me irrevocably and unquestionably to clarify hidden issues in the leafy family tree. Yes, to rescue Isidoro from oblivion. So I thought, *Isidoro, am I going to spend my life trying to find you!*

But the present is pressing. The present is more important than the past when you have a sick beloved. So, knowing the value of time, I devoted myself and my sisters to providing essential care for Mom while I tried to cast a net and rescue her ancestral memories.

THE BEST AGE

$\mathcal{A}$t first glance, the little house in Kendall, compact and cheerful, and as cute as it was didn't compared to the house in Santo Domingo, where I grew up; that house with white walls and rectangular tile floor that caused a furor among architects and engineers at the time it was built. According to what my father had told me, his friends and colleagues came to see it when the house was a shell without doors or windows in order to get ideas, because they had interspersed blocks of different sizes without tiling, the level of the floor in each room varied, and that was just the beginning of all the architectonically interesting quirks our house possessed.

The land for the house in Santo Domingo had been given to him by his father, Joaquín, as a wedding gift. My grandfather did the same with each of his children. Although it was not an immediate gift, since during the first years of their marriage, while the house was built, my parents resided with him, under the projection screen of the Autocinema Naco. Yes, they lived under the screen of a car cinema. My older sister, Cristina, slept in that house "under the screen", something she loved to say. Come to think of it, I don't understand how they managed with such a small space.

Once we went to visit my grandfather Joaquín in his eccentric home. The roof was the projection screen; flat, of course, but behind it was a back of wires and lights that was supported on an inclined plane, as if it were the roof of a northern European cottage. You entered through the living room, which was also a dining room; the kitchen was just a corner, and everything was filled with boxes full of reels and posters of classic films. Some of the celluloid tapes hung on the wall and others were on their sides, half-rolled on the desk. These celluloids were of three or four frames whose images to the naked eye were shapeless blobs. If one took them carefully and held them against the light, one could identify them. There were passionate kisses, romantic scenes and women dressed in sexy outfits on the squares. My sister Cris, without the adults noticing, would take one and go to the kitchen and put it against the windowpane. I would follow her, although she would try to stop me, being a younger sister and, for sure, a pain in the neck for her. Looking at the pictures, I remember her funny rabbit smile that she had inherited from my dad. The same one I also inherited.

My parents' house had a large garden where they planted fruit trees and many flowers that my mom liked. While lots of the little birds that came to coo in the morning, we discovered that a nightingale that had made its nest on our terrace. Dad said it sang to him at breakfast. In my room, Mami almost reluctantly let me paint the walls yellow. Why? She didn't understand my stubbornness. It would be the only different room in the house. She asked me if I didn't like white. I remember answering that the yellow invited the sun's rays to come in in the mornings and stay there longer; that I would snuggle into them.

That house was the one Mami sold after my dad passed away. And what happened to the house? The new owners destroyed it to make it into a parking lot. The loquat and coconut trees had been cut down. Only the almond tree from the barbecue parties remained because the corner was on the edge of the land. The parking lot served to alleviate the traffic to the offices that were beginning to rise in that rural area, and to the masses of buildings that muddied the native architecture.

This is how the old, with time, becomes fiction. Without leaving traces. In the end, the portraits fail to prove anything. They do not attest to what really was there. And the memories, which are true films of yesteryear, are intertwined with other collective ones.

There remains a concoction in our mind that can only be saved by the word; the stories that the memory changes according to the perspective of the one who tells them. I know this well. Memories are hard to catch. It's just that the images of memories are like wild rabbits. If you try to catch one, they scurry away among the green leaves, never to return. It's better to stay calm, to appease the feeling, to use indifference as a lure. Only then can memories be trapped in words.

I will become the catcher of memories. I will be the fisherwoman of untold stories of my ancestors' lives. Now it was time to catch them from the person closest to me: Mami.

"What is your best age?"

It was one of the interview questions I never finished asking. That list I wanted to keep for posterity, for my children. Now it was more for me. She was lying down and reading a book when I questioned her. We were both in her room, in her little house in Kendall. I had sprawled out on the bed next to her. As you might suspect, true to her trademark sense of humor, she answered me with another question.

"Why do you want to know?"

"Well, it's like a personal survey. I've already asked others." I knew that last one was going to pique her curiosity.

"Oh, yeah? So, what did you find out?"

"Mamma Chela told me that her best age was nineteen."

My mom smiled:

"Did she really tell you that?"

"Yes, because she wasn't yet worried about life; she just wanted to dance and be happy. When they were little, Mamma Chela and her sisters spent their childhood working at the hotel. Within a childhood of chores, the fantasy of parties helped her to detach herself from reality. Dancing was synonymous with freedom from the duties of the family business."

Mami did not answer. I wanted to pique her curiosity further.

"I also asked Aunt Ná. She told me that her best age was sixty-six." Aunt Ná had been an aunt of my father's and she had lived to the ripe old age of one hundred and two.

"Sixty-six!" This interested her more.

"According to her, at sixty-six she had learned to let go of everything that didn't matter. She no longer cared about her beauty. Nor the opinion of others. She decided not to worry about what people would say. She felt free. She took meditation classes, which she practiced assiduously and learned to dominate her thoughts. She said she chose to think only of the positive. I think that was the key to her happiness and longevity." I laughed as I added, "Although when I told dad about it he told me that, at sixty-six, Aunt Ná had already buried her husband."

"Oh, so...you asked your dad also." My mother's face looked even more attentive now.

"Yep," I answered, anticipating that she would like his answer.

"What did he say?" She tilted her ear, now very interested.

"He told me that his best years had been not one, but several. In particular, the decade of his thirties. In those days, we used to travel by car from Santo Domingo to Puerto Plata. Do you remember? We, the sisters, were small and we played all day long in Guarapito. There was the big tree called *Sombrero de Obispo* (Bishop's Hat) that I loved. We would impulsively run barefoot through the open field of grass full of *morivíes* on our way to the water. And once we reached the shore we had to jump over all the sharp rocks there to finally get into the sea. Our feet would land the sand, fine and freshly cool from the water, and then we would keep running until we could dive into the surf."

I let my imagination take me back to the pleasure of taking off my shoes, running across the grass and finding the path that ended in white sand. The continuous roar of the rough sea was so imposing, but also exhilarating! I remembered myself jumping over the jagged stones that embraced the beach. The prize was that fine powder and sparkling water. The enjoyment of putting my feet in the clear water is unsurpassed! And, when the sand was stirred up, the little blue fish we called angels would curiously approach us. Then, I turned my eyes from the past to the present. Mami had closed her book and put it aside. I settled in more, pulling the pillow closer and closing my eyes.

I sighed deeply and asked her, "And you adults, what were you doing?"

"We were constantly chasing after you and your sisters. When we weren't, we must have been sitting on the veranda of the house drinking rum and eating bits of seafood." Her tone had become quite animated.

"Do you remember the oysters they used to sell us at noon? No one would believe how we feasted when we went to the beach in Sosua!" I added, fascinated by the memories.

"Oysters came tucked between the ice in the square-folded *yaguas* that served as boxes. Freshly caught." Mami sounded wistful. "Your father would buy them all from the sellers saying, 'Don't worry about taking any of them back, we'll eat them all.' And they would open them one by one, and you would eat them all."

"A little lime and that's it!"

I raised my head to get a better look at her expression as I told her what my father had said and what his family meant to him.

"That was Dad's best age, according to my interview. We, his daughters, enjoying nature, the sea water, the sand, the food the fishermen brought us. *Nothing gives more pleasure than simple things*, he told me that time. You were unconcerned about everything. And so was he. You were happy."

"It was a peculiar, special world. Real living..." she said as if in a dream.

Puerto Plata was in the most precious part of her childhood too, because of her grandmother Bianca. Her beloved Babi. I was pleased with her questions about my survey because it gave me the opportunity to tell her all the answers I had previously collected from other family members. Which suited her just fine, as that's how she was; I had to tell her what everyone else had said before she would answer even the first question.

"My best age," she began, thinking carefully. "It was not one, but several, different and for different reasons. I liked the school I went to and I liked my friends. And I liked being your dad's girlfriend. He was so romantic and splendid and always cheerful; happy, as you say, in that same decade you were growing up. I loved it when the grandchildren started coming along. The truth is that every decade has had its charm. Every age brought good and bad things. Even now, without your dad, I've had many joyful experiences. Age frees you from everyday worries and invites you to fill your life with new experiences, if to take advantage of the time you have."

And it was true! As soon as Mami started feeling better after her first surgery and treatment, she didn't waste a minute and began planning trips. Selling her house in Santo Domingo freed her up, and it took a load off her mind. Surviving the first stage of her illness had taught her that time was short and she should do the things she wanted to do. She traveled as many summers as she could in the company of some of her daughters and her grandchildren. She traveled around Europe by car with my sister and nephews. Comically, I liked to remind her, "Remember the day I met you in Turkey?" It was a planned moment, but I loved that I had jokingly told Murat, "Husband, here are your children." And then I ran off to travel with my mother through Anatolia. Actually, being Turkish himself, he preferred to visit and introduce our children to family. And...me? I wanted to tour the rest of Turkey with Mami. With my husband's blessing and the blessing of those close to him, I went on adventures with her that summer.

I remembered how my dad loved his house so much. The gazebo and the orchid garden. "Didn't you get homesick after you sold your house?"

"No. The truth is that it was a very big house and my little house in Kendall suits me. Besides, I still have the apartment in Santo Domingo. You have to be practical in life and not be attached to things."

"So, tell me, what was your grandmother's house like? The one you used to go to when you were little."

"You really like to ask so many questions!" she said, rolling her eyes.

I confess that curiosity was eating me up inside. The rescue of potential sorrows did not frighten me because I knew that for every disappointment found there was a hidden joy as well. I wanted to collect memories and recollections before time swallowed them up.

"Yes, I want to know everything, Mami. I admit I have an insatiable curiosity about your grandparents. I wish I could have been there. I wish I could have been there when it all happened."

"Yes, but... if you keep looking, you're going to find something," she said as a warning. "And what you find, you may not like."

"What could it be, Mami? What could be so dramatic that I

wouldn't be able to stand it? I know what's currently there must be wrong, and that Isidoro is innocent. I'm sorry...I feel it in my heart."

I know Mami had her own fears. While I longed to connect with my roots and immortalize memories, she would have felt bad if we discovered another family that claimed her Italian grandfather as theirs. I didn't consider that to be an option. The more I looked into it, the more I realized that Isidoro and Bianca were inseparable. She would rather leave her children in Bologna in the care of relatives than travel without him. Perhaps I was naive in my search. This is what I think now, but still, at the time, there was nothing to scare me. I believed that if there were other people related to him in New York it could only benefit me. For example, if I found a picture of him, it would be a gain; if I found some trace that he lived for years after he left, surely there would be an explanation. But when I broached the subject, Mami insisted on not talking about it.

"What for? It happened ages ago. It doesn't matter anymore."

"Why don't you want to talk about it? What's the danger of inquiring?"

Honestly, more than finding out he may have had a separate family, I feared the possibility of not finding him at all. I feared not finding his whereabouts and never knowing what became of him again. That he would remain like that, forever, in the mist of a myth, fixing his hat in Puerto Plata, escaping from me. I was afraid of having an unfinished space in the line of our ancestors. Not recognizing it as my own or not knowing it, period. The alternative of continuing to think of Bianca alone, until eternity. The "something is missing" and to stay like this...forever.

"Because there are no answers," I heard her say. "When adults talked, we were not allowed to be present. *These are adult conversations*, we were told."

"That's why you think something bad happened. Because you were not allowed to ask about him. But I think Isidoro must be waiting for us to find him!" I exclaimed, and as I said it my heart beat like it was the truth. And this filled me with motivation. "I'll find him," I thought, "Even if I have to build a machine to travel back in time."

COMPARING GENEALOGICAL NOTES

One day when I was coming back from the supermarket, Mami opened the door and said,

"I just talked to Fernando. If you had arrived a minute earlier, I would have put him on. He's in Miami, but he's leaving tomorrow."

"Oh! I missed talking to him. But do you think I can call him?"

About the genealogical research, Mami always communicated to him and then informed me what he had said. She had been acting as an unspoken intermediary. Until that day when she urged me, "Call him before he gets busy with something else."

So I did. My uncle, ever so affectionate, greeted me with, "Oh, *m'hija*, how are you?"

As if it were natural, or as if we had been talking for some time, we engaged in a chat about genealogy. Fascinated with his enthusiasm, I could even imagine his broad smile through the phone.

I told him about how I obtained Isidoro's father's birth certificate in Italy:

"So, when I went to San Secondo, searching for the birth certificate of Stefano, Isidoro's father, it was in French! Not only did the kind local officer give me everything translated from French into Italian, but he also sent me the typed transcript, plus the certificate with a stamp, although I didn't really need all that, since it wasn't going to be used for anything legal. But they are so nice there!"

"His name was in French!" Uncle Fernando was amused.

I continued. "I didn't remember that Parma and Plasencia were considered French by that first decade of 1800, and even before... And there I was, searching and searching for Stefano's name and...of course the documents were going to be in French! His name in French is Etienne and I didn't even know it!" I put my hand on my head, holding the phone with the other.

"You can't know everything about everything, *m'hija*," he told me kindly.

"But how did they arrive in Puerto Plata??"

"The family's arrival in Puerto Plata has its own legend," my uncle answered, happy with the question. "They left Bogota with the idea of returning to take up residence in Bologna and they were carrying their first son, Isidorito, in their arms. They sailed the route that then passed through Puerto Plata, but the ship suffered a mechanical breakdown and they had to stay there for a couple of weeks. Grandfather Isidoro liked it. He thought it was a good place to set up business, although they did actually continue on to Bologna then."

"What year was that?"

"It was 1898. Upon entering Puerto Plata, Isidoro declared himself an *albergatore*, saying he had twenty years of experience."

On the notes I had at hand, I made a quick calculation with a pen. I commented to him,

"If he had the twenty years of experience he said he had, this means that he was twenty-seven years old when he undertook...I mean, when would he have started in the business, right? Because he was forty-seven when he entered Puerto Plata."

"Maybe in Bogota, I think he could have a business there, because originally they were going to leave Bogota to settle back in Bologna," my uncle continued. "My grandfather had promised my grandmother that their children would be born in Italy. Maybe that's why they were travelling so much during those years."

"In my research I found that Bogota had become an unsafe place for Italians. In the late 1890s, for a while, Italians were *persona non grata* in Colombia, because one of them, a proxy businessman, had wanted to start a revolution."

"It wasn't Grandfather!" said Uncle Fernando amused.

"No! Would Bianca have let him get into trouble? No! I assure you it wasn't Isidoro." We both laughed.

"Have you discovered the new genealogy websites? There you can find ship manifests and the names of the grandparents. On one of them, from the Ellis Island, Isidoro sailed from New York to get to my dad's birth in 1904 on time."

"I have it here. I recently found it too." I moved some papers I was carrying in my folder to read better while I wriggled to keep the phone from falling to the floor.

Indeed, as my uncle said, in 1904, Isidoro was on his way to Bologna for the birth of Uncle Queco, passing through New York. He departed from Santo Domingo, dated May 25. Apparently, he arrived on June 2. In the manifest he declared himself to be of Italian nationality, a businessman. During those days in New York, he would stay at the DeLogerott Hotel. His final destination, the document declared, was Italy, but he had not yet bought the ticket. He said he was traveling alone, that he was a husband and father, and that he was carrying five hundred dollars. I had investigated the DeLogerott hotel and found several advertisements for it in the newspapers at that time. The building it was in is still standing, there is a Barnes and Noble bookstore in it today. It was known for its gourmet French restaurant. I told my uncle about all this.

"No wonder. They were *connoisseurs* of fine cuisine. From family history, as a young man, we know that Isidoro headed north when he left Italy. We don't know exactly where, but we know that he lived in France too. Early in his youth. For sure he spoke French!"

"Isidoro knew how to speak French!" It was an affirmation. One more note from my dear Isidoro to continue coloring his life. "English, French, Spanish, Italian…"

"Although he traveled a lot, he had promised to be present at the birth of his children. On that ship's manifest from Ellis Island, he was passing through New York, perhaps he stayed a few days, it seems, but I know he was on his way to Italy to attend the arrival of my father, who was to be born on October 18 of that year in Castello d'Argile."

My uncle knew Bologna well. He had retained his father's Italian citizenship and traveled there many times. In fact, Queco's children and grandchildren retained family ties in Italy to the present time.

He continued with, "He was baptized in St. Peter's Church, which is on the same street and faces the corner of the square, on the same block."

I delighted in imagining the heroes of this story, Bianca and Isidoro, baptizing a child dressed in white linen inside that beautiful church.

"I saw another Ellis Island entry. Another ship's manifest," he said. "In this one he indicated that his profession was 'businessman'. He described his residence as Bologna and that he had four thousand dollars with him."

"I have it!" I said, waving the paper as if he could see me. "Isidoro and Bianca took a trip, accompanied by two of their daughters, Beatriz and Yolanda. They left on April 25, 1905, from Genoa, embarking on the Konig Albert and arriving on May 10, 1905, in New York. He declared four thousand dollars...at that time! How did you get around in those days with so much money?"

"In a suitcase, and just for that!" he laughed.

I told him that there was something else that fascinated me, that on the ship's manifest Isidoro declared that he came from northern Italy and he underlined the word "north" twice.

"I think he had learned that Italians were not treated very well in New York unless it was known that they were from the north. It was a way of protecting himself."

"Not all Italians were not treated well in New York in those late 1800s and early 1900s. The Italian unification or resurgence took something like twenty or more years to come to fruition. For Italy to come together as one country. Moreover, remember the great Italian emigration. Ever since Ellis Island opened, in 1892, ships would stop there, even if it wasn't their final destination."

I was curious and eager to see Isidoro arrive with Bianca from that trip. What did Isidoro see in New York back then? In my search for photos of the streets of this city, I noticed the crowds on the sidewalks, all walking from block to block. Back then, horseback transportation was the custom. Motor vehicles were still a luxury and not widely used.

"Why did they travel so much?" I asked.

"The house was in Bologna. It was what my grandmother wanted. On the one hand, we know that she had made Isidoro promise that all her children would be born in Italy. But my grandfather was also a businessman. He was a hard worker and passionately dedicated to his business. And his business was in Puerto Plata. He didn't allow himself to be separated from his work for long," he answered. "He was very enterprising, tireless and tenacious, but it was also a complicated time. Even so, he had managed to start his business, invest in it, and grow. He brought in Italian and Spanish products that he served in the hotel. That's how I found in the port registry that he stated that he was an *albergatore*. But in Bogota he declared himself as a merchant, which meant he was a business owner."

My uncle kept talking and I listened, trying to memorize all the fascinating details.

"So yes, he traveled a lot, but it is what he was, a businessman," explained Uncle Fernando. "And the restaurant in the hotel was a legend. Whenever people arrived in Puerto Plata, even if it was a local traveler, they had to go, no negotiation, to lunch or dinner at the restaurant. It was *de rigueur*! Without a doubt, it was the best Italian cuisine in the area! He had the reputation of choosing the right wine and the best spirits for each dish. He was known for bringing the best wines to the country. Grandpa was a *connoisseur*. He chose them with great care."

It is typical of Italian families to speak of meal presentation with great delight and I could hear the joy in Uncle Fernando's voice as he spoke of how the wine was selected according to the menu.

"Grandma was the great cook who trained her daughters. She was very famous in her kitchen and shared this task with them. They all collaborated in shifts; one day it was Yolanda's turn and another day Mayú's. They knew how to do everything. They knew how to cook everything, although each one had her own specialty."

"Mamma Chela made sensational *gnocchi*." I said, remembering my grandmother "And the way she made them... She almost carved them one by one with her fork. They looked like tiny snails; my grandmother was an artist!"

All his words were clues to me. Clues to my ancestor's actions and decisions. Pieces of an irresistible puzzle. I was still wrapped in a certain naiveté during the early years, thinking I was going to discover magical things, for the spell of borrowed memories brings us, descendants, closer to the ancestors.

"People send me things like newspaper clippings or make comments when they see me at parties. Older people, you know...especially if they lived in Puerto Plata. My grandfather's name appears in connection with two product import companies: one was Divanna y Grisolía and the other, Julio Simón and Associates."

I recognized the names of these companies from other notes I had. One of my desires was to look for the descendants of these companies in Puerto Plata and see if they kept any documents, receipts, papers or business letters. Perhaps even photos or family anecdotes that would color the life of that era. People can't even imagine the treasures they have hidden in their memories. They are dormant encounters with the past waiting to be awakened by future generations to connect us with our predecessors and enrich our lives and knowledge.

"But she was the one who really took the business forward," insisted Uncle Fernando, always putting Bianca first. "My grandmother, along with her eldest son, Isidorito."

The conversation turned to the Hotel Europa. My uncle described the rooms to me; someone had sent him some newspaper clippings from the beginning of the century.

"I can imagine how clean they must have been," I said, remembering my grandmother and her sisters' obsession with cleanliness. A legacy from Bianca.

There was a pause, as we both knew the conversation was winding up. But then Uncle Fernando commented, "I see you have really taken to this study of genealogy...."

I laughed because I didn't know how to make myself understood. I was lucky enough have met all my grandparents, all four; and better yet, a couple of their unmarried sisters who acted as grandmothers as well. My childhood with them was filled with stories. I have always been inquisitive, and I would follow them around at parties and gatherings, listening to their voices, questioning them about their lives in another era. They fascinated me and nourished my imagination. It was their hoarse voices and the cadence of their tones that sharpened my ears and enveloped me in mysteries and fantasies. Before the story of Bianca's abandonment, I thought I had heard everything they had to tell. I couldn't even believe that such a painful story had escaped me. Although I was already having luck convincing Mami that Isidoro was not the villain he'd been thought to be, his final whereabouts remained unclear to me. Why wasn't it known where he was buried? This chapter of the story, so touching, especially to our family's women, was still escaping me. Isidoro was still the center of my attention, or as Mami used to say, obsession. But genealogy research went with the characteristics of my being and came naturally to me. I think I was born for this endeavor. To recover my ancestors. Record their stories. To keep their memories. I had high hopes, but would I get to know everything? It was so pleasant to exchange research notes and anecdotes with Uncle Fernando. And the more I asked, the more information I gained. My subsequent days and the notebooks I wrote in filled up, and my soul filled as well. The stories in the memories of Mami and Fernando brought to life made me live many lives, many loves. And, of course, my uncle was the best and most entertaining source of information.

His soft and cheerful voice on the phone clearly communicated his affection for ancestral loves. I had my ear pressed eagerly to the receiver so as not to miss a single word or nuance he uttered.

"It's fascinating," he said. "Fascinating that I have the good fortune to receive newspaper clippings from people I don't even know. Usually they are genealogists and historians of Puerto Plata. There are some people who remember the hotels of that era and have sent me advertisements that were published in the newspaper from 1905 to 1911. Dad also left some information, now that I think about it, I will check and send you what I find interesting as soon as I can. From Isidorito, the oldest son, I have something very interesting that you'll like."

As unconcerned as my mother was regarding finding Isidoro, Fernando was eager and helpful. He wanted to create a pictorial family tree. We talked about this for a while longer, if only because it filled me with enthusiasm as well. I visualized a Florentine-style tree and let him know. I have always loved illuminated manuscripts and I wanted to integrate this style of ornamentation. He handed me dates and places of birth, the marriages of other family members, all of which I jotted down. Then, biting my lips, I waited for him to finish so I could broach the subject of what happened to Isidoro, but before I could he changed the subject himself.

"Don't stay only with Isidoro. Look down his genealogical tree, grandparents and great-grandparents. Look in Italy. Go and see how far you can go. In this way we will enrich the genealogy and your life too. You will be better for having done the searching."

The words that resonated in me the most were, *Go and see how far you go*. Upon hearing those my whole being lit up. It was not the first time he had expressed those words but hearing it directly from his voice made it something I will never forget. It touched my heart because...it was not a challenge, nor a command, but it was like an invitation to the enchanting game of life. Uncle Fernando made it sound like a playful search to investigate the clues that life offered us about all the things we like, to develop our ideas with avidity, to gather knowledge with joy. It reminded me of my grandmother's idea of "the love of work." She was referring to breathing joy into the tasks with which one toils. To commit oneself to them whole-heartedly. More than that, or more than anything else, I was moti-vated by the trust my uncle placed in me. It pleased me that he felt I could successfully elucidate answers for the family, and I was moved by his conviction in me. It strengthened me. It made me grow in self-confidence. It gave me the courage to dig out sorrows and turn hopelessness into life memories that induced us to improve our decisions. My family, in particular, is made happy by our genealogy. It is a source of joy because it connects us with rela-tives present and past, grandparents loved and known and great-grandparents yet to be known. It is as if we all form one heart. I think of descendants as cells in the hearts of our predecessors. Thinking this way turns genealogy into something mystical. Science explains that we inherit genes from one or another ancestor at random, it does not explain how we inherit manner-isms, dreams, or stories. How do we explain it? A little piece of them, something that never dies, is inherited in us and will always remain in us. We bring their hearts to the present. Their longings become our own; then we pass it on to our descendants in the same way.

Fernando was really the true guide who put me on my path of knowledge. He gave the invitation and provided the emotional support I need so that I could continue on, enthusiastically. His words edified me. He had a talent for imparting a spark of good humor that turned a tedious or laborious moment of research into an exciting and absorbing adventure. Whenever I remembered this particular phrase of my uncle's, it infused me with a thrill of epic adventure, and it reinvigorated me in the disappointing moments when my hands that searched and returned with nothing. I would think to myself, *Good, no more going this way. Now, that way!* When I remembered his positivity and confidence, I would think, *Yes, I can handle this. It's more than difficult, it's fascinating.* I also wanted to know *how far I could go.* What surprises awaited me? His words were an encouragement and a blessing.

I wonder if he had inherited that from Isidoro.

THE APRILS

*E*very year in April, Mami used to come to visit me for my birthday. She would always stay for the whole month. The room I arranged for her was the highest room in the house, with a big, beautiful window facing east. The light of dawn would come in with its subtle energy. My wish was that, when she opened her eyes, she would notice how the room was illuminated and that she would look out the window and admire the gardens of all the houses that surrounded the rotunda of my neighborhood. Some of my neighbors are great gardeners and in the spring blooming season the trees display leaves in bright pinks, such as magnolia and cherry trees. And although my favorites are the purple ones, like the cyclamen that blooms in early spring, I am blessed to have a Constantinople acacia at the back of the house. It is a wonderful thing is to see how the leaves grow directly from the hard, dark, bare trunks. As if the light of color insists on emerging from the darkness—like a miracle.

Every morning we went for a walk through my neighborhood, to look at all the gardens more closely. On one particular day, I was wearing sunglasses in the shape of two hearts that she had brought me from her most recent trip.

"Do you want me to see everything with little love hearts?" I had said to her with a smile as I put them and looked at myself in the mirror before going out. She was sitting on her bed putting on shoes.

The walks through my neighbors' gardens were very enjoyable. I confess that we walked in the opposite direction from mine as my garden was not as professionally-treated as the others. It looked like a somewhat groomed weed sanctuary. In my defense, I didn't have the time that my neighbors obviously had. Had it not been for the petunias that I had planted in pots that overflowed from every corner and covered their old containers, or for the white daisies that woke up every spring, erect in their simplicity and determined to cover all the weeds that tried to push through underneath, I would not have achieved an acceptable garden. I admired these daisies greatly; they were delicate, yet spiky and tenacious, and were unbeatable. I think it was the sheer volume of their numbers that drowned out any imperfections that dared attempt make themselves known on my plot. Their diaphanous white petals, so fragile in appearance, but so strong—like the women of my family!

"Look how the azaleas have caught fire today!" Mami exclaimed, stopping in front of some bushes at the top of the street.

She knew the names of the flowers and trees. I, on the other hand, did not.

"Look at the jacaranda tree, how intense!"

In Virginia, spring is beautiful, and the trees turn a kaleidoscope of bright colors. Fuchsia and purple hues abound. Begonias, tulips planted under the trees, and daffodils brightly paint every pathway. While gardening was not my strong suit, I learned a few things, like planting bulbs in autumn and letting them sleep through the winter until spring. They are the first to sprout just before the dry winter grass turns emerald. The stems of the daffodils and tulips come forward to grow and bloom. Before the lawn mower makes its first pass, I stop by to pick them. I rescue them! I fill my arms with tulips and spread them in vases all over the house to brighten our days. My dream is to live in a garden; maybe even put my brocaded iron bed in the very center surrounded by colors and the scent of fresh air. To wake up and see the smiling face of a gerbera or a rose. Why not? What a joy it would be to drink my coffee leaning my back against the trunk of a tree while enjoying the flight of a hummingbird. Like the ones at my grandfather Joaquín's house, my mother's father.

Mom's love for flowers must have been inherited from her father, whom we grandchildren used to call Quin-Quin. Every year, for his birthday, we would ask Mami what we were going to give him.

She would always say, "Give him flowers, that's what he likes the most."

Once, when he was in the hospital, I wanted to know why he liked flowers. He turned his eyes to me and answered:

"I can no longer go out to visit them, so I let them visit me."

"But you have to cut them to bring them in." I thought that was an act of assassination and it hurt me to see them cut. But my grandfather changed my mind.

"If you don't cut them and don't bring them to me, they get sad and wither faster. Then they die alone in the field. You have to pay attention to flowers. They like it when you delight in them. That is what they were born for. They long to be the best they can be; it's in their nature. And that includes being admired. They thrive on our delight. By bringing them in to a room, you allow them to fulfill their promise to do their best work and fill our lives with beauty," he replied.

Perhaps for that reason, when we rode in the car, Joaquin's daughter, Mami, greatly enjoyed the gardens in Virginia neighborhoods.

"What beautiful magnolias!"

"Lucky my neighbors planted some!" I would say, grateful for and even relieved at the neighbor's brilliant flower beds. I don't have a green thumb, as they say here, and I was grateful to witness the prodigy of nature growing. I loved that Mami enjoyed it and so I enjoyed it along with her.

I spent all year preparing for Mami's annual visits, arranging activities and acquiring odds and ends that I hoped would make her stay with us more pleasant. I tried to put something new and cheerful in the room dedicated to her. This particular time I painted the bedroom lavender and bought her flowered sheets. On the eve of her arrival, I lit a scented candle to infuse the air with perfume, so that when she came in, she felt like she was sleeping in her own springtime. I took a photograph of her and Dad, smiling forever, and placed it on the shelf I had installed over the head of her bed. It made her happy always, so I wanted that to be the first object she saw when entering her room.

One day we were going for a ride in the car and when we left my house and went up the hill, the myrtle tree showered us with pink leaves. It looked like confetti and felt like we were on a float. I slowed down almost completely and let them fill the front windshield.

"When you were parading in a queen's carriage, in the carnival of the roses, you didn't get so much confetti!" I joked.

This was a reference to the story my father had told me of the first time he had ever seen my mother. It was when she was parading with her friends in a *comparsa*. He said they were all dressed as nature fairies, with flower crowns pinned in their hair. Their ankles were also adorned with circlets of flowers, and they danced barefoot among trees made of papier-mâché whose branches danced, moved by wire and tied with brightly colored silk butterflies.

Next to me, Mami was immersed in the memory:

"I was on top of a chariot. It was the fairy float, and we were the queens of nature at the carnival. From far away, your dad spotted me. He was sitting in a restaurant, facing the boardwalk where you could see the whole parade. He sent a boy to talk to me. He said he was inviting me for a drink. I told him that I couldn't leave the other girls and he replied that he was inviting all of us. Imagine, all of us leaving the parade! So, I told him that I was barefoot because the costume did not call for shoes. His answer to that was to send me his own."

"So witty!" I laughed in amusement. The story was alive in my mind.

It was my delight—their stories of when they were young. My dad had told me another one, about how he had asked Mami out for a weekend date. That evening, they celebrated with a bubbly pink champagne. It seemed incomprehensible to me that they had pink sparkling wine at that time. This must have been around 1950, I think. Dad had told me that the chaperone of this event was Marocha Azar, who was another relation of ours. Aunt Marocha laughed heartily and enjoyed everything. I imagined them sitting in their long dresses and my dad acting very gallant. I imagined their amused laughter and the witticisms that passed back and forth throughout the evening.

So many years had passed and now I was enjoying a borrowed memory. I enjoyed the wind, the swaying of the car, and the pink petals that were still on the windshield, falling off one by one as we drove along. That day, we were visiting the Washington D.C. Botanical Garden across from the Capitol. I had suggested we take a stroll there as the Japanese cherry blossom trees were in glorious bloom. These trees were a gift from Japan to the United States in 1912 and they surround the Jefferson Memorial Pond. Everyone came to see them at this time of spring. The plan involved a whole morning of traffic to get there. I was sure it would be impossible to park anywhere nearby, but we were sure to find a spot by the Botanical Gardens, since no one would think of visiting the orchid garden that day. The cherry blossom trees, at their peak, are the stars of the spring season. But we could easily enjoy them from the car. Arriving at our destination, we entered the orchid exhibit. Mami was very fond of orchids and knew a lot about them. At my childhood home she'd had a beautiful garden where they stood out. Now we could enjoy them again; it would be like visiting old friends. However, I was amazed when I noticed that Mami seemed to be comparing in her mind this blooming garden with that family memory of her own orchid garden, as if she still had it.

"At home I have this one and this one. Ah! look how pretty! I don't have that one!"

I stood next to her, a little stunned, looking at what she was showing me and listening to her comments. *Her house? She didn't have a house!* I didn't want to remind her that she didn't have that big garden anymore, and especially not the orchid garden! There were no orchids in her apartment nor in her little house in Kendall. But still, I listened to her nodding all the while.

"Yes, yes! Those pink ones...ooh! Spectacular...yes."

Although a bit skeptical, I didn't want to stop joining her in her appreciation. She kept using the present, as if she still had an orchid garden, which I knew she did not. She would walk a few steps and stop at each little sign they had placed in front of the flowers with information about what was planted there. One by one she read each sign, pronouncing their names, both the scientific and the common:

"Ansellia Orchid...Brassia orchid..."

She said them quietly to herself, then repeater her words louder, so that I could hear them as though I was a child in school.

"Masdevallia, also called hummingbird orchid; I have those, and they grow in poppy yellow...."

She also asked me to read them and that reminded me of the beloved joke emails she used to send me.

At first, I was glad of her interest, but after a couple of hours, I would check the clock every moment as I did not want to get caught in traffic on the way home. I had not yet learned to be in the present and appreciate the beauty of flowers as they are a blessed prayer to nature. In that space and time, she was teaching it to me, and I should have been gracious enough to receive the lesson. But my mind returned to its normal obsession with time, and I just kept watching the clock.

She kept talking about the flowers, enjoying each one.

"I also have these, but in orange, with black dots. When they bloom, they last a long time. It says there that they come from Indonesia, oooh, I didn't know that!"

I almost, almost corrected her and let it slip to remind her that she didn't have a garden anymore. There was no orange one black dotted no purple nothing like that. What's more, the house with its orchid garden no longer existed. It had been destroyed! Or didn't she remember?

Suddenly, an idea began to light up my mind. It was like a sigh of infinite patience from the divinity: *Learn from your mother*, it seemed to whisper to me. *Lesson number one: admiration for nature is a prayer. Lesson number two...what was lesson number two?* As my mom enjoyed and treasured the flowers in her chimerical garden, alive and thriving, in real life, I realized that she saw beyond the obvious. She had in her mind her garden completely intact, healthy and bursting with color. She had in her mind an eternal springtime resembling the garden she once had. While I envisioned my house destroyed, she, in her being, had it fully intact and full of flowers forever, all year round. Ideal and indestructible; better yet, it made her enjoy the beauty forever and not just the external. Her appreciation was like picking flowers in her mind and filling her inner garden to overflowing. Beautiful, healthy, limpid flowers, what's the difference between that and any memory? The flowers she had chosen for her garden were flowers she kept in her memory. In her eyes, there was no difference between the *real* garden and *imagined*. All of them she enjoyed with her soul.

Then I understood. *Lesson number two: treasure an inner garden.*

Later, as we were driving back and I was preoccupied with traffic, watching the tail end of the car in front of me, she was looking at each side of the road. Thus she said to me:

"What pretty flowers there are along here! When you go to and from work every day, is it always like this?"

I took my eyes off the bumper in front of me and looked at each side of the road. In amazement I noticed that she was completely right! To my left and right were riots of marvelously blooming flowers! On one side, the yellow color of daffodils adorned the green grass that separated the roads and, to my right, red wildflowers like tiny poppies filled the green carpet with vibrancy. It was a marvel I had never noticed before! Scattered along, they accompanied the drivers until we left the road. If she hadn't made me see, I probably wouldn't have ever noticed them. I would have lost myself from the present moment. Softly in me, like morning dew, the lesson settled. And I, humble student, finally accepted. I looked up to heaven to thank it. *The present is full of beauty*, and *beauty is in the normal* were part of the same lesson.

"Now I see them and notice them, Mami. Thanks to you."

DREAM

$\mathcal{W}$henever Mami came to visit, we would have breakfast on the back deck to enjoy the nice weather with the flowering trees of spring. My children loved to sit next to her. Alex, the middle one, affectionately called her "Grandma Cookie" and would follow her all over the house. Up and down. That's how we discovered that Mami secretly gave him cookies that were not organic.

"Mami, stop giving those cookies to Alex, he's already chubby," I said when I discovered her game.

She replied, "Let me be a grandmother. If you don't like it, don't look!"

One cool and rainy morning, we decided to stay at home. Sitting at the table in front of the window, we admired the green grass, the trees with their colorful leaves and the multicolored begonias. While I spread some jam on white cheese, Mami said something very strange.

"Since I got here, I haven't dreamed about your dad. I think it's you who won't let me dream about him. You did something..." she accused me.

I opened my mouth in astonishment. First, because she was accusing me of something unusual. I was not the owner of her dreams about dad. Secondly, because I couldn't believe she wasn't able to dream about dad anymore. Those dreams with him were the most precious thing to me, to her and to all my four sisters.

Let me explain what dreams with dad are for us like, they are like gold. Even more than flowers or winning the lottery. The most precious jewel is dreaming about dad. After his death, every time one of us received a visit from him, we shared it in great detail and enjoyed it as a real privilege. They were like desserts for the soul.

Could dreams of our absent loved ones be true visits? To answer I must ask you to suspend disbelief. Let's take a look at beliefs. It is a familiar belief that good people go to heaven. Therefore, Dad is in heaven.

According to Catholic folklore, St. Peter guards the gates of glory. So I imagined my dad, a mischievous hero, managing to distract the gatekeeper and tiptoe through the sacred entrance to cross dimensions and slip into dreams and visit us that way. For our sake, I'm sure my dad would manage to do it, but what if in heaven not everyone who arrives is well-behaved and stays quietly at his post! I know that mischief happens there too, otherwise it wouldn't be heaven! And according to what dad's cousins tell me, he was naughty as a child. So, what's more, I knew he would manage to visit us in our dreams!

"Oh, what more could I want than to dream of Dad!" I breathed in the aroma of coffee as I closed my eyes in longing. I remembered a dream my sister Cristina and I had the same day, a year after his death. In the dream he was on his back as if following a path of white stones that ended at the limpid blue of the skyline. It was as if he was walking away. Then he stopped and turned around while smiling and, at the same time, we both ran like children to each other. We hugged tightly and for a long, long, long time. When we parted, we looked at each other, laughing and saying goodbye. Then I saw him walking back toward that bright blue sky.

That was the same dream Cris had with about our dad. A dream that also ended with a big hug before he returned to the big blue. I don't doubt that all of his daughters had the same dream that night, but only Cristina and I could remember it.

I came back to reality with my cup of coffee and was surprised when I turned to look at Mami. She had a frown on her face. How had I done something to stop her from having dreams about dad?

I was mortified.

"So, what did *I do* to prevent you from dreaming about dad? How do you think I could even prevent them?"

I sighed. It never crossed my mind that I might lose my dad so early in life and that my children would not get to enjoy their grandfather, as I had enjoyed mine. Before his death, I thought I would hear my children ask their grandparents questions and that I would hear their voices passing on their wisdom to them. As happened on one occasion when we were riding in the car with Dad, my oldest son, André, asked him, "Grandpa, how do you fly?

"Grandpa, how do airplanes fly?"

We had just landed at the Santo Domingo airport. My son already thought his grandfather knew everything. I loved his question. And my dad, without wasting a second, very simply explained to him that speed generates the force that lifts the airplane during takeoff. He wanted to do an experiment. He asked my son to hold his arm outside the window with his hand flat, parallel to the ground and said, "Tilt your palm slightly and you'll see how the speed of takeoff lifts it..."

I sighed at that memory. André, seven years old, and smiling as the wind lifted his arm just like his grandpa said it would.

He would say to me excitedly, "Mami, look I think I could fly too!"

My son's laughter and my father's laughter...together they were a melody in my heart. I longed for more moments like that, his legacy passed on to the grandchildren without interference or interpretation, but that was not to be!

Sigh.

Mami insisted, "I suspect you did something."

You did Something.

I wanted to make it clear to her that I had no power whatsoever to prevent a loved one in spirit from visiting us in our dreams. But she persisted with the absurd suspicion that I had done...*what?* I felt somewhere between fascinated and alarmed, for we had unwittingly entered mystical territory. And she wasn't much for putting cabalistic tones on anything.

"What do you think I did, some kind of incantation? How I wish I could dream about Dad and other loved ones who have their residence in heaven! If I knew I could influence dreams, that I could somehow prevent them or not, I would invite him to come to our dreams, not keep him out. I would have sent out invitations beforehand! And I would dream about my ancestors all of the time! All of them!" I was going to add, *"Even that grandfather of yours that you don't want,"* referring to you-know-who, but I stopped there because our surname has the reputation to get very...*Italian*, if you know what I mean.

"Well, go and see what you do."

"Let's see, Mami, explain yourself." I put my cup on the table to look at it so it wouldn't get away from me. I didn't know whether to laugh or cry. Well, if there was something to do, I would do it! I was ready.

"Something you did because I can't dream about your dad." She was so adamant in her certainty.

"But whaaaaat?" It had been a long time since I had heard her express herself like that, with that familiar tone from when I was a little girl and she scolded me, and I naturally responded as I would have when I was young, like an old habit.

Thoughtfully, she crunched a delicious piece of toast with her teeth. I had spread Mediterranean orange marmalade on it, and she chewed it slowly, as if weighing each bite.

She finally said, "Like you asked some saint to protect your house or something. To keep spirits out."

This idea exploded in my mind as implausible. I shook my head vehemently and even laughed. And I saw her expression turn to offended. She really believed it!

"No, Mami... how could that be!"

Suddenly, my words sounded hollow. A cold wind hit the memories in my head with undeniable clarity. The lucidity of an event. An act I had performed long ago flashed in my mind and I stopped laughing. I looked at her stunned. I couldn't believe she was right. Indeed! Something *had* happened and...but could it be possible? I looked at her with wide eyes.

"It just can't be...it's just a coincidence..." I murmured.

Now my brain was spinning. If the idea of having dreams about a loved one sounds a bit esoteric and mysterious, the idea that I had done *something*, some magic or spell, was much more far-fetched.

That idea beat the other one by a lot! And yet, the more I thought about it, the more I realized that she might be right. I gawked at her.

"I told you so!" She smiled triumphantly.

I tried to remember in detail what had happened when Alex was suffering from nightmares. With stammering words at first, I tried to explain myself as best I could.

A few years before, my family had experienced a very painful and difficult situation when my children's caregiver had tragically lost his life. He was driving home when he suffered a cardiac arrest. His car was found in the back of a neighbor's house, in front of the school. He hadn't crashed or anything. He had simply stopped to die.

The sudden loss of someone so dear, so close to the family and who was part of our daily life, was devastating for my family; especially for Alex, who must have been between six and seven years old at the time and he began to have nightmares. One night he jumped awake. He ran from his bed to our room to come to me. He pulled on the door with such force that the wood cracked. He jumped into my arms. He trembled with fright. I'm not afraid of death and, oddly enough, I don't believe in ghosts. But I also know that too much fear hurts and that a calm mother is the best medicine for a child trapped by anxiety. And since I'm not like Chela, my grandmother, who knew everything, I did what I could. I sought help, professional and alternative, I even concocted home remedies to appease anxiety, such as chamomile or lavender tea.

So my mom was right after all. I had done "something". I had done more than "something". I had taken Alex to doctors, psychologists and professional counselors for help. In fact, we all went. I used every means at my disposal to assist him and put an end to his nightmares. Still, while all the other members of this family were recovering more or less and getting better, Alex was still nervous. It was fine to take him to the regular doctors and physicians, but why not try something else to ease his pain and fears? By that time, I had learned to meditate and knew that the power of intention and prayer is powerful in mothers. So I decided to raise a prayer to God and all the saints. I sat in the center of my house and imagined it bathed in light that dissolved the negative and enhanced the positive. It was like a combination of a prayer and guided meditation that I had learned somewhere. Maybe I made it up. What difference did it make? With my eyes closed, my feet on the ground and my mind calm, I made a request to the great spiritual powers. I asked Jesus and the angels of protection not to allow any energy to come near the house. I said "Neither good nor bad" so that there would be no mistake. I pictured in my mind the walls bathed in a divine light of protection. A dense, strong, loving light that sealed everything and let nothing in.

I did not do it with fear, but with conviction. My conscience is clear, and I have faith in divine compassion. I stay positive, confident that we have His protection. I am one of those who think that worries are a prayer in the opposite direction of our desires, like negative prayers. That the only fear to be afraid of is...fear itself. We must review our thoughts daily, lest, by worrying, especially if we do it automatically, we attract negativity.

This action was just a complement to all the other traditional things I did for Alex. It was one more effort of a desperate mother who did not want to see her son suffer even for a minute. After having visited all the doctors and counselors I could, it was a complement to all the treatments, a "just in case." It was such a small thing, I even forgot about it. I got off the couch and never attributed the subsequent peace that reigned in the house to what I had done. Now, in Mami's presence, I thought that it was all of this together...doctors, meditations, prayers...they all had worked. I explained it to her, that longed-for peace was achieved when Alex never had nightmares again.

"I knew it!" she said, lifting her chin in triumph.

"Maybe it was a combination of everything: the doctors, the weather...."

I was justifying myself too much. If she believed it, so what? Besides, if she trusted, I could trust too. I could trust that God has a preference for mothers protecting their children. Mothers' intentions, in and of themselves, are powerful and can produce peace and conviction in the hearts of children. I felt Mami's security in me.

Mami was so sure that this prayer-meditation of protection was the key to everything, so she said,

"Well, do you still need the protection? Not anymore! So, take it away so he can come visit me in a dream and...because I say so!"

She was very serious, and I reacted quickly.

"I already took the light-protection off! It was easy," I answered with a giggle. But she wasn't laughing, so I had to close my eyes and imagine the house with the white light, but with the intention of letting the good in. "Let only the good come in!"

And especially my dad.

I opened my eyes and looked at her. I raised my eyebrows so she would believe me and took my cup of coffee in my hands.

The next day, she arrived very happily at the breakfast table. We found ourselves in the same positions as the day before: sitting next to each other, drinking coffee and admiring the courtyard.

"I woke up today with a kiss from your dad."

I looked at her stunned. Yesterday's visualization was just to play along, wasn't it? But I made a nodding gesture along with an *unhu*, very typical of my grandmother Chela. "Tell me about it, Mami. What was it like?"

"I was asleep, and he was standing next to me. I woke up when I felt him. Your dad woke me up with a kiss."

THE OLDEST SON, ISIDRO

*J*n November 2006, I had back surgery for a herniated disc. Mami came to stay with us for a week while I recovered. During those days, I received an email from my uncle Fernando in reference to Isidorito, Bianca's oldest son. He enclosed a newspaper clipping. The email read: "It is an anecdote that talks about an event that happened in 1918. Isidorito is mentioned as Isidro. He was the eldest and the great support of my grandmother. He was in charge of the hotel because you know that my grandfather was no longer there. My dad, who was younger, was still living in Italy."

I showed Mami what I had received, "Look what Uncle Fernando says," I said while I showed her on the screen the yellowed image of the piece of newspaper "Did you know they called him Isidro in Puerto Plata? I like that name for him: Isidro. It goes with his way of being, changing from a boy to a young man. An adolescent who is not quite an adult yet but has a strong personality and character."

"Strong personality? It's not because of the name, but the surname!" Mami said energetically. "This family has strong characters. All of them!"

She read with me the piece of the family legacy we had just received. Then I looked up the historical context of what was going on in the world to find out what a Bolshevik, the term used in the

213

publication, was. At the 11th hour of the 11th day of the 11th month, an armistice was signed declaring the end of the "war that would end all wars", later called World War I. I discovered that a Bolshevik was defined as a "member of the majority," in connection with the events that took place in Russia in the early 20th century. When the Russian monarchy was overthrown, Bolshevism aimed, among other things, to distribute land to the poor and peasant class. It would be part of the movement that would lead to communism. This ideology had been observed as news in Puerto Plata, but it never took root. It was the people who lived in this place, highly enterprising individuals dedicated to their businesses, like my ancestors, who had come to establish commerce and prosper and they did not want privileges or gifts, but rather to earn their own living with their work. It was businessmen and women in Puerto Plata, who paved the streets and connected the wires for electricity, before it became a state order. And it should be made clear that the townspeople kept their city impeccably clean and their reputation was well earned. The citizens, whether foreigners or educated locals, influenced innovation and progress. But it was not only order and cleanliness that distinguished them, but an amalgam of welcome foreign customs: in the afternoons they drank tea, English style, instead of coffee, and played bridge instead of *canasta*. In short, it was a town that naturally wanted to be cosmopolitan and welcomed diverse cultures. A stimulating progressive mosaic of entrepreneurs.

Apparently, our brave Isidro had seen a new guest arrive, just like any other. He noticed that he had stopped to look the hotel up and down. A three-story building with a balcony surrounding the second floor, where the rooms were arranged. From the doorway of his office stood Isidro, tall like his father and with abundant brown hair and light eyes, watching the visitor enter with a suitcase, looking somewhat disheveled. He saw that his appearance was somewhat distressing but attributed it to a long journey. And if there was anything on offer at the hotel, it was basic dignity, support and rest.

One of his sisters would have welcomed this man and asked for his signature for the guest book. Bianca's daughters, still in their teens, would attend to the demands of visitors and provide them with the best hospitality. Beyond the reception area, the dining room could be seen, with the chairs and tables neatly set. The girls were moving around incessantly, arranging tablecloths and dishes, wiping any surface that came their way, polishing every space and straightening anything they found out of place. The one in charge of the kitchen, for which they took turns, wore a white apron and a cotton hat, and in the steaming pots she moved a ladle or two with very clean hands that protruded from rolled-up shirts. Another sister measured the flour, another melted the butter, preparing to knead the dough to perfection, whether for lunch or dinner.

Isidro was the epitome of a gentleman and, at eighteen, he was working hard for a demanding business. The newspaper account said that the young man had agreed to put up the unusual individual at the hotel. The guy claimed to be Venezuelan at first and did not immediately admit to his Russian connections. Guests from all over the world were respectfully received at the hotel without any concern for their ideological leanings.

As was customary, he was provided with a room for a few days. But the next day, his manners became a bit alarming. Bianca and her eldest son noticed something about him that made them pay special attention. The guest did not allow entry to his room to clean it. This raised a couple of eyebrows in Bianca's family, as they prided themselves on the hygiene and tidiness of the place. In the newspapers the rooms were described as "sanitary." And I know from my heritage what that means to these women! Although the attitude was cause for alarm, they let it go for a day, but...two days? That would be stretching it too thin. Management remained vigilant.

Then they were struck by the arrogance of the individual, who kept criticizing Puerto Plata businesses. While tasting the food in the hotel restaurant, with the white napkin tied around his neck and raising his fork, he declared himself a supporter of the Bolshevik movement. Without further ado, he accused them of exploiting their workers. This went down badly with my great-grandmother Bianca, who was already called Doña Blanca by that time, and whose children worked shoulder to shoulder with her employees. I could imagine this guy, not very hygienic looking, bad-mouthing everything and everyone, criticizing the impeccably prepared and succulent dinner in front of him while he sat in the most prestigious restaurant in town. Demanding more wine with exaggerated hand gestures and gobbling up a second course while his voice heated up the ears of more than one person in the room.

This abuse of hospitality began to offend other diners. Young Isidro could not stand it any longer when his sisters, who were attending the restaurant, called him to observe the scene and he heard him saying indecencies. With a determined attitude, the energetic boy asked the man to pay his bill and leave. But the punk responded with a belch. "Don't you know who I am? I'm a Bolshevik!" And he waved his fork arrogantly in young Isidro's face.

"I don't care," replied the young man vehemently. "This may be a hotel, but it is first a family business. And you must pay for your stay and all the meals you were given. It is an abuse of our hospitality. And not only to us, but to our employees who make a living from their hard work."

The offended man grumbled with the courage that alcohol induces. He argued that it was the State that should pay, since everyone was equal to him.

The writer of the anecdote in the newspaper exposed that, apart from the verbal offense, he gave off a stench that polluted the entire place. It was his lack of personal hygiene which was the straw that broke the camel's back and the fine sense of smell of the members of this family. And to wrap the scene up neatly in a bow, he erupted with a series of bad words in front of the locals. The decent clientele who was expecting to receive a delicious dinner in an elegant but cozy atmosphere became uncomfortable. The diners stirred in their chairs.

Without thinking twice, Isidro entered the man's room, took his suitcase and all his belongings and threw them into the street. The writer explains that it was an act of heroism since the suitcase stank more than the owner. When the Bolshevik saw this, he got up from his chair, and Isidro took that moment to give him a kick and send him out with a single hesitation. Afterwards, the odious culprit seems to have been consequently driven out of town amidst shouting and expletives.

I imagined Isidro mending his coat while shaking his head. A worthy son of Bianca, he treated those close to him with honor and the highest rules of cordiality. But he had to do what he had to do.

When I finished reading this anecdote from Uncle Fernando, I asked Mami if she knew more. What else did Isidro's sisters say about him? Who was he like? She didn't think much about it.

"He was the father figure for them, but...I didn't know that story from the newspaper."

"I guess he was like my uncles, Frank and Fernando, with a cheerful temperament. In the only photo we have of him with his sisters, he's smiling, and they're so serious!"

"In those days they didn't smile in pictures," my mother replied. "They didn't show their teeth."

"Ah, but he didn't get the memo because he was smiling!"

"What memo?"

"Mami, he was an Italian teenager in Puerto Plata. As much as he worked and had a strong temper, I can't imagine him stern. My grandmother inferred in her stories a lightness of character and good humor in him. And that he liked music and dancing, as she did.

Suddenly, and as if it was part of my talk, piano music wandered to our ears. I made a gesture to Mami of "See!", as if hearing the tune gave me the reason. And my mom made an astonished face at me and then smiled and nodded. To add to the coincidence, the music that reached our ears, as if transported from Victor's piano, had a splash of rhythm from the times of yesteryear."

"The universe conspires to support me. It's a sign that I'm right about his personality." I lifted my finger just like Mami did and together we listened to the piano.

My children's childhood was accompanied by piano music. From an early age, and once I noticed their inclination, they took lessons, and it was music, more than sports, that excited them. But it was Victor, the youngest, who became a great pianist. I never had to remind him to practice because he imposed it on himself. In the mornings, the first thing he did was sit at the piano. The piano teacher was of the opinion that all three of my sons were talented, but it was Victor, with a keen musical ear, who was able to repeat the notes he heard almost immediately. He would pick out music from his Japanese games and pull out the primordial sounds. He would give my mother great concerts. Today was one of those days when, by happy coincidence, we were talking about music at the hotel. Mami listened, enjoying, and I went on.

"In those days, restaurants had pianos for people to play and sing along."

This coincidence made me smile. I think our ancestors speak to us through symbols. I felt Mami give in to my point when she remembered something:

"My grandmother had insisted that one of her daughters play the piano. As far as I remember, of my aunts, Mafalda was the one who played well. But everyone likes music." When she saw that I was gesticulating, she added: "Yes, of course I accept that Isidro could have liked music and that, if they had a piano in the hotel, which was the usual thing, he could have started to play like Victor."

"There were victrolas or machines that played music with a cylinder, but it was nothing like listening to live music. What if Isidro liked to play like Victor? Maybe he played some keys trying to make them sound and then, in the evenings, let them flow. What if that was his way of relaxing and disconnecting?"

The music filled my house, and in a pause we heard, "Grandma, do you hear? Grandma, do you hear me playing the piano?" Victor spoke from the living room with great enthusiasm.

Mami answered in the affirmative and we both approached him to watch him begin a piece with great enthusiasm and mastery. His indigo eyes narrowed in concentration. His slender body straightened on the bench and his long fingers caressed the keyboard. His hair fell in spikes over his aquiline nose. At its conclusion, we all rose to our feet and gave a standing ovation. The applause of my other children could be heard from their rooms where they were, as it was a family custom.

"Wonderful! Bravo!"

Mami hugged him, telling him how much she had enjoyed it, and Victor, more enthusiastic than ever, began another little concert. After the meal, we enjoyed clapping and asking for more. Perhaps as they did at Doña Blanca's restaurant on occasion.

In my imagination, at the Hotel Europa there is a piano in one corner of the dining room. I don't know for sure how much or how little it was played, but, for lack of information, I draw on my son's personality to describe it: I visualize a slender young man playing and enjoying music whose sense of responsibility did not bend to these moments of art. Music made him feel alive and he did not miss the slightest opportunity to play, even though his obligations were ahead of him.

I compare Isidro to Victor, a practically solitary or self-taught apprentice, who, without much help, takes every opportunity to practice and manages to play by ear. One day he pushed a key with one finger, and so, one day, quite simply, he began.

According to a document I have, young Isidro had arrived in Puerto Plata at the age of twelve. His father taught him with certainty everything about the family business and he had in him a firm support. In the absence of his father, he became the father figure for his sisters even in his early teenage years. All the sisters mentioned him with longing and affection. My grandmother said that he had a cheerful personality, that he got into the Puerto Plata culture as soon as he arrived, and that he loved the diverse music that came from various parts of the world. He was gregarious, cheerful and even learned to dance. The only photo we have of him shows us a handsome boy of innate joy.

Today Victor is twenty years old, which was almost the age Isidro was when he died during a pandemic; a pandemic much like the one the world lived through in 2020. But my thoughts do not stop with death. In me, they all live. In my imagination my grandmother is six years old. She is happy with her sisters listening to her older brother making music in the living room of the hotel in Puerto Plata. Isidro plays with his body bent and fingers caressing the keys in the middle of the musical act, his hair falling over his forehead and curled in spiky locks; his eyes, gray and attentive, like those of his father. Music is his outlet. The sound of the keys enlivens the room, and the diners appreciate the candor of his music. But it is the youngest girls in the house who are the most enthusiastic. When they heard the melodies, Mayú, Chela and Ana ran from wherever they were to start dancing. They would hold hands and dance in a corner next to the piano. There was no one who did not succumb to the sight of these three, who looked like little angels, forming a wheel, laughing and dancing together. The atmosphere was transformed into a heartwarming and festive moment. The girls even took their bow at the end of the song to which everyone applauded. And they would ask their brother to play again and again.

I close my eyes. I'm with them, there...being part of the audience. A time of fairies, of candlelight and oil lamps and plank floors. Little pieces of girls dancing and creaking wood. A time of truce where there were moments of innocent joy between times of tragedy. Big brother playing music and his little sisters dancing forever. A time in me where everyone lives and celebrates life and happiness.

BIANCA AND HER SON, ISIDRO

*J*n those days, while Mami stayed at home, I wanted to address the subject of Bianca's abandonment. With death we feel so abandoned! We are haunted by that feeling of being left behind, with our feelings wrapped up in an inevitable situation. We cannot stop the river of destiny.

"I understand that every death is an abandonment," I said to her without ceremony. And I added, "I felt abandoned when dad died. Maybe it is an emotion without logic, but it is what it is."

But my mother was going to defend her grandmother's feelings.

"Leave my grandmother alone. Whatever her feelings were, they were a response to what happened to her; whatever happened, that's hers. She had a right to feel abandoned, if that's how she felt."

I accepted that because it's a way to honor each other's feelings. But that Mami's loyalty, while respectful, made me nervous. I understood the sentiment and I could not refute it because I still had no hard evidence of his whereabouts that could give us a clue to his decisions. But we did know about Bianca whereabouts. She had been left alone, it was a fact, in a country that was not her homeland, with her children separated on two continents and she was pregnant.

After all, with all that mettle and fierce love with which the family remembers her, she was human. And it is that part of human nature in her that I also wanted to bring to light. To also give that respite to those feelings that perhaps she herself did not deign to feel.

How did Bianca feel when Isidoro left without her?

He never came back.

When did she learn that he had passed away? Whether it was an hour, a month or a year after his departure, the desolation could have overwhelmed her deeply. Perhaps, even from a social point of view, she felt vulnerable. She had lost her anchor, her security; and being as she was, a foreign woman, alone, with small children, running her own business and pregnant. When she took stock of the situation, she must have wanted to leave the past in the past in order to dedicate herself body and soul to the present and provide a future for her children and herself. She informed those she had to inform and continued in her daily life like everyone else. But, as a foreigner, I wondered if she ever had the illusion of returning to her native country. Surely it would have been better to return with him. And so she must have spent her days debating: go back or to stay?

"I just have to wait for the baby to be born, I just have to wait for it to get strong, to sell the business, to wait for my children to grow up more, I just have to...I just have to..."

But, left responsible for so many things, she wouldn't even have time for nostalgia.

At dawn sometime in January of 1913, she walked with her swollen belly through the streets of Puerto Plata. Alone, she advanced towards the sea at the first light of dawn. Perhaps the full moon had been pinned to one side and illuminated her way through the empty streets with its splendor. It was her intention to see the horizon at the precise moment when the sun kisses the sea with its radiant flame. To breathe in the salty scent of iodized water and receive subtle relief. She reached the coast and climbed the stone steps of the ruins of the fortress of San Felipe, when there were still vestiges of its tower, which had not completely collapsed. Did she fear the myth that her belly had awakened when Isidoro no longer returned? He had promised to accompany her always. "You are my strength," he had told her on the eve of previous tragedies. "You are the strongest woman I know. Fiercely loving and...formidable." But she felt it was easy to be strong next to him because he validated and admired her for it.

The next ship would anchor early this morning. She wished to see him come down with his hat and small suitcase fulfilling his promise; a promise broken since his departure seven months ago. "No man could take care of himself on a voyage without his wife by his side." Hadn't he told her that? He had said it to make her feel indispensable. Isidoro did not need anyone. He himself had taught her so many things, such as how to carefully select the best, so one did not have to carry too much. He was even-tempered, without great attachments, and this made him the most independent man she had ever known. He was impeccable in his personal care and attire, his neatness, and minimalism.

Once in the bedroom, standing in front of the mirror he looked at her as she entered and winked at her with a smile. It was what he always did when he saw her enter. But, this time, thumping his chest, he said, "Look at the gentleman you've won!" He was joking, alluding to the lottery jackpot, betting that life at his side had been a prize.

She disliked proving him right. Any exercise of his vanity did not go with her principles, as she was so demure and modest. So in response, she lifted her chin, proudly, denying him an affirmation. But she adored how he tried in vain to flatten the lock of his hair that started from a swirl.

Their childhoods had not been easy. Each of them at home in Italy had labored from a young age to help the family. Isidoro had told her that his father, Stefano, was tireless and, although not as tall as he was, he was extremely strong, like a cannonball. But he was also affable and dynamic and could hold a mischievous smile. He worked hard but did so in good humor and liked to laugh and feel useful. He did not refuse help to anyone. As for his mother, she had knowledge of herbalism. She would restore any affliction with a tea or an infusion that she prepared and offered for the sorrows of the body and soul. The people of the region would visit her for health advice, and she had passed on her knowledge to her son. After his father died, and at his mother's urging, he set out on an adventure to become a businessman. The world welcomed him and imparted what he needed to learn. He was fluent in several languages. He had learned to prosper.

Bianca had lost her mother in her childhood, so she had made it a point to be a perfectionist in order to please those who cared for her. Unlike Isidoro, who was the youngest in his family, and whose sisters went out of their way for him as a child, she was the eldest and, therefore, the one who took care of other children. Once married to Isidoro, her great pleasure was to take care of her own. Her devotion was to take care of her own family. Together they formed a tireless and efficient team. He trusted her completely with his organization and decisions in the house and in the business. And being married to Isidoro had provided her with many experiences. It had filled her with life, adventure and abundance. He himself never stopped moving, as restless and industrious as he was. His quiet moments accompanied him when he traveled by ship. Since he first set sail with other dreamers, he realized that the sea brought him clarity. On the sea he did not waste a minute; he thought, planned, took the opportunity to put his papers in order and placed orders by letter. On land, he slept little. To answer her question as to why, he replied, "We can dream to a certain extent. We came here to realize. I dream while at sea; on land I set about the task of making the dreams come true."

Bianca knew him like that, in a constant hustle and bustle. Organized, planned, and meditated movements. His manner was precise and industrious. His inner joy was immutable. On the trips they made together, they won everyone's sympathy, including that of the captain, whom he always entertained with a gift. A good bottle of wine. From the first time they traveled together, he would introduce Bianca with such pride that she never forgot it.

"May I introduce my *madame*. The cultured Madame Rainieri." And he bowed.

On that first occasion, she looked at him closely. Her husband was a gregarious fellow whose smile followed a glass of wine to toast with remarkable eloquence. From that first time, she appreciated the meals they shared and sympathized with everyone present. Only she knew of his daily toil. Whether in the wee hours of the morning by candlelight or by oil lamp at night, he would push ahead and move forward with his commitments. At times, he seemed not to want others to know how hard he worked, as if he intended to make them believe that it was easy for him. Both she and he were alike in some things and different in others, as was ordained by the fact that they came from different parts of Italy. One and the other had suffered similar hardships growing up but had reacted differently to the vicissitudes of life.

And, unlike him, she had become hardened; without him, life had changed her. Within months of his departure, the new baby would arrive at home and she would have to welcome it alone.

With all that pain sealed in her soul, Bianca unknowingly climbed the highest tower of the fort of San Felipe. Her feet, hesitating on the porous stones of this ruined place. She had never before dared to climb the steps to the top, suspicious of the heat and the slippery danger they held. But that January morning she felt an urge to reach the highest point and look out the narrow window formerly used for shooting and now framing the overseas cobalt. She knew a ship would arrive.

It was arrivals day, although from the top she could barely make out anything but the colors of the water and the waves swaying to the whim of the wind. She watched the rain coming down in a gray cloud, holding its breath in an instant of eternal waiting. She was looking out to sea, her eyes fixed and fogged with water, when she felt the presence of someone. It was her eldest son, Isidro. He had come out to look for her.

"Let's go home, mother."

He had his father's eyes and was, like him, extraordinarily handsome. Without a doubt, the best son a mother could have. As a child she had left him in Italy to cross the Atlantic with Isidoro. The boy had grown up in Italy and arrived later in Puerto Plata with his sister Blanquita. He showed infinite gentleness toward her and his sisters. When she was pregnant with the twins, she remembered the moment when the midwife had informed her that she had two babies in her womb. She had already felt it, attentive to the two hearts that played to push each other in the brief space of her uterus. Isidro and Blanquita had arrived on March 11, 1911, just in time, since a month later, on April 21, the twins were born, one of them was my grandmother.

On this January day, in 1913, as mother and son stood up in the tower of the fort of San Felipe, she looked at the horizon, towards Italy, where only two of her children remained. Mafalda and Queco were still growing up, away from their siblings.

Suddenly, a pang in her abdomen brought her back to reality.

"Come on, Mom, I'll help you. Lean on me," said Isidro.

She knew that the time of birth was coming and that it was going to be a girl.

"I'll call her Ana," she said.

Isidro nodded slowly, quietly. He could see the treacherous steps they had to go down.

"How did you know I was here?"

Her son smiled, amused:

"What secrets are there in Puerto Plata?" he answered, as if she had forgotten that in this town everything is known.

Bianca looked up as he held her by one elbow. This tall, baby-faced teenager was her only support at the moment. She hadn't needed anyone's companionship during her adolescence either. But, even then, everyone seemed to cling to her. The clinging of others to her seemed to be the theme of her life. In the myth that would awaken last, they would believe to be made of iron and, eventually, she would come to accept it as her own belief as well. She realized that she had climbed to the top of the fort to say good-bye, to say goodbye to who she was. From now on she would be without a companion, alone, with her children. She did not know, but she suspected, that she would become a lady of tenacity and mettle. From that moment on, she would be Doña Blanca, as she was already called in town. She would assume that character as a prescription of destiny. The unblemished reputation. The strength of iron. In the ruins of San Felipe, she decided to let herself be helped one last time. The stones could be as treacherous as life itself.

"Mom," he said, smiling, "don't come up here again, because next time I won't come looking for you."

She smiled; these days, only her son made her smile. Like Isidoro once too, but Bianca never wanted to give him the pleasure of letting him know it. How much unnecessary pride!

"Next time I'll send Beatriz to come and get you."

"Oh, no! I'd better not come back!" she replied, playing along.

Bianca knew that her daughter Beatriz was becoming a living imitation of her. Unlike Blanquita, whose strength did not detract from her sweetness, Beatriz and Yolanda could be severe with everyone. As much as they demanded from themselves, they demanded from others and began to instill in the younger girls the daily discipline required to run such a business. All this was the fault of the example of strength that Bianca herself projected.

She promised herself to stop being so hard on her daughters, a promise she immediately forgot.

That night Ana was born, with a nice shock of bright yellow hair and lavender eyes. Bianca asked her eldest daughter, Blanquita, to write to her siblings still in Italy, Queco and Mafalda, telling them of the event.

And what became of Isidro? How did he die so young? Now I will describe here what happened.

In 1919, influenza struck Puerto Plata. It was a pandemic from which few would be spared. In those days penicillin had not yet been discovered and the treatment of diseases was according to their symptoms. For the relief of this disease, there was nothing but aspirin, quinine salt or cinnamon tea. I think some guests might have become ill, but he didn't. He looked healthy. On one occasion, Mamma Chela told us that Isidro had gone to visit a friend. How surprised he was when he realized that he had been infected!

I can imagine him on his bed feeling doubly distressed, with remorse for being sick and for not being able to help his mother.

"Forgive me, mother."

"For what?"

"For leaving you alone again."

She took her son's hands in hers; he was feverish and didn't have the strength to look her. She couldn't see, just one last time, the color of his eyes. There was no cold water on his forehead, no miraculous tea or ointment, no pious prayer for divine intercession to stop the course of impending doom. Bianca saw her son's eyes go faint and felt him fall...defeated.

She got up and made a decision: she ordered Blanquita, who could not stop crying, to write her brothers and sisters, Queco and Mafalda, a letter.

"Tell them to get ready, that you are going to fetch them from Italy."

"Mom, who is going to pick them up?"

"You are. As soon as you come of age, you will travel to Italy with one of your sisters... And stop crying, you're going to get the paper for the letter wet. Get to work!"

HOSPITAL VISIT

*I*t was 2007 and it was one of the last times I traveled to the little Kendall house to take care of Mami. I walked into her room and saw her lying down. She looked up to greet me as I kissed her forehead. Her eyelashes had fallen out from the chemotherapy. Her pale skin, dry eyes, and baldness were witness to her battle. With her cheek on the soft, white pillow, and body tucked under the covers, she looked very beautiful to me. Her lips, in a half smile, beatified the tranquility of her rest.

"How cute you look—like a baby!" I would tell her every morning as I helped her get up. They were my love words to her, an endearment like those in a love letter. I've always loved her, but the consciousness of my love had deepened by the spirit of the women of her lineage who loved her through me.

Caring for my mother at that time was a labor of love between my sisters, my niece Laila and myself; we felt it was divinely inspired. We felt we performed our duties at a higher level of consciousness. Perhaps at the soul level they served to reestablish the tangled ties she had had with her own mother. When she was nine years old, if I remember correctly, her father sent her to a boarding school in Santiago, where Catholic girls attended. It was, in a way, being taken her away from her own mother, or so I understood. The deeper reasons behind that action I did not comprehend. Was she happy in that school with the nuns? She told me she had been. Her best friends, her heart sisters, came from that school. During her last years there, her cousin Billy, who lived with family also in Santiago where the school was, picked her up every weekend to stay with Mafalda's family—could that have made her a bit happier, then? I suppose so. I didn't see photos of her and Billy in their youth at that time. But in the black and white school photos that I found, my mom was smiling broadly with her thick braids. It's my favorite picture of her and that's how I imagine her now, from here to eternity.

This particular morning she was resting on her bed, smiling with her eyes closed and this made all her stoicism stay outside the door. With that vulnerable look of a baby, I recited the names of all her mothers as if they were part of the beads of a rosary: "Socorro Ginebra, daughter of Chela Rainieri, daughter of Bianca Franceschini, daughter of Raffaellina Galletti, daughter of Maria Guizzardi…" It was her own personal rosary. I prayed that their names would inspire in her the strength to continue the battle.

This morning I did not dare to wake her up completely. I let her rest in the half-light and I spent my time keeping her company in silence. I looked forward to when she would wake up feeling better, and thought she would surely take me to her garden to show me the new shoots and her discovery of a tricolor palmetto enthusiastically growing among the embrace of the lilies.

That day, she had an appointment at the hospital. At the beginning of her illness, she visited medical professionals until she found a Colombian oncologist who turned out to be wonderful. He received her with great affection at Mt. Sinai Hospital. He'd came out from behind his desk, made her sit in a comfortable armchair and, holding her hand with the eyes of a lover, spoke to her softly and with immense compassion. "My little queen, how beautiful you look! Tell me, my queenie, how do you feel?" Then he'd look into her eyes as she spoke, inviting her to unburden herself as if this was a romance. He took all his time with her and for that I was overflowing with inner appreciation and gratitude. Admittedly, I compared him to the professionals my dad found in New York. Of them, I have stories that are better left out of this story. This doctor made her look twenty years younger at every visit and she spoke of him with equal candor.

That morning she was scheduled for a scan. When we arrived, I saw with despair that the parking lot was full. I drove the car slowly around until I came upon one after more than half an hour had passed. As we entered the waiting room, we were told that the machines and doctors were running late, so the wait would be a couple of hours. Visiting hospitals causes in me a physical state of aversion. My stomach churns like a tank of heavy water, And I would feel dizzy and nauseous. I say it here, even if it sounds like an exaggeration, that I'd rather visit a cemetery thousand times more than a hospital. Now I foresaw that we would stay there the whole day.

I admired Mami's calmness as I helped her settle into a chair by the window. She had her knitting bag next to her. She pulled out her yarn and needle and started at it with a high state of concentration. For a while I watched her spin the needles quickly, until we were called up to the second floor.

"This is where the waiting begins," I murmured, hoping she wouldn't hear me.

In the past, I had asked her about how she occupied her thoughts inside those machines. I think that the whirring of the machine must have been excruciating and the minutes must have seemed like hours. But that's not what she indicated. She said, "I repeat to myself the phrase, *Jesus, I trust in you.*"

I told her that in India such phrases are called mantras and that it is a form of meditation. At yoga class some students usually wear a string of round beads that are used to focus the mind while saying the mantra.

"It's like the rosary," I explained. I loved praying the rosary with her. But at that moment there was no rosary to calm my anxiety. Sitting in the waiting room, I turned pages of magazines without looking at them. Sighing and looking around, I looked for what to do. On top of the counter behind the nurses' station, I found some free hospital calendars. I grabbed a pen and started scratching a made-up story on one of these. I kept writing who-knows-what in the blank squares on empty dates—after all, it's not like you could use it to plan ahead when you know nothing that would happen. During my childhood, I wrote daily in a journal all the happy things that happened during the day—not because happy things were the only thing that happened to me, but because I am an optimist at heart and made myself look for only the good. But that was my childhood and this time in this perfunctory waiting room I didn't feel like making the effort to find anything positive—what could it be after all? My mind found nothing in my reality that I could write. I set out to invent. At first, the ink came out tremulously, barely filling the squares, but then a current of ideas took hold of me and I filled in day by day and, little by little, month after month.

Someone called Mami's name and we both straightened up. A couple of nurses with a wheelchair helped her sit up. As they took her away, I breathed in the smell of the hospital. With more energy perhaps due to the heightened anxiety I felt, I wrote and wrote on the calendar pages in small letters. After a long while, between the lines, I saw the wheels approaching and the nurses returning my beautiful legacy, my mom, back to me. They accompanied us to the car.

We crossed the bridge over the island that joins to the highway and she pointed out the direction with her finger, since she knew the route better than I did, and I let her guide me. Once on the highway, she looked at me and asked, "And what were you writing?"

From between our seats, she took the calendar scribbled with my uneasy handwriting. The paragraphs look like a long rant of slanted letters small or large depending on the space. From January through December the text flowed through each square that indicated a day to the next. My writing crossed all the lines, ignoring them, as if days did not exist. Now I felt ashamed for I didn't want her to discover that in this tragedy I had written a trivial and fanciful children's story that with no relation to the serious moment we were living. But it would be obvious, if she started reading, so I decided to confess the truth.

"It's a story I made up...a fantasy...it's not that important."

My conscience now pricked at me for having devoted myself to that—wouldn't it have been more useful to have use my time for praying?

But her face lit up in curiosity.

"What's it all about?"

I'd forgotten that Mami loves to read!

"It's about," I began cautiously. Seeing she was interested, I continued, "It's about a teenage girl who decides to become a witch to save her sick father from an illness that has no cure.

Out of the corner of my eye, I saw the corners of her mouth lift.

"How does she do it?" She was genuinely curious.

"She goes out in search of a healer, against the will of the towns-people, who think the shaman is, in fact, a witch. They follow her to kill the witch. In a scene where the healer gives her the cure, the townspeople show up, they fight and the potion is scattered on the floor. They accuse them both of being sorceresses and try to kill them both. The girl has to figure out how to save herself and remake the medicine to save her father, all at the same time."

"And does she manage to cure her father?" she asked me, getting into the story.

"I don't know. I didn't finish it."

The answer was no. But I didn't want to tell Mami that even in my imaginary story everything had been in vain. I thought that perhaps she could tell me how to finish the story the way she wanted.

"How do you think I should end it?" I asked her.

"If only it were that easy," she said with a long sigh and looked away for a second.

Then, determined, she turned back to me with a strange light in her eyes.

"But I liked the story. It must have a happy ending." She surprised me when she said with energy, "You always wanted to be a writer. When you were little, you wrote in that journal of yours every day without fail. I'd look at you and think, *What does she write so much for?* And then I thought to myself, *Someday, my daughter will be a great writer.* I was amazed when you didn't—when you chose something else to do with your life."

My jaw dropped. I never imagined she would think of me like that.

She continued. "And do you remember when you went to the wedding in Cappadocia? You emailed me stories of what happened to you that day in the form of fables. I waited for them each day."

"Mami, they weren't fables! They were real stories. The water coming out of the rocks, the pigeons carrying messages..." I laughed because I had forgotten them. But it was true that I colored them more to charm her, thinking that was the only way she would be interested in them. I did it for her. In those stories I also brought records of the time we were together—I wanted her to reminisce and remember her trips. She was sick when I went to the wedding in Capadoccia and it was hard to leave her, so I wanted her to remember the time we were together there and weave those anecdotes with new events. At that time, my sister Cris received them by email and read them aloud to her. Mami was too sick to check her emails herself. After she got better and I went to visit her she would ask me to tell her more travel anecdotes. She had said, "Your travel anecdotes are more engaging that any travel writing I've read." But I always thought she was trying to make nice—just because she was my mother. The truth was that I had forgotten all that and I was thrilled that she remembered.

My mom didn't listen to my protest that those stories were true and not mere fables. But I was smiling while I was protesting, because well, my heart had lifted in the knowledge that those stories had mattered to her as much as they had mattered to me.

With the energy of her personality she gave me an order.

"Finish the story—and make it a happy ending. It's *your* story and you can make it whatever you want. So—end it happily!"

"That's right!" I said, softly hitting the steering wheel with gusto.

That day I loved her more for not criticizing me. She wasn't very expressive and I never thought she had enjoyed my stories so much. But that day she was giving me permission; permission to dream of fairy tales and impossible stories made possible; permission to dream and to put down on paper those dreams in my head. From that moment on, I decided I would not apologize for my different way of looking at life. I would not apologize for seeing life through the heart-shaped glasses she gave me. I would listen to her. I would write a happy ending!

We drove in silence, the lines of the road rapidly moving past us while she leaned back, resting with her eyes closed. Admittedly, I wore a big smile of gratitude, but I thought it was strange that her illness had given another quality to our time. It had certainly been a strange way to love each other in these times of dealing with this cancer. We healed wounds, we forgave each other, we conversed and understood each other a little better. We got to know each other a little more but most importantly, we connected with that current of love that came from before—and we beat the disease in that way. We took the chance to exercise this eternal love. Consciously, we deeply and profoundly loved each other again. That was the biggest surprise about her illness—that it brought about in us a transformation; not only me, but with my sisters as well. I can say that her inherited steel temperament had helped her not to let herself be discouraged, she was the calm in the midst of the storm. I never saw her being defeated by her illness, and in that I don't want to make light of it, because she suffered, but I never saw her defeated. It's hard to define it in words, the emotional change that took place in me and I am sure in my sisters too, but the fact that I had inherited this fierce love through the feminine way, *jus sanguinis*, made it all the more precious.

After that day there would be other dawns, sunsets and springs where we would talk and accompany each other. For now, all that remained was to rest. When she got home, she crawled into bed, curled up like a baby and dreamed her happy ending.

WAIT!

$\mathcal{I}$t was mid-March 2007 and I was in Virginia. Mami still hadn't arranged her April visit.

"Mami, when will you be arriving?" I asked her over the phone.

"I don't know. I'm not feeling well these days." Her voice sounded languid, weary.

I didn't want an April to pass without her coming to visit me, so I suggested May instead as there were still flowers then. What's more, in Virginia, buds cheer us up from spring to summer. I tried to convince her.

"Then you'll enjoy the wisterias, Mami...I think that's what they are called. They ornament the neighborhood on the way to Alex and Victor's school. Also, you won't believe it! The bluebells bloom like carpets at the end of May, you're going to love them!"

I let her make her decision and kept my hope intact. I continued in my daily routine and one Saturday I went to the subway to pick up Myrna, the mother of a friend who had offered to help me sew on some buttons and mend the hem of my children's pants. Growing up in Santo Domingo, sewing was a habit at home. I have in my memory the image of Mami spreading out fabric on the dining room table to cut out patterns and make little girls' dresses. My grandmother taught me to embroider too. I thought having female companion would comfort me. Just in case I was going to spend an April without Mami visiting.

236

Myrna had short gray hair, just like my mom a few months before chemotherapy. She rode next to me in the passenger seat as we drove down the hill to my house. I spotted a group of children on the grass of one of the neighbors at the top of the slope. I slowed down and pointed to my son, who was playing with his friends.

I said to her, "Look, that little boy in the red shirt, with straight black hair. That's my son Alex."

From the grass, Alex looked up. His eyes lit up and he turned to his friends and said, "That's my grandmother!"

He sounded so happy, "That's my grandmother, that's my grandmother!" He kept repeating, "It's Grandma! Grandma!"

In the distance, he was mistaking Myrna for Mami. And as my vehicle continued to idle down the street I heard him say, "Wait, Grandma, wait!"

I didn't start braking until I heard him say, "Wait, Grandma, wait!"

Quickly, he dropped what he was holding and ran toward the car as fast as his legs could go. I saw him in the rearview mirror. I stopped the vehicle as he continued to shout:

"Wait, Grandma, wait!"

I thought, *Oh, God, he's going to hurt himself.* I was afraid he would trip and fall behind the car. *What if a car was coming behind me without being so careful?*

I lowered the passenger window so he could see that it wasn't his grandmother. I will never forget his happy face thinking that it was indeed his grandmother sitting next to me. Once he reached the car, he leaned down and both his head and hand came through the open window in anticipation of an affectionate greeting. "Grandma, it's me, Alex. It's Alex."

Suddenly, his eyes got big when he saw that it wasn't his grandmother sitting next to me after all. Realizing his mistake, and as if propelled like a spring, he jumped backwards and stood upright on the grass with his mouth open, in shock. I had a feeling, and perhaps he had the same feeling, that he would never see his grandmother alive again. His brown eyes watered and his mouth curved downward.

"Grandma...?" He looked at me as if wanting to know why this was not his grandmother—as he had seen her arrive during all those other springs. His disappointment was palpable and it seemed as if he had been suddenly planted in reality.

Myrna was perplexed, but she understood the boy's confusion and was touched. In a soft voice, she spoke to him, "Sorry that I am not your grandmother, Alex. How cute you are! And how you love your grandmother, don't you? Where is she?"

His disenchanted expression made my heart sink even more and I tried to explain to him. Referring to Myrna, I said, "She is the mother of a friend who is coming to help me with my sewing."

Embarrassed, Alex stepped away from the car.

"Go back to play with your friends. Go with them, go on, they're waiting for you," I added.

But he didn't want to; he didn't move. He looked at the lady and looked down. Then he would look at her again and avert his eyes; his hands were deep in his pockets.

I hesitated. I didn't know what to do. I didn't want to leave him in the street like that when he seemed so...confused.

"Do you want to get in the car? Do you want to ride the rest of the way home with us?"

Our house was a few meters away. To get there, he could have walked across the neighbor's lawn, but he followed us along the edge of the driveway, self-absorbed, serious, as if oblivious to his surroundings. He was only eleven years old and looked so frail walking beside my car that I became worried. When I saw that he was finally heading home, I let the car slowly glide past the circle and into the parking lot. Myrna repeated, "What a cute little boy, what big, endearing eyes, how beautiful that love for his grandmother!"

For me it was a metaphor that took me back to another era. It was myself running behind my parents—like Alex in that moment; it was *me* asking and begging them. "Wait! Wait!", I yelled, trying to beat time. I was never ready to let them go.

I was left with the consolation of her last April, when she told me that my visualization had helped her dream of Dad. I enjoyed it like never before. I understood that it had been our final goodbye as she took the plane and walked away from me. The summer that followed she said she felt fine, but in the pictures she looked deteriorated. At the end of that summer, Adelaida called me.

"Mami is very ill in the hospital."

I began a series of short plane trips to see her. The dates depended on the cost of airfare and the projects I was busy with at work, but I was lucky in the flexibility I was awarded at the place of my employment to be able to go at least once a month and stay for three to five days, sometimes up to a week.

During my stays, I slept in my temporary *sandwich* bed in her room listening to the enchanting angelic bells. It gave me comfort, that tinkling of the breeze caressing the wind chimes. It was as if hope was peeking through the window.

In early January 2008, Mami was walking with a walker and needed assistance with everything. The first time she got up to go to the bathroom at night, she didn't want to wake me. I watched her walk past my bed trying to figure it out on her own. I got up to help her. I teased her about her maneuvers, "You almost beat me!" In the morning, as we ate breakfast, I admonished her, "For the love of God, Mami! When you want to go to the bathroom at night, wake me up! Please! That's what I'm here for." And she would reply, "But you looked so peaceful sleeping!" And I would reply jokingly: "Yep! How peaceful I would be if you fell down on me!" The roles had switched and I looked like the mother. "Accept the help, Mami...accept it," I would repeat, making her laugh. But for the granddaughter of the formidable woman that was Bianca and even for Chela's daughter, accepting help was something extraordinary. The women in this family have a hard time with that. And that's the female lineage I inherited!

I flew back and forth whenever I could, trying to keep up with my responsibilities, maneuver back and forth between two lives and make them minimally compatible. One night, back home in Virginia, something happened to me that I couldn't call anything else but esoteric. Asleep in the middle of the night, I heard Mami's clear voice calling me by my nickname: "Lache, Lache." Her steady intonation woke me up in the darkness and I raised my head. "Mami! Mami?" I jerked upright in bed, realizing I was in my own home in Virginia. But I was sure *her* voice had awakened me. For a split of a second, I was confused, thinking she was indeed visiting me. Or...was I in her house?

But it was my house!

Now my eyes sprang open. I touched my husband's arm to wake him up.

"Did you hear? Did you hear that?" I was sure that Mami's voice came from outside and not from inside me. I was sure I heard her with my ears and it wasn't my imagination.

"What?" he answered sleepily.

"Mami was calling me," I said. I tried to explain quickly that her voice was not coming from my imagination, but her voice had been picked up by my own ears.

"You dreamt it." He turned over and fell back asleep.

"No. I'm sure that I heard her voice!" I insisted, even though I knew he was no longer listening to me.

"What do I do? Should I call her on the phone?" I wondered to myself. I felt that something had happened to her and my heart was pounding. The clock read four o'clock in the morning and I began to bargain with myself. If I called her and woke her up, I could be robbing her of a good night's sleep and alarming her for no reason. She was sick and rest was essential. It was better to wait until five o'clock and then call. It was one of the longest hours of my life and I used every single relaxation method I had been taught in my yoga classes. I meditated. In my meditation I felt my mother's life and concluded that I did not feel her "on the other side," as I did with my dad.

The phone rang at five in the morning and I jumped with fright. I picked it up at lightning speed and without a hello or anything else, I asked:

"What happened to Mami?"

It was Cristina. She answered,

"I'm calling you because we are at the hospital with her. Everything is fine. She just fell out of bed. Let me put her on the phone so you can talk to her."

Mami's voice was thin. "I'm fine," she assured me. And she explained to me that what hurt her most was the fact that she couldn't get up from the floor on her own.

"I just heard your voice in the middle of the night. Did you call for me, Mami?"

"I called everyone!" She put such emphasis on the word world that it made her chuckle. Inside me, I had an intuition and a deep uneasiness that I was soon going to lose her, at least from a physical perspective.

"But me too? Did you call for me?" I insisted. I wanted to know if she had called me by my nickname.

"Yes, I said, *Lache! Lache!* For a moment I thought you were here...."

Those words squeezed my heart. With a sigh, I answered, "I heard you, Mami. I heard you as if you were here."

As soon as I could, I got on a plane. As soon as I arrived at her home, I sang aloud her name as I always did from the front door, "Mami, Mamiiiii!"

She came to meet me with her walker, which she irreverently called the *old lady's walker*, assisted by a nurse. The nurse had told me to wait, that we'd meet in the living room. She came out of the hallway slowly holding on to her walked in a cheerful gown with pastel-colored flowers and I hid my urge to cry. One whole side of her face was badly bruised. The bruise ran from her cheek to the top right of her bald head. Before hugging her, I exaggerated my horrified expression to make her chuckle—and she laughed heartily. Her teeth looked like those of a toddler. She looked so fragile to me that I didn't know where to go around her to embrace. Bianca's formidable granddaughter seemed as delicate today as the flowers on her dress.

"Oh, Mami!" I said, finally putting my arms around her. She thought it was funny.

"Don't exaggerate—it's over now!" she said.

I hugged her. I didn't want to let go. I didn't want to scare her with my outburst of grief either, so we looked into each other's eyes and laughed.

"Stop making drama. Relax," she added looking into my eyes, smiling.

I will never forget the look in her eyes at that moment. In the pallor of her face, they were two wells of water from a crystalline spring. Her love for me was palpable, spilling out like little stars, as in gushes, resembling the look she gave to her grandchildren. I could have knelt down from the divine love so immense, overwhelmed by her wellspring of affection. I could have fallen to my knees with my forehead on the ground and that wouldn't have been enough for the reverence I felt on the receiving end of that love.

Even today, as I write these words, I cannot stop the tears. Where were our childhood quarrels and fights? How we loved each other so deeply, beyond our different personalities, illnesses, faults and opinions! We realized that we loved each other for thousands of years with an ancestral love, a love that overtook me, embraced me, fierce and delicately, through my whole being. It was full, plenty, bittersweet, infinite, and inexhaustible. We were like soul mates coming from the same spiritual source…beyond understanding. We were standing before each other—or embracing, and our bodies were there but we travelled to a place where only souls can travel. I know that only love can bring us there.

Now I think, "We did it, Mami! You and me. We did it! Love won! Despite our differences, love triumphed. We loved each other deeply, profoundly."

Now I know. You are the love of my life.

I stayed with her at her house in Santo Domingo as long as I could. We said goodbye because I had to return to Virginia. I left with a broken heart. But before I left, I did something for her, thinking of the power of visualization she trusted I had.

I sat in the living room of her house and clasping my hands together as if in prayer, I imagined her in baby form, right there in her bed, snuggled between the sheets that would see her die. I prayed to God to come and get her in person. That the moment her soul left her body, the Divine Mother would receive her in her arms as a first-born, as if she were a baby of light. I visualized her spirit, wrapped in diaphanous clothes of pure love. And, Divinity, as a first-time mother, holding on to her first born. That She herself, the Divine Mother, in all of her light, would welcome this baby into the afterlife with loving whispers. She would tell Mami how happy she was to have her in her arms. She would tell her, "Before I was born, I loved you. Before you were, I missed you. You gave me the reason to live and I learned the greatest love from you." Like mothers to their daughters and daughters to their mothers in this family. And I felt the certainty that Divinity herself would embrace her like a baby and place her little bald head on her own chest so she could listen to the divine mother's heartbeats.

242

I did this visualization with my full conviction. I believed it on Mami's behalf, as she once believed me to be, I don't know exactly but...so powerful and so talented that...even her dreams about dad depended on me. I went along with her in an imaginary way, at that time. If I was so confident in my energies it was because she instilled in me that confidence that I could influence her dreaming. So I would do it once more, this time, for her, and make her trust count. I had faith that my prayer had paid off. She was a baby wrapped in light in the arms of her heavenly mother. Traveling now through the cosmos directly to the divine source of love.

The next time I returned to Santo Domingo, Mami was gone. It had been sixteen hours since I had said goodbye to her with a broken heart. I came back and I saw. I was alone, standing by her bed, witnessing in my mind our last goodbye. Her bed was now in perfect order and the window bells were in complete silence. Her beloved computer was off; there were probably unread jokes left in it.

Later, my sisters and I cleaned out the room. On the bedside table, in the first drawer next to some medicines, I found the diary-style booklet I had once given her. It was small and on the cover was an illustration of Leonardo da Vinci's calligraphy. I remembered the day I had put it in her hands with the instruction: "Mami, every night, you should write down the things you are grateful for." My intention was to help her heal. I believed that a positive state of gratitude contributed to the effectiveness of any medicine. I prescribed it for her and wrote it down on the first page. "This is a gratitude journal. Every night, write a gratitude list." And on the other side of the page, I wrote an incantation. "May all the gratitude written here be multiplied unto you."

It lay alone. Untouched. In the same place I had left it. Mami never used it. My mom was grateful at heart, that I knew. Now I imagined that, between all the things people suggested and doctors prescribed, she didn't have time to sit down in peace and write. Now I held the journal in my hands, its pages waiting for ink, thirsty for words of gratitude and love. I understood that the notebook was a gift to me. An inheritance from her. It was up to my soul to do the exercise of gratitude I had prescribed her. For giving me life—I'd exercise love in this way, because a grateful heart is a divine treasure.

Since then, I have cultivated gratitude in a practical way. Every night I write at least five lines, and sometimes more.

Dear Holy Spirit: thank you for my mother, my father, my husband and my children. Thank you for being the divine treasure of my ancestors and my descendants. Thank you for the sunrise that you gave me today when I was on my way to work; for the colors of the sunset that I enjoyed when I sat down to dinner. Thank you for the flowers in the field that I observed on the road that reminded me of Mami. Thank you for my memories and for my cool window and wind chimes. For sharing with my children every day and for their voices when they say "Mami" to me.

I understood that love does not end when souls leave their bodies. There is something that lives beyond the physical. The soul never dies, rather it travels to meet Divinity. Today I am smiling because, at the beginning of my research, I thought I should do something for my ancestors, like go out and save them or something. Rescue them from the diaphanous haze of oblivion. Yet they seemed to have saved me. I wanted to find Isidoro and, rather, I found something inside myself. A deep love in me. The research was a vehicle of connection. The divinity offered me the genealogy to guide me to them and from them to myself. It taught me, through experience, what my soul has always known: that they are never gone, that we are souls who never truly die. That we are, in soul, infinity itself. That we are of God and when we die we return to God.

The ancestors are like ambassadors of the Spirit. They are a way to bring us closer to our understanding of eternity and its infinite love. My ancestors linked me more consciously to my mother and her storytelling. Through ancestral story research, I had conversations with her about her life that I would never have had otherwise. Through genealogical research I was able to connect with so many family stories, family members, such as my uncles and cousins, and even to know things about my sisters on a deeper level. Through this art and science, I learned about the personalities of our predecessors and revived their threads. I discovered that everything is written in our blood and that when we reach them we renew ourselves—at the very least, we renew the love in us, when we go searching for them. Love is in their names.

In the end, it is they who are waiting for us, even before we start looking for them. They are there, patiently waiting for us to turn our eyes and attention to them. And if one has the inspiration and the joy to go in search of them, one can reach them soul to soul, encounter them and their experiences. In fact, the more we reach out to them, the more they reach out to us, from their spiritual being to us. Through their memories and even their tragedies that we know of, we are able to understand them and make them our own. A collective of experiences that makes us grow, to be fuller, more resilient individuals, vibrant and courageous. To the extent that we want and accept them, they give vigor to our existences. I believe it and I feel it.

I close my eyes and in my meditation I remember Mami...her eyes, her voice. I have developed a new relationship with her. As if we had started anew. Feeling this way fills my heart. I imagine her with my other ancestors, encouraging me like never before. "Live, travel, laugh, and be alive!"

Or as Chela would say her invented word, *"Alebrécate"*, which means all that and more.

PART 4

ISIDORO'S DESTINY

THE BEYOND IS NOT SO "BEYOND"

 wo months or more after Mami's death and that first April without her, when the leaves of the jacaranda were giving their spectacular welcome to spring; when the lilies and petunias were bringing their splendorous flowers overflowing with colors, I set out to clean her room in my house to adapt it to any new visitor. There was the picture of her and dad laughing on a trip. I decided to leave it in that spot, on top of the shelf, next to the books she had left behind over the years. When I knelt down to open the bottom drawer, I was amazed to find a beautiful, hand-made album, bought from the catalog of an Italian store. I had put it in there myself almost a year before and had forgotten about it. I had prepared it for her. It was her surprise gift. Now the surprise was mine.

It had been almost two years since I had presented her with that huge square notebook with its empty pages. Some other spring, I had asked her if she liked the color of the cover, the shape and the color of the pages. Naturally, she wanted to know why I was asking her so many questions about this object that did not merit such an interrogation. Calmly, I replied that it was a surprise. I did not inform her that I was preparing a collage of her ancestry. It would be a compendium where copies of the research documents would reside. I would call it The Family Book. And I wanted to know her opinions on the book styles I was showing her.

"Mami, but which one do you like best?" I insisted, showing her the photo in the catalog, "This one or that one?"

She reached out to choose the cover with a brocaded flower urn embossed in leather.

"And which color do you like better, this one or that one?" She chose the brandy-colored one. What she chose, I ordered. So she knew something, but she didn't know what she was going inside this decorated masterpiece, much less did she know that the subject was her Italian genealogy.

In this Family Book would be artistically presented, preserved and treasured documents of her Italian lineage. In pictorial form, I represented Isidoro and Bianca at the same level of love, as heads of this family, together for eternity. They appeared with their genealogies in parallel. In their pages, they exhibited the same filial value. Isidoro's ancestors came from San Secondo Parmense and Bianca's from Castello d'Argile. Their trajectories, from an aesthetic point of view, were adorned with Florentine motifs, in the style of the Italian illuminated manuscripts that I loved so much. On each page we could glimpse the historical journey of my great-grandparents, their travels, from their respective beginnings, their births in Italy, matrimony, the countries where they had lived and each birth certificate of their children. To give it a visual efficacy simulating the ancient times in which they left their mark, I decorated each page with a document in a special way. Isidoro's birth certificate I put in the form of parchment. It had a thin ribbon with a bow that could be opened and closed. Bianca's was being longer, so I folded it like an accordion that extended when opened. With the marriage certificate from Colombia I did something even nicer. I obtained a photo of some stained-glass windows of a church in the style of the Notre Dame de Paris and printed it on transparent vellum paper. I cut in the middle the gothic window that was trans-figured into a double door, with two silk ribbons as doorknobs that, when opened, revealed the document. It gave the impression of entering the church through a door of brightly colored stained glass. The marriage certificate, which I obtained in Colombia thanks to Sandra's nephews and nieces, was "on the other side of the doors", on parchment paper. It looked heavenly and even of artistic and historical value! On another page, I painted a tree with the branches of her children with their respective photos: Isidorito, Blanquita, Beatriz, Yolanda, Queco, Mafalda, Chela, Mayú and Ana.

I had imagined telling Mami, when I had the chance to place this in her hands, "This is a Family Book and these are your Italian ancestors. Isidoro and Bianca are equal in love." I imagined it as a triumphant moment, between mother and daughter. Cherubin angels would suddenly appear in the ceiling of her room and peek curiously to see what heavenly missive I was declaring. Well, nothing less than the moment of the delivery of this album of ancestors to my mother.

Kneeling on the floor, with the album in my hand, I was a bit baffled regarding what to do with it. As I placed the large book on top of Mami's bed to look carefully at each page, I realized that in the past year, I had discovered other documents that I wanted to add in there. I remembered my speech, "It's an epic story. Their travels, their lives, how they met, what they went through," I said triumphantly. "They were always together. Yes, Mami, they traveled together. And together they undertook an enterprise. Together they had adventures. I have the evidence of many of them here. And the ones I haven't, those documents are yet to come!"

I wanted to change her story from one of abandonment to one of love. I thought then that I had achieved my goal with the family book. But we already know that she never saw it finished, as on February 11, 2008, she was taken away.

"And that was how my mom became one of my ancestors," I said aloud to myself. And that was how she herself would be captured on one of its pages. As I now would like to add Isidoro and Bianca's grandchildren.

When I turned the page and I saw the pictorial representation of each of them and their ancestors, I realized that each parent and grandparent on both sides looked like angel wings. Fathers on the right, mothers on the left. Then I understood that the guardian angels encompass the ancestors. And, that there is an angel for each family. The same as Mami had taught me when I was a little girl for my guardian angel, "Guardian angel, sweet companion, do not forsake me night or day."

Then I spoke to her as if I had it in mind,

"You taught me that every child is born with its guardian angel. Likewise, every family has a personal angel. It is the same!"

It is an angel that accompanies a family in all its generations; that mends broken hearts and brings the love of people who are no longer physically with us. I don't know how the angel does it; I'm just glad it's like that. An angel of a family whose goal is to unite its members in love, and who is in charge of repairing the tree. As if in response, I turned another page and saw the little family tree I had made with Bianca and Isidoro's children. That was the one I would show Uncle Fernando. Yes, I would add the grandchildren. I would paint the family angel that watched over everyone and cared about unveiling the truth. That only love is truth and only love exists.

"A restorative angel for each family."

I don't know if it was sensitivity or an innate desire. But now a desire for a family alliance was growing in me. And in that longing I had a sensation…I sensed that someone was coming after me to fulfill certain designs for this ancestral love. Who? I did not know yet, for it was only a premonition.

I realized that I had been instrumental in renewing my mother's memory of her grandfather. Likewise I was to be an instrument to renew the memory of this great-grandfather to all his descendants. To forgive and to strengthen ties. Just as the stories of Mami and Uncle Fernando had been for me, this timeless book served to capture it visually. So that so many future descendants will remember their names and thank them for their lives. So that their names will never be forgotten. They will exist in this consciousness and will be reflected, between the lines, passing from page to page, from word to word, from consciousness to consciousness to each heart of their descendants.

Leafing through the pages, a letter slipped out. It was from the New York City health department. It dealt with the matter of Isidoro's whereabouts. I had received it in 2001, before the Twin Towers fell in New York. Of course this document had never been pasted, or embellished, as a family document. At that time I did not know if it was real and could not corroborate it. I hesitated to add it now because I wondered if this would be another case of "the two Isidoros", as it happened with his birth certificate that said that in

San Secondo there were two babies born in the same week. So could there be two men with the same name...in New York?

I took it in my hands. *I've been searching around the world trying to find you!*

"If it's you, I'm sorry I'm late. Sorry, because you have been waiting for so long for someone to find you. There's no more hurry for Mami because she knows the truth in heaven. But I don't know. What do I do? Will I finally be able to go out and look for you? Will I find you? Do you want to be found?"

"Mami," I said to the air or to Mami's spirit if she heard me from beyond, which I wanted to think she did, as I held the book in my lap, contemplating it. "Now, what do I do with this book? I don't want to go on if you are not with me. I don't want to go on dreaming, searching among the memories of your ancestors if I have no one to share them with."

Uncle Fernando came to mind. "Of course, with him!"

Then I felt that the book was not mine. I had not created it to keep it. Not even to give it to my mother. A different feeling came over me with this one than with the gratitude journal. This was an instrument; this book had a life that would go on after mine. I would give it to Isidoro's descendants from the male side, Fernando and Frank sometime in the future. After all, they were the males in the family who carried the family surname forward and it would be that way for generations. I had the conviction that their descendants would enjoy it more. Their children, my cousins, would appreciate it more.

If so, there must be a larger plan than my mind could foresee yet; moreover, I even felt that, at some future time, there would be a child, a young girl, or adult already, but... a descendant, a granddaughter of Frank or Fernando, who would have a desire to know her roots, a desire to get to know her ancestors. She would call one of my uncles *Great-Grandfather*, as I call Isidoro. She would be inspired to love and to search within herself with that same love that transcends generations.

And why not, if the same thing had happened to me? If someone before me had intended it. If even Isidoro in his dying breath had wished it so?

"How did I get here?" I thought, happy to have conquered the idea of "here". Thinking of the texture of time that sometimes undulated and sometimes drove in a straight line. I had fallen in love with the story of a great-grandfather, with his life journey, and with the idea that there was more than could be perceived on a merely human scale. As I hugged the book to my chest I thought, *And in searching for you, I found so many adventures and so many divine treasures!*

I didn't even know something had been missing in me! But now, I got it.

I concluded the book for now by adding photos from Mami's album. That day I asked the family angel to place a very special blessing in the book for each member of the family, present, past and future generations. Then, turning pages and pasting real and dreamed images, the idea came to me that each time these future members would capture a photo of themselves or their descendants, they would at the same time capture their dreams and pass them on from generation to generation. This project was not only mine, but a divine gift to those other generations who would keep this representation of the divine treasures of this family.

This book will be a sweet and irresistible object of union for the whole family.

In conclusion, the heart rules. The feminine way is strong in this family. It is the lineage of great warriors of truth. The men of this family are great supporters of this feminine force, and through this Family Book they will become great guardians of our history in its future context.

I honor all the ancestors who gave life to our grandparents and parents and thus gave life to me as well, even those whose names I do not know. I love them all, and I know they love me from other lives.

This convinced me to make a decision about Isidoro. As soon as I had time available, I would clear my schedule and leave for New York to follow up on the lead I had once received in that envelope which had been sealed for so many years.

I left the New York letter folded inside because I suspected that the familiar spirit was still had more inspirations and surprises in store for me. But I did not suspect that the wheel of a new reunion was already in our destiny. I did not know that there was also a descendant, apart from Uncle Fernando and myself, who was on the same quest and waiting for his turn to take over and take the lead. The family angel was going to unite me with him and unite everyone in his name, in the name of our ancestors. For the first time, we would be connected in the adventure of searching for our unforgettable ancestor.

I concluded my visit to the drawer of memories by taking a last look at the research, unaware that, by closing the cover, wrapping the book in delicate tissues, placing it inside a beautiful box and closing the lid, a cycle was ending. However, something unknown awaited me, because where something ends, something new begins. A genesis of unknown adventures: other trips, other investigations, other happy moments to which our ancestors moved us toward. Not only me, but also many of my other relatives. It would lead us to recover lost ties and to build new memories.

ISIDORO ARRIVES IN NEW YORK

*I*n June 1912, Isidoro arrived in New York amidst the intermittent smoke of the steamer that overshadowed the big blue sky with its black clouds. He arrived along with dozens of passengers, some of them dressed in jackets to block the wind. He was leaning on the handrail of the gunwale, watching the ripples of the water that moved and stirred the ship. He turned his gaze toward the distant city he was approaching. What must have caught his eye? Probably the oyster barges huddled between the piers parallel to the wharf. And, what about the hustle and bustle of a hyperactive city with its skyscrapers lined up? Neither the *Empire State* Building nor the *Woolworth* had been built yet, still rows of tall buildings were already unfolding on the wide, rectangular streets. When the ship finally came to a stop, Isidoro picked up his suitcase and prepared to step out onto the dais. Just like that, he made his way through customs. That was my Isidoro: tall and well-dressed, walking purposefully and with good humor because everything in his life, so far, had been an adventure.

At the time of this evocation, I was sitting at my desk. I had just opened the ship's manifest of his last voyage. Whenever I see his name on some genealogical document, my curiosity is piqued. What caught his attention when he arrived alone New York City? I often pondered all the information on documents that I found. I was curious to know how people were dressed or what was happening on that date. So, I did some research on my beloved Google and before it even showed me pictures of some streets from 1912, I could already imagine them! I knew that most of the carriages were still horse-drawn, although the rhythm of their legs was mixed with the rhythm of the occasional motor carriage that filled the atmosphere with small explosions of intermittent rat-a-tat-tats!

The black and white images showed me the people moving on foot and crossing the corners of the wide streets, dressed in hats and long coats. They all looked the same! I turned my eyes to the manifest on my screen and reviewed the information about Isidoro's arrival on that ship. I was struck by the date of his entry into New York on the manifest: June 12, 1912.

It was clear and bright as if it was waiting for me to notice it.

I looked up and checked the date on my calendar . It was June 12, 2008.

A current of electricity shot up from my back and made the hair on my nape stand on end. I turned looking back as if by instinct, as if there was a presence, and when I only glanced at my familiar bookcase, I smiled. Why had this research been so tangentially magical?

How come the day I sat down to review the research was the same month and day of his entry into New York?

It was as if there was a direct line drawn between that day of his arrival in New York and this day in Virginia. I was here, sitting in my chair looking at the screen with this information. It was as if, through time, that imaginary line linked what he was doing and what I was doing. He was standing in line and going through customs, with his small suitcase; and me, with my pen, my computer and the phone by my side. In one hand he held his entry permit and in the other, his hat. When it was his turn, he approached the waiting customs officer.

If there was a thread that united us at that time, I think that he, among the New York crowd, looked south, toward Virginia, at the same instant that I raised my head and felt what I felt. Perhaps he, too, felt the shiver on his nape as I did. What if for a moment we suspended our belief in linear time and stepped into a new time; into a time lapse where he is there and I am here? If we are peeled away from the scene, hovering in a modern drone and then zoomed out from this map, we could see the straight line from north to south; from his position in New York to where I was, in Virginia. That line would reach my desk where it would touch the back of my neck like a tickle. A greeting from his time to my time. A smile of a goodbye. I think that one line would cross time, space, and belief. Then, I raised my pen and stood upright because I heard something and I wanted to write it down. An idea about our perception of a flat time. A humming of a machine in my room and the bustle of people's noise where he is. He turns his eyes in my direction, maybe feeling my yearning thoughts toward him.

Internal opinions move from the *"can't be"* of disbelief to confidence in what I feel. I suspect there is much more to what we know regarding science and the science of the spirit realm, than we think. There is more to learn about the texture of time too. Time and space are mysteries. And between imaginary dimensions, I know I heard a whisper.

Is it my *name?*

Is it his *name?*

And sharpening my inner ear, I want to know more. What could it be that urges time and space to speak to me? So, in the dimension of this imaginary parallel time where everything happens at the same time; where miracles happen; where imagination dilutes with reality...at that very moment when I raise my head and close my eyes, he takes his small suitcase, adjusts his hat and walks up the slope, away from the boat.

And in the crowd on the Hudson River waterfront, I call out to him. Yes, it's me. I decided to visit him in my imagination just then like a lucid dream. I decided to run to him. I'm disguised as a little girl and dressed in white; I'm wearing my long curls like that time in the dream of the farewell. And in the crowd, I call out his name.

"Isidoro!"

He listens to me. I see him stop. He turns and looks at me. Towards that little girl who is looking for him but can't find him. He tries to look where I am because he thinks he heard someone calling his name. But he only sees the people coming out of customs and the boat he came on and can no longer return to. He cannot see me. Because I do not exist where he exists. So, ignoring his own insight and intuition, he gets moving, crosses over the threshold that takes him out of the dock area and into the bustling city streets. He walks determinedly uphill away from me, closer to his destination and moving towards what really happened—his destiny.

But what did happen? I still couldn't find the final truth because how do we know the truth of the truth? We will never know what exactly happened and in this there is an infinite longing for a life. However, I am determined to see between times, to travel in dimensions. I too have a small, light suitcase. I too can make short trips into the past. I will trust Einstein and his theory that "time is elastic" and that there are events in history that happen at the same moment. And as if there is a time crystal for us, I am a little girl who insists on calling out to him in the New York crowd. Like me, he tries to see out of his translucent crystal, his dimensional realm where he exists. Then, something unusual happens. In the crowd, Isidoro stops and looks off into the distance and raises a wish into the air...a piece of this story. He hands it to fate.

Who will receive it?

Who will discover his destiny?

Who will rescue it from the bowels of oblivion? A destiny traced and orchestrated. Between us there is a great time and a great space. A translucent distance that even today we do not know how to eliminate. We still do not know if one day we will be united in the same time and space beyond imagination. There is the straight line drawn by destiny from him to me on this day. This line advances, begins to undulate and become a spiral as if it were a sacred cornucopia. And it is through that spiral that a clock-like circle is activated with a pair of hands that go round and round between numbers that mark the hours. And in this clock of life the needle moves, and begins Isidoro's life (1857), Bianca's (1875), theirs as adults dancing in Colombia (1896). That of their children being born (1897, 1899...), that of a daughter dying (1900). The birth of Chela and her twin (1911), of him leaving on a boat (1912). Ana, the posthumous daughter, being born into this world (1913), his eldest son dying (1918), that of the last children arriving in Puerto Plata from Italy...with other dates and actions appearing and, as smoke, vanishing as well...

All these images of events rise and form, mark the hours, then vanish to make way for others. Like a beautiful dance of lives that emerge surrounded by colors and laughter. They, the descendants, are born, grow, fall in love, play, and cry. And with these images sounds also awaken, and so I hear tender babies, little girls laughing like little birds playing hide and seek in the lobby of a hotel in Puerto Plata, and much more. Like a dance in the mists of time, their descendants do some action as they rise on the flat clock, the hands spin and then, disappear to fall into the next hour. Some I recognize and some I do not. The image of Chela makes me smile when I see her as a young woman parading through the flowers of a garden towards her beloved. Other lives go by in fast motion. They grow, they fall in love, they live they laugh, they play, they grow old. I hear the word "Mami". I see my mom at the end of her hour as a bald baby being lifted by the divine mother of light as her physical body passes away in one last breath. Like a diaspora of descendants fanning out, they rise in the early morning, work, play, lay their head on the pillow in the moonlight. In parallel, other descendants enter and exit trains, travel, embrace their children as they return home... These images of circular time fade and dissolve. Again, only the straight line from New York to Virginia remains. Destiny searches for whom to choose. Isidoro looks up and I raise my hand. It is the magic of the ancestors. It is the angel of my ancestors who coordinates, searches, chooses the person who is willing.

"I am willing."

Maybe I said it before I was born.

Destiny approves it. It will be the one who has the special sensitivity and loves them all with a deep, undeniable, inherited and inevitable love, without judging. She will be the one who has the longing to exist between times. Destiny chose and it was me, when I raised my hand, who chose me too. The one who understood that I chose myself.

A document does not explain the reasons for abandonment, nor does a tombstone. They are just silent witnesses of destiny. I remember the day I called Mami with the letter in my hand from the New York Department of Health. At that time, I did not have this ship's manifest that I was now seeing and I realized that the letter I received with the date of what happened matched! And just like that, all my doubts dissipated. Suddenly, that blank piece of paper on which this information was written represented a handkerchief wet with tears. Tears of loss, of abandonment, yes, but our tears.

I remember that, in that summer of 2001, I almost ran to take the train to go there and verify that tombstone with my own eyes. I almost hopped on a train to New York, but just that weekend one of my children got sick. Then, on another occasion, other events prevented my departure to corroborate this part of the mystery. How did things happen like that?

It was not time yet.

This investigation seemed to have its own rhythm. It had its own mind, even its own…angel? Whatever it was it all seemed to be uncontrolled by me. So how dare I think that I had any control over destiny? Did I have anything to do, or say, beyond letting myself feel the flow and follow it? Did it mean that it was time now?

I felt determined. Finally, I was going to do it. New York was calling me. I would go there and review everything I had received previously and corroborate.

I was happy to have made a decision! I was sorting out dates and the hotel I would be staying at when I received an email that made me slap my hands to my face and nearly die laughing. What was I planning to do—and what for? I wasn't even in charge! What I found in my email inbox was an invitation to my next destination.

And it wasn't New York. It was Puerto Plata.

DESTINATION PUERTO PLATA

*T*he invitation that arrived by email was a summons from Uncle Frank to all the descendants of Bianca and Isidoro. A family reunion was to be held in Puerto Plata. It said that the celebration was more for her, in honor of her temperance and fortitude. "My grandmother was one of the most prosperous businesswomen in the area. Her children became good men and women. Love of work was a virtue she instilled in her descendants that led them to be known as honest, upstanding and hardworking people. But of all the gifts she left us, love of family has been one of the most valuable. Family is a person's greatest success. The union of this is fundamental in the joy of the human being. I am fortunate to have both. I invite you to share this joy of being together in love as family, and to celebrate where it all really began."

I sensed that it would be a magical weekend, of descendants' meeting where time would merge with that of our ancestors. That weekend, more precisely on Friday, would begin with a reception. On Saturday we would travel to visit the "Callejón de Doña Blanca.", Bianca's alley, where the town of Puerto Plata was honoring her. It was where the Hotel Europa had once stood. In the evening, there would be a celebration of family stories. I knew that together we would connect body and soul with the true story of Isidoro and Bianca. I trusted that the past would speak in this present.

Uncle Frank, as the head of the family and as part of Queco's descendants, invited all the successors of his sisters for a reunion the first weekend of August. He asked us to contact, pass on the invitation and add those family members who were not included in that first message. Please don't miss anyone! As expected, the family was in an uproar, that is to say, the enthusiasm exploded into a hullabaloo that fed the expectations of the reunion. It was all expressed in the email messages that were fired off with great enthusiasm and seemed to dance when they arrived in our inboxes. With them, memories appeared supported by short jokes and comments. Due to distance, some of us who lived abroad had not attended smaller reunions in decades, a situation that meant we saw very little of our childhood cousins. Some emails arrived with current photos so that we could recognize each other. So it was that I saw a picture of Frank Elias, Uncle Frank's son, with a big smile on his face. I don't know if I sensed right away what part he was going to play in this story when I saw his picture, but I knew I felt an immediate kinship with him. Since he is younger than me, my memories of him were as a child. When he was nine, I was seventeen and about to head off to college. And now, he was a man looking so much alike as his father! But I didn't stop there, I got to work sending out memories in capsules of anecdotes because I knew how much we needed that family love! In this explosion of enthusiasm, the more comical members of the group took the opportunity to send their funny notes. I remembered the famous jokes that Mami received and sent forever ago. And guess who was the first one who started sending humorous, off-color jokes? Uncle Fernando, of course! Using modern technology we looked like kids in an amusement park and we hadn't even seen each other's faces yet! The list of cousins grew, not only in enthusiasm, but in number until there were ninety of us! All descendants of Isidoro and Bianca's children: Yolanda, Queco, Mafalda, Chela, Mayu and Ana.

There was no reason to wait! I contributed to these messages the pictures of our beloved Babi, and childhood pictures of uncles and aunts. They were pictures that Mami had lovingly kept in the albums of her youth. I scanned and sent them. Immediately, the photos caused a sensation. Each one seemed to awaken stories stored in dormant memories. Of course I shared the one of Mami at nine years old, sporting her long braid and posing with her siblings, dear Nelson and Blanca. I also sent a photo with Luis Manuel Machado, one with Frank and Fernando that looked like it had been taken at Frank's fourth birthday. He, with his adorable little boy's smile in front of his cake, was clapping his hands happily. The Harpers also sent new photos of Billy and Frank David, thirteen and fifteen years old at the time, which they had never seen before. Some Harper told how Billy used to pick up my mom at the boarding school in Santiago to spend weekends with the Harper-Rainieri cousins. In that house there was an exotic black bird—they couldn't decide if it was a crow or a cockatoo. Someone remembered that Uncle Harper had taught words to the birds. I would have loved to interview that bird! In Mami's album there were images of other little cousins that looked familiar but were unrecognizable to me, so I shared them so the owners would recognize themselves. One little boy with long golden curls was posing with big tears in his eyes. He seemed to be complaining about the photo.

Uncle Fernando commented, "That one must be saying, Cut these for me, it's warm in the tropics."

"That's my brother Giuseppe," replied Aunt Maria Filomena Barletta in another email. "He was just like that. He had an enviable head of curly hair that my mother, Mayu, thought was beautiful and she didn't want to cut it! He was a beautiful boy."

Another picture showed a six-year-old boy dressed as a baseball player with a cap and uniform of the *Escogido* team. When I sent this last one to the group, there was an outburst, as there were several who didn't know who it was and it remained an unknown for a couple of emails that went back and forth until Uncle Miguel Maltes wrote, "Oh, my! I see myself as a child! The little ball player is me!"

I also shared one photo that I considered a particular treasure. It was my grandmother's photograph, so beautiful! Her clear eyes, one blue and one green as she always liked to point out, looking straight into the camera. I had subtly enlarged and painted it and had it in a frame above my desk. Sometimes, I would take a break from my work to look at her and thought that this is how she looked from another life—that thought would make me smile in satisfaction. "I'm doing this for you." But that was no longer entirely true. I was also doing it for me. I loved holding the image of my grandmother close to me, remembering that she was once young, and sharing her with my cousins. They all marveled at her beauty.

Uncle Frank commented, "The only one of the sisters who didn't have a snub nose was Chela, she always laughed out loud at everything. We would go to the theater Elite to watch Italian films. She let us in for free and filled our hands with candy."

How much I treasured those new memories and how much I thanked my grandmother for having such a joyful family! I thanked the photo of her for the shared memories and told her I was going to her favorite place, Puerto Plata. It had never occurred to me to make this request to any ancestor, but the joy enveloped me and I wished she was with me. I would take her to her hometown. We would go together to Puerto Plata to meet and recognize the descendants of her brother and sisters. That image would escort me on my journey from the moment I packed my bags, boarded the plane and arrived at the plaza in front of the church in her beloved town.

Then, something fantastic happened. Between the messages that came and went, descendants began to ask for pictures of their grandfather while others responded and exclaimed that they wanted to see their great-grandfather. They were referring to Isidoro! As always, the comments alluded to him. Speculation of his whereabouts continued. "He left and never cameback. They say he died during the trip and was thrown overboard." This squeezed my heart. Someone wrote, "He is buried in the Santo Domingo cemetery." And this made me think that maybe the one I had in New York was not him. But soon, Maria Filomena answered: "That is not Isidoro, but the oldest son, Isodorito, that my mother (Mayu) exhumed from Puerto Plata to bury in the family plot." Then, she added that Mayu had brought from Italy the statue of an angel and this made me think of the family angel that protects us all. Someone commented, "They say Isidoro had other children in Colombia," while others added, "He died of influenza." These claims too were quickly denied by one or more of the elders.

Still, I was attentive to every email that came in as I packed my suitcase with my grandmother's picture off to the side on top of my desk and me folding clothes. My trip would be short so my luggage was small, with only the essentials. *The promise of a short trip,* I thought as I carefully arranged two dresses, one for each night and two changes of evening clothes. I interrupted what I was doing when another email arrived.

Suddenly, out of the blue, an email came in with the subject: ONLY EXISTING PHOTO OF ISIDORO. Unintentionally, I threw all my folded clothes to the side and rushed to the monitor. I almost threw the chair! After the double click I waited for it to open as if a century was slowly passing me by. My eyes were fully focused and my breath held, and then...there it was! My eyes were drawn immediately to the black and white photograph of their wedding two figures looking at the camera while tilting their heads toward each other. Both were dressed elegantly. Isidoro was distinguished by his cheerful expression while Bianca looked very serious.

So this is you. This is you...my dear Isidoro...my divine treasure, the one who started it all.

The email explained where the photo came from. It was a keepsake Mappy had from her grandmother Mafalda. Later, she would tell me, "When Tuta passed away, I went through and cleaned out all the trunks. I found this one among her papers and photos. It is the only one of Isidoro and Bianca's wedding. For this reunion I sent it to Aunt Filomena."

Aunt Maria Filomena was collecting this and other family documents along with a list of names of all the descendants to present them in a booklet at this reunion. It featured photos of the hotel, the family and a list of the descendants, all compiled by her and thanks to family members who had sent in the oldest photos they could find. There was even a receipt for the sale of one of the hotels. In short, it was a small treasure. This was the only photo of Isidoro that existed until that day. His marriage to Bianca celebrated in Bogota in 1896.

I didn't wait long to download the photo and examine it with a professional program. Using Photoshop, I opened the file and enlarged it; I zoomed in as close as I could. Indeed, Isidoro was very handsome! He wore his hair in the style of the time; he looked like Valentino, the famous Italian actor. Because of his build, he looked quite tall and relaxed. *I thought you were slenderer.* The hair was like Uncle Frank's, a bit unruly and with a little tuft like a swirl. Although his body and build were more like Uncle Fernando's and he also resembled him much more in the face. Next to him was Bianca with her brown hair in curls, a fashionable style for that time. She looked delicate, however, her strong personality was already standing out. Her expression was serious, her thin lips were a little tight almost as if she was nervous, or didn't know how to smile. She was not the one that was going to abandon anyone— that's for sure. "Ah, the things you will go through, my dear great-grandmother! The adventures and misadventures that fate has in store for you after that day in March 1896 when you joined Isidoro."

And then I went back to his smile. Although not completely open, it resembled that of Uncle Fernando. His eyes were full of light and life as if he were happy that day, happy to be married. He had the countenance of a dreamer. He was definitely enjoying the moment.

I looked at Isidoro's eyes through the monitor. I've always wanted to know their hue, but I'm not sure if they're aquamarine like my grandmother's or lavender-hazel like Aunt Ana's. Although I could tell his pupils express an extra light, trying to imagine the color in a photo from that era is very difficult. I zoomed in on the digital magnifying glass and glimpsed the mischief in his eyes. I set the magnification to 200 percent on the screen and then to 400 percent until the tiny squares of pixilation were visible. I moved the image again and again, near and far, and thought, *What is the color of your eyes?*

When I moved the magnifying glass away I felt that he saw me...as if he opened his eyes and observed me. As if he was my mirror. I smiled and imagined him winking at me. *"What are you looking for, Graciela?"* he seemed to ask me in that familiar, husky voice similar to Uncle Frank's and which, in turn, resembled my Uncle Nelson's.

I laughed because in this family we all think we know every-thing. I have my grandmother Chela's "know-it-all" genes and, following this fictitious game, I replied, "Isidoro, I've been looking for you and now, I can see you in a picture!"

I stood in order to tidy up again and finish packing. I said to Chela's photo, "This time it's not Italy or Bologna or San Secondo. It's another poetic and mythical place. It's your Puerto Plata. Will you come with me?"

The plane took off from Dulles International Airport with a stopover in Atlanta where I made a connection with Mappy, and then we flew together to Puerto Plata.

Thus began this adventure to the 2008 family reunion, with a small suitcase as the promise of a short, but immensely fun trip!

FAMILY REUNION, 2008

I began this story with the moment Mappy and I landed in Puerto Plata. The customs officer had asked us the following question, "How many family members are you traveling with?"

Now it is clear why this question comes so loaded with stories. And before Mappy answered, and before I raised my voice to tell "the truth" based on *reality*, I wanted from the deepest part of my being, to tell the truth based on *my experience*. I wanted to answer once and for all with the knowledge of my soul. To tell the customs officer and the whole world that we all travel through life with a lot of family. I wanted to warn him, laughing with joy, that...there is more out there! That I carry my ancestors with me! That, if he would only take off the glasses that cover his eyes and put on the glasses of the soul, he could see them too. Like me, they are all standing behind him... and behind Mappy too. Smiling, moving, waving. Dressed differently—and of varying appearance and stature. I realize that neither the officer, nor anyone who considers themselves sane, would understand. Perhaps, if he were the one who would have told me before I did all of my genealogical research, I wouldn't have believed it myself. I say this because *now* I know, and it seems natural to me to feel them all here, with me.

It is true that I did not know it before—as no one informed me or told me. Neither the wind, nor the sea, nor the celestial vault that surrounds us. The knowledge came to me by realizing all this with my experience—as in, "you had to be there," to understand. When I decided to unravel past stories and when I discovered that not only do we inherit the biological, but that we also inherit thoughts, dreams, longings and, above all, the Love.

Before I opened my big mouth and scattered the diamonds of my soul on the frame of this window that divided us, Mappy, as sane and normal as can be, just answered while laughing, "With more than ninety relatives." And she added mischievously while looking intently and me and softening her voice, "Some in spirit."

I remember that the customs agent had looked behind us as if looking for more people and smiled thinking it was a joke. The smile I gave back to him was worthy of my grandmother Chela.

I mentally deliberated whether it would be a good choice to reveal the truth to this professional. The young man with the starched shirt and doubtful expression would have thought I had a screw loose. I decided to remain calm and quiet. He looked and made sure, relieved, that there were indeed *not* ninety people behind us and went on with his work of noting down the number of passengers we were. Meanwhile, behind my right shoulder was my dad. And behind my left shoulder, my mother. And behind him, standing in the same way, his parents. And so on with all the other ancestors. Their fathers and mothers who are my grandparents. I know that, if I move to the right, everyone in perfect formation moves with me to that side. Likewise, if I move to the left, all in coordination and in unison move to the left. A spiritual knowledge. The certainty that our ancestors accompany us at all times. And although he does not know it, he is also accompanied by his own! They are there, supporting him, providing him with truth and love if he wanted to receive it. All the strength of their lineage at his disposal—should he ask for it. Mine, with me—always with me. Mappy with her own—always with her own. Eternally.

On that flight we took together, we both felt how the energy and love accompanied us, for the almost empty plane felt full. We laughingly commented that the multitude of people we were walking with inside us was uncountable! We felt intoxicated with happiness, it couldn't be anything else, for we had only had water. Therefore, we recognized that something had taken hold of us and it had to do with the strength of union, love and enthusiasm. If I had suspected that family stories were uplifting, the proof was the feeling we carried with us as we landed. It was the first time I realized the impact of genealogical research and rescued stories. But right there, thousands of feet up in the air, I saw my cousin's beautiful dark eyes full of the question that surfaced time and time again.

"But did he abandon her or not?" Mappy's heart and hope were bent toward our beloved great-grandmother Bianca. And I didn't know if I was carrying the truth—not just yet.

When we landed at the airport, the first one we saw was Rosa and her family who had come to pick us up. She and Chelo had come with their children from Santiago to take us to the hotel. Carlos and Javier were teenagers.

"You don't know me, but I am your aunt," I said, hugging them. And they laughed with the fun that youth brings.

Mappy and I entered the central garden of the hotel, jumping happily into the arms of our dear people. The *peloterito* in the photo, our uncle Miguel Maltes, Ana's son, had grown to over six feet. Billito came running to hug us too. Others came and joined in the hug.

The garden was beautiful, full of flowers. From the balconies surrounding the rooms more family members came out to greet us. My sisters came down and we embraced happily. Fernando also came to greet us with his unique smile. We were all welcomed with open arms, it had been true all along, we were ninety relatives and some there in spirit!

That night, we spent the evening in an *enramada* on the shores of the sparkling blue sea of Playa Dorada. Music filled the place. We descendants enjoyed the sound of the sea and the band. The party lights adorned the coconut trees and looked like little stars dancing to the rhythm of our favorite melody, the merengue de *tambor y güira* (drum and güira merengue). Uncle Frank had hired a *Perico Ripiao*. Surely, our bare feet dancing in the sand made hermit crabs flee from their lair to avoid being crushed and fled at full speed to take refuge in the sea.

I already knew that we, the women of this family, are the bravest dancers. I knew it because when we arrived at the terrace, which was also the hotel's clubhouse, most of them were already on the sand moving to the musical notes. As soon as I could, I joined a group of cousins. Uncle Moncho's daughters, whom I had only seen in pictures when they were little and today, they were hugging me happily, without missing a beat. Mappy also joined us, this is what we had come for! There was no time to lose! I'm sure, if they let us, we would dance until dawn. I realized that the Imbert cousins had asked more than one of us to dance and that whoever sat down was liable to be asked to move again before long. The women of this family were dancing with great rhythm. And this joke of not letting the men or anyone else sit down made us all laugh. Yvonne, cheerful and beautiful like her mother, was in the lead. Then, she met me with her gaze. Without speaking or missing a beat, she waved me over with her hands. Tacitly, we agreed to ask our uncles, Frank and Fernando, to dance.

Uncle Frank was farther away, sitting with some cousins near the table where the food was. He was making hand gestures and laughing. Meanwhile, Uncle Fernando was at a table talking with Aunt Pilar and other couples. I saw Yvonne go ahead toward Frank. I went toward Fernando, inviting him to dance. I knew it was going to be difficult to convince him to move his skeleton and join the dance in the arena. He only dances accompanied by Aunt Pilar. Unlike Frank...who even dances in commercials!

Anyway, I thought it was nice to play along with Yvonne and give it a try. Amused, my uncle and aunt looked at me when I approached because they guessed my intentions! To please me and play along for a minute, Colorao got up from his chair like a gallant young man, took my hand and gave me a twirl. I responded with laughter because he was smiling with a half-smile that one never forgets.

My dear Aunt Pilar is of singular beauty. Her eyes are large, penetrating and full of light and life. She has a wide and captivating smile. At that moment, as I was close by, she took my hand and said into my ear,

"Your mom was one of my great loves." She touched her heart, filling mine with tenderness. With a wave of gratitude inside me, I took advantage of the fact that our cheeks were brushing and I answered her tenderly,

"Thank you, my beautiful aunt!"

In return, I received a kiss on my face.

Yvonne motioned for me to join the line that had formed behind Uncle Frank. He loves to laugh and is inexhaustible. If it were up to him, the party would never stop. Moving with rhythm, he would make each person he passed stand up and dance with him. He called them by name with his characteristic loudly coarse voice. The line of cousins was very long; we all laughed. When we reached the center, he took his beloved Haydée by the waist and gave her a twirl. As part of the celebration, we all made a circle around this adored couple and clapped rhythmically. They looked at each other smiling; they knew they were complicit in this joy. Frank and Haydée were the organizers of this reunion and the ones who lit the flame of love, happiness and magic of this meeting.

The descendants of Isidoro and Bianca had grown up in different countries, and we had been separated for a long time. But, at that moment we were all the same, as if we were all of the same age, contemporaries of one heart. Our grandparents who were brothers and sisters had protected and supported each other amidst so many tragedies. Now they had inspired us to come together so that we could create memories.

NEW MEMORIES

*T*he plan for Saturday morning was to meet in the central garden of the hotel in Playa Dorada. From there, we would embark on our journey to the *Callejón de Doña Blanca* for its inauguration. We would hold a ceremony, take pictures and listen to family stories.

I left my room on the second floor to walk down the hallway-balcony to the garden. A door opened and I was greeted by Josemaría, who with her wide smile and olive eyes, held out her hand for us to go together. From each door that opened, a beloved family member joined us—imagine that! Cousins joined us with hugs and pleasantries like, "Good morning, darling!" or "What a beautiful day!" Together we all went down the white stairs and entered the garden. We found our Uncle Frank and Aunt Haydee and their son Frank Elias sitting on benches adorned with large and beautiful green leaves. These leaves are called "elephant ears" because they curl up as if they were listening.

After greeting them, I looked around for Uncle Fernando, but he was still not there. My mission was to take the opportunity to talk to him about genealogy and tell him about the new documents that I had organized in the Family Book and thus, to enliven his imagination and listen to picturesque comments with which he painted each document. Luis Manuel, the eldest brother on his mother's side, greeted us all and immediately began to tell stories of his childhood with a style of his own but just as endearing and engaging as Fernando's. With his humor, he infected all us nephews and nieces. I was fascinated trying to remember the childhood anecdotes he was sharing to later write about them. Then my cousin Frank Elias approached me.

"Uncle Colorao tells me that you have dedicated yourself to genealogical research...that you have been rescuing and compiling family histories."

I looked up and felt an immediate affinity. I admit it's like that with anyone who talks to me about genealogy. My cousin was a handsome man in his thirties and, resembling Uncle Frank in his youth with his head of black hair. He wore a short beard on this occasion and his eyes seemed eternally noble and as frank as his name.

"That's right. What did he say?" I was a little astonished by his comment, for I did not know who else in the family was fond of genealogy. Now I understand that the love of our ancestors envelops us all. The love that flows from the family tree takes any excuse to bond us. In our case, I thought his interest was about Bianca and her story. About all the peculiarities of the inherited stories, I asked him which family story had caught his attention or aroused his interest the most.

"It's the one about Bianca's abandonment, isn't it?" I assumed.

I was surprised when he answered, "I have also been attracted by family stories, but not by the abandonment from Bianca's point of view, but by Great-Grandfather Isidoro. Because I think there is something else to know. I have been looking in Colombia..." He told me something he knew about that city.

"Well, I have found something in New York." I nodded thoughtfully as the pages inside the envelope came to my mind. The one that I had read that was still scratching my soul, waiting for corroboration at the slightest opportunity. Suddenly it was the only thing I had in my head. As if everything had disappeared and only that white envelope remained floating in the center of my mind. Sealed.

Open it and tell him. He'll know what to do.

I was about to speak and tell him about the letter resting within the pages of the Family Book, but suddenly, a space opened up in front of us and Uncle Fernando appeared, dressed in a white suit and sporting a Panama Hat. Next to him, and very beautiful, Aunt Pilar matched his attire wearing a similar style dress. They looked like two movie stars from another era—a radiant couple!

"They're here!" said the nephews and nieces clapping their hands.

"They arrived!" His older brother shouted at Luis Manuel, "And it looks like he's just back from filming the movie Casablanca!"

"And what panache!" added Uncle Frank "Not even Humphrey Bogart wore a hat with such a style!"

"I don't know if that's Humphrey Bogart, but I do know that's Ingrid Bergman," replied Uncle Luis Manuel.

The jokes between the brothers seemed to me like amusements that took them back to their childhood. Uncle Fernando, undeterred and with a mischievous smile, raised an eyebrow as if to express that he was the one who was in order and in accordance with what the act required. For a moment he looked aloof, frowning like a big celebrity at the attention, then his lips burst onto a broad smile.

"And now, the whole cast, I mean, everyone in the family, wants to have a hat like that!" The nephews and nieces commented amidst applause and laughter.

Uncle Fernando broke his pose and came to greet and hug us all, with Aunt Pilar always at his side.

"Are we all here?" Uncle Frank asked, getting up and starting to walk.

I think that, in this garden, we were more than ninety family members dressed in afternoon clothes, joyful and holding hands, divided into groups.

We boarded the two buses. At the head of the first was Uncle Frank. And in the second one, Uncle Fernando. When we were all seated, the latter moved parallel to ours with its loud engine rumbling. Some gossip floated through the windows. Rosa caught it and brought us the report.

"They say that they have it better because they are serving champagne and chocolate. It's better over there! They ask what *you* have for this group?"

Uncle Frank's answer was followed by his laughter. "Don't believe it. It's a prank."

. . .

"THEY WANT TO MAKE US ENVIOUS!" someone else added.

As always happens in this family, everyone started to give their opinion at the same time.

"Let them show us! I don't see anything! They are bluffing."

"Because the sisters all had snub noses except Aunt Chela. All of them on that bus resemble Mafalda's grandchildren!"

"Uncle Frank," I jumped in. "Tell the driver to leave them behind and get lost!"

"That's the hat's fault!"

"I want one!"

We were laughing until our bus started moving ahead. At the head, Frank stood next to the driver and took a microphone to narrate the family stories.

"Isidoro and Bianca were married in Bogotá. Still newlyweds, they decided to return to Italy to live in Bologna. The year was 1898. They were carrying their first baby, Isidorito, when the ship stopped in Puerto Plata. My grandfather liked the place enough to establish a hotel. So, a few years later, the grandparents returned to work first on the Hotel Europa and ended up buying it! And they followed that with the Hotel del Comercio in Puerto Plata and the Grand Hotel Rainieri in Santiago, which was the old Hotel Central, the one in front of the park."

From the back, someone asked something that I didn't hear, but Frank answered.

"The children of Isidoro and Bianca were growing up separated between Bologna and Puerto Plata. The ones who grew up in Bologna were Isidorito, Blanquita, Beatriz, Queco and Mafalda. Yolanda was born in Puerto Plata, but as a child she also lived in Bologna for a while. In 1911, when Chela and Mayu, the twins, were about to be born in Puerto Plata, their mother sent for the older siblings to come and help with the youngest children. However, they left Queco and Mafalda, who were five and seven years old, behind because they were too young. Besides, they were already used to Italy and wanted to stay in Aunt Maria's care. There they grew up with their cousins as if they were siblings. I think the grandparents' intention was to let them finish their studies in Bologna before joining them here in Puerto Plata."

The bus made a turn, causing the engine to shudder. We were heading towards the *Malecon* to roll down the avenue that borders it. Uncle Frank continued to tell us about his father.

"They stayed living at Aunt Maria's house, the grandmother of the cousins we have in Italy."

As the wheels of the buses rolled down Malecon avenue, he paused in his narration. We all turned our eyes to the horizon. We were fascinated to see the clarity of the sky and the sparkling waves. It had been years since I had seen the sea to the north of our island and I felt a great emotion. The avenue was lined with palms and coconut trees, but the beach grapes were my favorite. These small trees are not afraid of the rocks and grow in front of the sea as if they want to touch it with their branches and their leaves look like crushed apples. They have that strong green color that later turns orange and yellow as if they were trying to compete with the colors of the sun. More than one comment of admiration came out of the mouths of the cousins. "Look at this beautiful land!" "How lucky you are to enjoy this view whenever you want!"

We turned and headed away from the sea and into the center of town. We kept asking questions because we wanted to know more of the family stories. Yvonne was interested in her grandmother Yolanda. Uncle Frank listened attentively and answered her over the microphone for all of us to hear.

"The first of the daughters to marry was Yolanda; she married Manuel. The family history tells that when she left for Bologna for a year or two, to go with Blanquita to fetch their younger siblings, Manuel had remained very much in love here in Puerto Plata. Manuel and Yolanda's love affair had begun when they were fifteen years old. As her grandmother did not like these adolescent romances, she sent her to Bologna so that she could forget about this fantasy. Actually, she sent both sisters with the idea was that once Queco and Mafalda finished their studies, they would all return from Bologna to Puerto Plata to live here permanently. During the year and a half that Yolanda was absent for her trip, her lover was waiting for her. Then, when Yolanda, Blanquita, Queco and Mafalda were arriving on the boat...oh, here comes the most romantic and funny part of the story! They say that when the ship was arriving, bringing his beloved Yolanda, Manuel, desperate to see her, came up with the idea of getting on a small boat and having them take him to the anchored ship. Manuel jumped on board and searched for her among the passengers."

My imagination was running rampant. I could see Manuel, managing to get a ride on one of those little yolas to get close to the ocean liner. Everyone on the gunwale had seen him arrive. He got on, and in his exuberance, hugged and kissed her while all the passengers cooed and applauded.

On the bus, Frank pointed to the place where the old port was located, past the Fortress of San Felipe, "Meanwhile, there in the harbor, my grandmother was waiting for the passengers to disembark without having any idea of the boldness of this young man in love. Bianca, standing on the dock and in the crowd, spotted her children coming down the steps of the ship. Suddenly, she noticed that, among the passengers there was...Manuel! And...with Yolanda! Both of them giggling and joined arm in arm!"

We all laughed, enjoying the anecdote.

He continued. "You can imagine my Nonna's face. She almost fainted! And thinking that Manuel had traveled with them or that her daughter's virtue was at stake...she took them to a church and married them!"

I imagined the lovers arriving at the parish, dragged by Bianca, who made furious gestures with her arms and explained to the parish priest what had happened. Holding hands, the two lovebirds kept looking at each other and were happy to be together after a few years, completely oblivious to the chaos their love was causing. The priest, resigned, ended up putting on his cassock; he took out the wine to give them the host and blessed their union in the name of God.

The bus turned again in the direction of the center of town, passing through streets of houses painted light blue and pink with triangular roofs and romantic crossbeams.

"Look how pretty that little Victorian house is!" we said to each other, pointing to particular buildings as the transport moved along.

"And look at this one!"

There was a little house painted pink that I loved. It looked like something out of a fairy tale. The gothic-romantic style buildings in Puerto Plata were very famous. They had remained intact for over a hundred years. The mountain, which is now called "Isabel de Torres" and used to be full of *yagrumos,* together with the shape of the bay constituted a protection against hurricanes.

I had the joy of seeing small old houses more than one hundred and fifty years old, with their elaborate wooden balconies and uniquely designed transoms that had been hand carved by crafts-men. From between their slits, they let in the breeze while adorning the tops of the doors and the facades of the windows. And so, admiring the little houses of this Victorian village, we arrived at the square.

THE FAMILY

$\mathcal{W}$e stopped in front of the central plaza of Puerto Plata. Long before sunset, when the sky was still the same shade of blue as one of the cozy little houses we had passed. We got off and walked towards the central gazebo. It was here that I remembered my grandmother Chela as if she were standing next to me...she told me that every Sunday she and her siblings would visit the plaza to enjoy the music. My mind was filled with melodies and dancing until a male voice burst in and dispelled my memories. It was the photographer and his assistant, who, armed with big cameras and lights, called each group of descendants by their grandfather or grandmother's name: Yolanda, Queco, Mafalda, Chela, Mayu and Ana.

"Queco's descendants, gather here!"

The photographer pointed to the gazebo. The assistant in charge of the lights followed him. Frank and Fernando's groups, with their respective families, moved to pose. Then, the photographer continued to call out to those who remained, enlisting the help of the cousins.

"Chela's, now, here? Yolanda's, here, and Mafalda's, there."

Some of the family members obeyed the orders... But not all of them!

"No, that's not Yolanda's. They're pulling your leg! That's Mafalda's. What's she doing in that group?"

Typical of the Harpers! They started joking around pretending to be someone in a group that wasn't theirs and confusing the professional. I was standing next to Johnny and posing with the Mafalda's when my sister Gina called me out to me.

"You think you're Mafalda's, but you belong to Chela. Come back here!"

At the end, we were laughing and passing each other from group to group. In closing, we all took a picture together under the church.

Later, I stood next to Uncle Frank and listened to him talk about the family heirlooms and who we were at that moment as a family.

"And all that we have been through, which is a lot, is in our DNA."

"I think that, now, each one of us is stronger because they went through what they went through," I added to his comments.

"That's right! And after Isidoro, it didn't take so long to lose the oldest son in 1918," Uncle Fernando concluded.

"Yes, we lost Isidorito to the virus called Spanish influenza. It must have been hard for her!

"He was a real support..." added Uncle Fernando. "Not six years after Isidoro left...and suddenly, her oldest son is gone too! Do you know what that must have been like?"

"That's why *Nonna* had such a strong character." Uncle Frank was always ready to defend his grandmother. "Back then, being left alone with her daughters wouldn't have been like being left alone now. After all, as strong as they were, they were young women who didn't have a male to represent them. My dad was still in Italy. She was the mother hen defending her chicks—she had to be strong! She had to assert herself and be emotionally and socially unbreakable. And she did not need anyone's endorsement nor did she crumble before what destiny had prepared for her. It was not in her plans to be vulnerable. She, who was delicate in appearance and short in stature, made herself an unshakable frame and took on the presence of a giant.

"At a time when women did not vote or have a chance to rule, and when they most likely did not even inherit, she was a shrewd businesswoman!" Uncle Fernando added.

We started walking towards the plaza to take the buses back to the hotel. I followed in their footsteps.

"Why does the idea of running a hotel jump from one generation to another?" I wanted to bring up the subject that was my greatest curiosity. "The idea jumped over your dad and landed on you."

I would have liked to ask him the question in a more direct way. Talk to him about "inherited dreams," the idea that kept dancing in my mind, but it was the only thing I could think of at the time. Did Uncle Frank inherit this dream of becoming a hotelier because of some influence from Isidoro? Maybe it was a dream of dreams. Maybe it was a dream borrowed...from Isidoro! At least, that's what I wanted to suggest. Or perhaps, it was nothing like that, but rather as he grew older, he heard some anecdote that intrigued him. As I could see that Uncle Frank was still thinking about it, I added, "From your grandparents directly to you."

He finally answered. "Look, I can't say that from the beginning I was planning to be a hotelier under any circumstances. For whatever reason, after the Hotel Europa closed with the death of my grandmother, no one in the family ever talked about a hotel again. My generation, which is your mom's generation, it didn't cross our minds. That's understandable. You realize that all the sisters had to make sacrifices in their youth and take on a thousand tasks from an early age. In other words, they had adult responsibilities from the time they were very little. Perhaps, the daughters, seeing that their other friends in society had a comfortable life, that they danced and walked in the park, and had it easy. Meanwhile Bianca's daughters were working. So I'm sure a light went on and they decided *not* to follow on in this so sacrificing business. I remember as a child listening to the aunts talking about their childhood. They said that Grandma Blanca divided up the chores: *"You, the cleaning. You, attending the reception. You, cleaning up the dining room."* Mafalda was spared because she was with Queco in Bologna and Yolanda was able to avoid that fate for the couple of years when she traveled to Bologna, but the others were teenagers when all of this happened!"

"Grandfather and Grandmother were demanding. It was the doctrine of the house they had to follow until they got married," added Uncle Fernando.

"They were not treated as less because they were women. They had instilled in them a love of work. Later, they all contributed to their husbands' businesses. Your grandmother Chela worked in Uncle Joaquin's movie theater business."

I nodded and Fernando spoke, "And Grandma didn't just maintain that stoic and strong personality in the business, it was part of her entire life. She was close friends with Castellano, a famous anti-Trujillo priest in Puerto Plata, and she used to go to him for confession. She would walk to mass with her daughters. People commented, "Here come the Italians. The mother in front and all the daughters behind, in line." They would sit on the first bench on the left side. It was Doña Blanca's bench. If anyone dared to sit there, when she arrived, she would touch them with her cane and order them out. Whoever did not want to be embarrassed, had better respect her space!"

We laughed at this anecdote. Uncle Frank explained, "She had to be a formidable character by force. Maybe not in her youth, but her children have memories of her as a widow. It was part of a defense mechanism she had to create for her and her family's safety. Her reputation could not be derailed, nor could someone be allowed to think it could be derailed. She needed to be unshakable, and so she was!"

Tio Fernando added a comment. "The story goes that when grandma would go to the Union Club in Puerto Plata where the older daughters would go to dance, she would sit with them. When a gallant gentleman tried to approach the girls, she would look him up and down. With the cane she would give signals. If she didn't like the boy, she'd order with the cane, "Turn around!"

We listeners were all fascinated by the anecdotes.

I asked, "Uncle Frank, when you started the business, your dad...Queco...would he have claimed it was his parents' dream? No?"

Shaking his head, he answered, "Mom said it on occasion, but Dad didn't. As far as I remember, he mentioned it only once. It was when we inaugurated Club Med. He was with mom, Colorao, Pilar, Haydée and I. We already had the children. I remember that when the ceremony was over, Dad turned to look at me and said, "Well, the family tradition continues!"

I wanted to go deeper and murmured to him with intent, "Uncle Frank, I believe you inherited this dream, the one from your ancestors.. the dream of being a hotelier."

"Ha ha!" He laughed and added, "Sometimes when I think about it, my grandmother comes to mind. But I can't say I did it on purpose or that I had the idea from a young age. It was little by little that the vision was born in me. Now, I tell you, it was impossible to say no to that vision—impossible! It wasn't that I had the certainty from the beginning or that I knew the magnitude—not at all. It was simply that I couldn't stop it! It occupied my whole mind. Can I tell you that I loved that vision from the beginning? Yes, of course I did! And I still didn't know much about the future or where it could lead me. But I did feel that I had to strive day by day. Step by step, doing what I had to do on that day and without much thought...holding on to the vision."

As the sun's rays began to lower and the city lights came on, we walked down the street together. We followed Uncle Frank who was walking hand in hand with Aunt Haydée and Uncle Fernando with Aunt Pilar, just as they always do. For the first time, we saw the monument to our great-grandmother. The alley was freshly painted and full of flowers. Although it was long, we were all crowded together and close to the plaque with Bianca's photo.

Uncle Frank continued to relay more anecdotes before cutting the ribbon. "I tell you one more story. I want you to know the intensity of her integrity. And I want you to take with you the love with which I see her."

Then he told us, during the time of Trujillo, when Bianca was already called Doña Blanca and she only had one hotel and Isidorito had already died, a man arrived with a bloody shirt asking to be accommodated. It was night and she had already retired to her room when they called her to tell her about the situation. She went out to see the man who had just arrived. There were rumors of a massacre somewhere, but what had happened was not clear at the time. But she recognized him and refused him entry. The man tried to defend himself; claiming he was just doing "the boss's work", which was what they called the dictator. Doña Blanca replied: "I know that you work for a murderer. And just as he is, so are you. Go away, murderer, go away now! This is a hotel, but it is also MY home and therefore a family home. And we don't accept ASSASSINS here."

We were shocked by this story, and even more shocked to learn that this legacy was within us, in our genetic information! It is the strength and mettle of the women who make it up and that includes the love and support of our men. How could Isidoro not love a woman like that? A woman of fierce love and a clear mind. An autonomous, sovereign and dignified woman. A woman who belongs to all of us and is inscribed in our DNA.

Uncle Frank cut the silk ribbon and we all applauded enthusiastically and felt special for being descendants. Soon, a line formed so that everyone could get a closer look at the photo and plaque that were on the wall inaugurating the space. I took my place and when my turn came in front of the picture surrounded by flowers, I read the copper metal inscription and admired the image. I was surprised when I realized what was happening. Would it be crazy to say that I felt that she was watching me from another dimension?

I had come prepared to reopen the New York letter and finally determine her whereabouts and her death. To tell "what happened." Or, rather, what I thought had happened. My cousin Frank Elias' voice reverberated in my head with his "I never believed it." Remembering his words from that morning filled my body with chills. "It wasn't like that." We had both felt it, each in turn. This made me confirm that I had to read the document in front of everyone. I would lay out what I had found before all the descendants and together we would decide what to do with that information.

THE FATE OF ISIDORO

*T*hat night I arrived at the party with the book stored in a white box that I left on a table. After dinner, dancing and enjoying ourselves, Uncle Frank stood in the arena in front of everyone. He spoke to us as the head of the family.

"People ask me, 'What is the key to success and happiness?' The answer is family. That is the greatest success of a person. The union of the family is fundamental to the joy of every human being. I am happy to have you gathered together today to celebrate family and legacy."

We were all moved by his words. He continued.

"I have the conviction that a united family is the source of happiness. In every family meeting we have, this truth is expressed. I often sit with the young people. I love to listen to them, to hear the stories of their worlds, their opinions, their ways. I get about ten years younger! Thank you all for coming, young and young at heart! Thank you dear family members for responding to this call! A call to recognize and thank our ancestors, especially Grandmother Bianca, who, left alone, raised her family with admirable courage and strength. This is something that has marked the Rainieri descendants. The family has gone through pandemics, abandonment and loss. She had young daughters. She was a foreign entrepreneur, a hotelier, a sacrificial business. No tragedy was obstacle enough to raise the whole family and instill values, principles. She kept them all on two continents until they were united and practically created a legend around them, always looking with confidence to the future and with great faith in God! Today let us give thanks for the good and the not so good. Let us be grateful for everything. Let us learn from our predecessors. For the sake of the *Nonna*, let us keep our principles and values. Let us look at life with optimism and give thanks to God. May the family continue this legacy, I love you very much and God bless you!"

His words turned that moment into something very special. As if stars of blessings appeared to cover us all. A soft breeze came in from the sea and those of us who were close by held hands or leaned on the shoulders of our elders.

And so, under the starlight that matched the colored bulbs hanging from the coconut trees, I found myself standing next to Uncle Frank, barefoot on the cold, fine sand that felt like cloud dust. Wearing my white cotton dress and with the box containing the book in my hands, I approached him. He was also barefoot and wearing white pants and a linen jacket. He had the microphone in his right hand. He looked at me with a surprised expression. In front of everyone, I placed my gift in his hands...without reverence, even though I knew I was holding a treasure. Together we opened the pages of the Family Book to discover its richness. Until that moment, I myself was unaware of the immense value of this compilation. Unbeknownst to them, this book also contained the whereabouts of our Isidoro, but before we got to it, we saw the photos from Mami's album that they had never seen. One was the picture of his dad, Queco, that my grandmother had kept and cherished.

Uncle Frank's eyes stopped on his dad's picture and his hands touched the edge. Queco was posed like a movie actor and looked so much like him, as if he had cloned himself! His very expression. A portrait of his father I had never seen before.

Passing the pages, I kept explaining each document to him like it was a precious jewel. Each page I turned, I unfolded a document decorated with Florentine paper.

"This is beautiful," he said, and I was touched. I didn't know how to tell him that every finding in this research began with a hunch, or rather, a heartache.

"How did you make such a beautiful book?" asked some of the cousins.

"I'm a nerd," I answered, laughing, addressing them all. The group burst out laughing.

Some descendants were sitting in the chairs at the tables and others were listening while standing. Suddenly, someone raised a voice to the defining question, "What happened to Isidoro?"

From among the , without decoration or anything, I took out the envelope containing the death certificate I had received in 2001.

I remembered the day that letter arrived in my mailbox from the New York City Health Office. I had opened it and was surprised, for it was the death certificate of a certain Isidoro in New York, who had died on July 3, 1912. I agreed to go to investigate and corroborate if he was our Isidoro. But first the Twin Towers fell and then Mami's illness prevented me from doing so. We still did not know for sure if Isidoro was buried in New York or not.

Now we were together in 2008...again, opening the time-sealed envelope. Only, this time, Uncle Frank was in front of me and, all around us were the fixed eyes of the descendants not wanting to move. They were expectant. When I peeled back the flap of the envelope, even the sea swaying behind us was silent. I think even the tiny grains of sand, snails and starfish paid attention. I began to read it slowly. A few borrowed memories took hold of me, drop by drop at first, then the images flowed forth as a deluge, a torrent of shapes, colors, and sounds.

Isidoro disembarking in New York, lining up at immigration with the small suitcase that was his promise...up the hill, out the threshold of the port designation and into the city. Days later, he was visiting a hospital in New York City.

As I read aloud, I let the images flow because it was impossible to stop them. It was a completely visceral reaction. My mind was filled with memories of light and shadow, of voices and silence. I saw him sitting in the hospital bed, dressed in a patient gown after undergoing several tests, perhaps x-rays, and waiting for his diagnosis. The next image was a scene with a doctor standing in front of him, explaining what he was reading in his file.

I thought about that image. *Was he a new patient or had he been there before? Where could his medical history be found?*

Then, when he was alone, Isidoro leaned back against the back of the metal bed. He wanted to rest for a second. To think about what the medical professional had just proposed. The pillow was hard. The cleanliness of the room left something to be desired. The noise of the construction next door distracted him for a moment with the "tap tap tap" of the hammers reminding him of the sound of a clock. He asked the doctor for time, a few minutes alone to think, during which, however, he stared out the window into the void. Between the rectangle of the window and the heavy, stiff curtains, the thought crossed his mind that he had embarked to seek help for his pain, when life had ambushed him and made him doubt his decision. As he traveled on the ship, nothing hurt... and now, he was to undergo an operation? If everything went well, it would be quick. It would just be a matter of healing in New York and, in a couple of weeks, once he had recovered, to return home to the hotel management—back to Bianca. The doctor had conveyed to him that everything was so simple, but life had taught him that nothing is.

He remembered the hotel, his work, his plans. He even remembered that something as simple as the last order he placed for the big party at the hotel restaurant had triggered a problem. A glitch in the process. Until then he had had good luck because he had taken care of things in good time and planned everything with enough time to spare. According to him, everything had been solved and he had personally settled the matter with customs. He was an expert at solving things! More than once he had heard his father say to his brother and him, *"Don't stop to worry, just take care of it!"* To each son he would give the right advice according to his personality. He felt his father's eyes on him, eyes filled with pride and love. Although he was the youngest in the house, he had always been confident that his personality was such that he would solve everything.

Isidoro realized that he was remembering something from his childhood that had been lost in his memory. His father's words resonated with him. "There is time to work and time to be with the family. With your health and strength you will have time to enjoy yourself too. Work hard and treat yourself. There is no time to waste." If only his father could see him now! Isidoro, with his tenacity and good humor, organized and with clear goals, had advanced with a lot of effort. He was in charge of every aspect every managerial aspect of his business. Almost everything had depended on him until he met Bianca. Then, life has become the work of a team. With her by his side, he could accomplish everything.

But this operation was different. The surgery was in the hands of someone else. A surgeon he had never seen before. A doctor that had been recommended at a party and between spirits served in colorful glasses, a colleague in Puerto Plata had told him, "This surgeon is an eminence!" Confident with such a reference, he embarked and arrived here, to this private clinic and this doctor who, after examining him and doing an X-ray session, had recommended surgery.

Of course! A surgeon recommends surgery. A therapist recommends therapy. A shoemaker recommends a type of shoe. Everyone recommends what they know, he thought.

At that moment, he made the decision to leave the hospital and go back to his family; to return to Puerto Plata. He had come so far. He thought he was right to be suspicious of everything. An operation? He was already feeling fine! He got up, took his clothes from the rack and took off his hospital gown.

Now dressed, he looked out a third-floor window at New York City. Before going out and putting on his hat, he looked in the mirror and noticed a few silver flecks in his once completely dark hair. As he always had a swirl that made a rebellious lock of hair fall on his forehead, he tried to pull it back for the umpteenth time in his life. He thought of Bianca, and of his children separated on two continents...of the trips he still had to take. Of the food and drink imports from Spain and France that he sourced for his customers with great pride. He had other plans for life! Plans to go further and see just how far he could go. To focus his life further. To extend it and enjoy his family and the effort he had achieved...someday.

Someday...

The surgeon had made him a promise. According to him, with the operation he could end the pain once and for all. "Operating is an everyday thing for me. The anesthesia will help you with the suffering. You are a strong man; recovery will be quick," the doctor told him.

Trust him, trust science, and trust medicine. But he felt fine now. He had improved along the journey. Thinking about it for a moment, he confirmed that the boat trip always felt great. And he was determined to get home. All he needed was to leave and get home to Bianca and his children. Perhaps it was time to reunite the whole family on one continent, and, if possible, to gather them all under the same roof and in the same house. That would be best.

But a new ailment intervened, a pain in the abdomen on the left side that split him apart. He decided to have surgery.

Once again he was dressed in a hospital gown. Now the doctor was in a hurry and had arranged everything to perform the surgery in the morning before the patient got cold feet. The patient was urged to relax. He debated in his mind whether he should write a letter to Bianca in case something happened. Wasn't that a bit unlucky? Better to trust in divinity. After all, his life had been full of wonderful surprises. He had been healthy and never tired of hard work. Moreover, his last years had been filled with success. He decided to think about this. He remembered the last celebration they'd had. He'd had the joy of organizing meetings in the hotel restaurant. In addition, he had managed to find and bring the best wines and spirits from Europe and ended up as banquet manager of the Masonic temple where his presence was always welcome. He had been praised as a refined and cultured man of impeccable taste and pleasant conversation. The last time he had been in the temple before this trip, he had been greeted with a warm welcome and dismissed with great wishes for success and early return by the companions.

His belongings rested on the table next to him: his watch, his clothes carefully chosen and neatly folded for the trip. He sat on the bed to wait for the nurse to arrive. The window was open, letting in the heat of the summer. He felt overwhelmed by the temperature; he was on the third floor and the building next door was under construction. The dust, the hustle and bustle, the cars, and the midday sun all seemed to be conspiring against him to make him feel worse. Everything hurt.

Minutes later, the stretcher was rolling down the half-lit corridor. The walls were wide, however, as he was lying down, it seemed as if they wanted to come together to pounce on him. He wondered if it was a good decision not to have left Bianca a note. A letter...something. But he didn't want to worry her in her condition. The first letter would arrive perhaps with the second where he would say that everything had turned out well. For a moment, he had felt like he was missing something, like he was leaving something undone. There was no turning back now. The stretcher ride took forever; the wheels squeaked and turned. It lasted a couple of interminable minutes that, paradoxically, passed quickly at the same time. The doors of the operating room opened and gave way to a large room with a central light that hung over and encompassed everything. There were several lamps on either side of the surgeon and his assistant. Both had their mouths covered and their hands washed with alcohol. He could smell the pungent odor of chemicals. He did not allow himself to become dizzy when he saw the nurse approaching with the syringe. It was full. *Enough to put a horse to sleep, was the thought that drifted through his mind.*

Another unfamiliar, feminine face approached his; it was the other nurse who had pushed the gurney. She rested her eyes on his. Although they were not like his mother's, he still remembered her and longed for those times when, as a child, she would come up to him to kiss him and lay him on his bed. But this person spoke to him in English and not in Italian.

"Very soon everything will be over and you will wake up like nothing happened," she assured him. She tried to smile to encourage him. Isidoro knew that she was not very experienced; she was very young and thought that with a few gentle words she could dispel his doubts and soothe his soul.

By now, he understood little and felt that he was leaving. The lamp had too much light and it bothered his pupils. Everything was beginning to look blurry. In that state, between sleeping and living, time was already meaningless. Sleep quickly enveloped him and, suddenly, he lost consciousness.

· · ·

MY MIND CAME BACK to the present. I was there, under the eyes of all the descendants, with the document unfolded in my hand. I looked up. My cousins were focused on me; whatever I read, it was going to touch their hearts.

I read the doctor's notes, *"I attended the patient on July 3"* in scribble he wrote it and now I know he was also a surgeon. "He signed it with a big squiggle," I said.

At the word squiggle, there were giggles, but soon silence returned. I read on. With all that I already knew of Isidoro and Bianca's life, it was as if I had met them personally. My heart was filled with a deep sorrow for my great-grandmother and for him because I knew of his desire to live on and return home. His end could not have been sadder!

I continued to describe the details aloud. *"Isidoro, age 52, residing in Puerto Plata, of Italian nationality, died of surgical shock on July 3..."* The age was wrong. I looked up to see them all, who were listening to me with genuine devotion. *"He was 56 years old when he sailed for New York."*

I didn't tell them that I was offended because the hospital workers clearly did not take down information well. I would have expected a little more from a private hospital in New York City in 1912! My suspicion was that, at the time, Isidoro would have been in severe pain and would possibly not been very coherent. As it happened to me, I have had two back surgeries and I know that pain can prevent you from speaking or responding coherently to questions asked by nurses and doctors. Sometimes, in those moments, the suffering monopolizes the mind and any question outside of that lacks logic.

With a sigh, I continued reading. "We are waiting for someone to come and pick him up..." This is noted on another line on the back of the document. From what I can gather, they waited for days without someone coming to claim it," I concluded.

Then, I looked at the bottom of the form on the lines below that also contained atrocious handwriting and showing it to Uncle Frank.

I added, "There you find the designation of the funeral home and the address with two names, but at first glance it is not understandable. It took me a long time to untangle this knot of letters and decipher what it says..."

I remember thinking that, if it was up to me to decipher, letter by letter, I would do it; perhaps I was entrusted with it. These names of people and businesses represented crucial data in genealogical research of this magnitude. But it was difficult. Two more dashes equaled a long name in a tiny square. It was impossible to understand its contents.

"What I suspect is that, at some point during that wait, his remains were cremated. So, look," I pointed to the corner where it was written. "This is the undertaker's information. Apparently, here in this scrawl it says, *Removed and buried on July 10.*"

To make a point, I said, "Seven days after death!"

I was indignant with the doctor as I raised an internal question to my great-grandfather, *What is the reason you put yourself in the hands of this matasano? Why did it have to be in New York?*

Years later, with the help of a friend, I was able to decipher the name of the doctor. This friend helped me with the death certificate, with the visualization of this and other documents, and with finding out from the doctor as much as possible about his life. For example, his surgeon was Cuban and that his first marriage had taken place in Cuba. Later he had his first wife declared crazy and sent her back there, all so he could marry the daughter of a colleague in New York. That much we could find out. But aside his personal life, what I wanted to know was how many more patients had died under his scalpel. To my disappointment (but the blessing of the world), I didn't find many, so I had to absolve him.

Also, my aunt Maria Filomena Barletta Rainieri, daughter of Mayu, my grandmother's twin, explained to us that she knew of a group of Masonic friends from Puerto Plata who had recommended this trip to New York to Isidoro to be treated for an illness he had. There were many such pieces of history in the family. Bits and pieces that had been left among descendants. All of this helped me to piece together the story.

A little less than a decade after this family reunion at which I was describing this event with the attention of all the relatives, I had a coup de grace. The photo of the private clinic where Isidoro had died appeared. Because the National Library of New York scanned and posted his old photos and hundreds of images of the city from the early 1900s and before, I was able to look at the photos that depicted the city at the time he had traveled. All of the professionally taken photographs of the city were displayed to the public on his website. They were wonderful black and white grainy memories of the buildings and old constructions that no longer exist today and some were replaced by skyscrapers.

One of the photographs posted by the library struck me as the most interesting. It was taken in 1911. It clearly showed a five-story private hospital building; I was almost one hundred percent sure it was the one that housed the private hospital where Isidoro ended up. It was noticeable in the photo that the adjoining building was under construction. That made me think of the dust on the floors, the echo of hammers and construction men that must have been heard from some points. Sharpening my eyes a bit to the details of this private hospital building, I noticed that if I zoomed in, I could see a sign that read something like , *"Horse stabling in the back."* This also gave life to my imagination, tinting the moment of his arrival at this hospital. But the most chilling thing about the photo was an almost ghostly figure that showed in some detail in the background. In one of the windows of a room on the highest floor, a person was observed. He was standing almost behind the white curtains. It was easy to deduce that it was a nurse the figure was wearing a bonnet. Behind the window frame and glass, she seemed to be looking out. I could tell she was watching the street. That faint image was creepy to me in the sense that she also seemed to be watching the camera. I felt the shiver run up my spine. I felt awe and fascination and let my imagination piece together the scene described above. Could it have happened like that? It will remain an unsettling and unknown. A restlessness that, now, thanks to the photograph, was reproduced again and remained crystallized as eternal.

FINAL QUEST

J did not share all the details and visualizations that went through my head, although I did feel that many sensed them and that they were all with me. When I read the last sentence, "We are waiting for them to come and get the body," I turned to look at Uncle Frank and said, "I think he died alone."

I saw in his eyes that my statement moved him. The room was silent. There was nothing more to add. Isidoro died alone, in New York, in a country that was not his own, without anyone to take care of his remains. And Bianca, without knowing point-by-point how it all happened. Those were other times, difficult situations. Perhaps the only thing that came true was destiny.

At that moment and as if driven by a decision, Frank Elias stood up and took his place in front of us. He asked the same question I had asked myself some years before.

"And where is he buried?" His eyes roamed over the paper in my hand.

Finding the cemetery had been a kind of puzzle, one that often felt like it had a thousand scattered pieces! After receiving the death certificate that I had in my hand, I started to look for where he would have been buried, because the document did not make this clear at any point. In the rectangle where the name of the cemetery should appear, there was a scribble with no logic! The doctor may have used his best handwriting but it rather resembled Picasso's. To put it more finely: it was my first exercise in paleography, a science that I didn't even know existed, let alone that there were people dedicated to its study. I almost went cross-eyed deciphering such a blot of ink. Receiving this certificate was by no means the resolution of the whole mystery. Knowing the cause of his death and not knowing where his remains rested kept the mystery open.

The next step was to decipher the hieroglyphically written name of the cemetery. At that time in 2001, Google did not autocorrect, so the search had to be spelled precisely, placing each letter in its proper position. As no matter how hard I rolled my eyes, I could not detect the first letter, but I could detect the letters that followed, so I pointed out two possibilities: The first letter would be followed by "enrico" or "ensico." I tried each letter of the alphabet in order: B, C, D... When I put the letter "K" before "ensico" and tried Google...I saw it!

Like with a sudden magic, Google returned an answer, "Kensico Cemetery and Shannon Gardens." I gasped in surprise—I had hit the nail on the head! I immediately clicked and found the information for a huge cemetery north of New York City.

The richness of the description of the place was not just anything. Located in Merrifield, it was also now considered a botanical tree garden or *arboretum* as well as a cemetery. Some celebrities are even buried there, such as the parents of the famous actor Robert De Niro, and for that reason tours are offered. Shannon Gardens, which is at one end of the property, is the burial ground of New York's Jewish Faith.

A letter of confirmation quickly was sent and I asked for more information. Since it was so long ago, had his remains, well, remained there? Or perhaps, if no one paid for the lot, would he had been, well, exhumed or placed somewhere else? What if by having no one coming to claim him, or pay for the space, perhaps he had been erased or forgotten?

Luckily for me, the following week I received a letter from the cemetery's director stating that Isidoro was buried there—in the oldest part of the cemetery. In addition, the director had kindly added a booklet with photos and details of how the place worked and, to my astonishment, a page at the end with a map of the cemetery's streets.

I related this whole saga in detail to Frank Elias. "The cemetery is called Kensico and is located on the outskirts of New York." I showed him the scribble where it said "Kensico" and went on to explain: "It's huge so I got a map of the territory showing me where his grave is located."

He looked up and asked me, "Have you gone?"

"No," I answered.

"Why not?"

A visual avalanche of reasons passed by the inner vision of my mind as I thought, *Wow, what a simple and loaded question!* Searching in my mind for the least complicated answer, I managed to mumble, "I haven't had the opportunity."

I thought I would add the missing details later. He turned to his dad and uttered the magic words.

"I'm traveling this week to New York."

I turned on my ear-to-ear grin as I celebrated in my thoughts, *Someone like me!* The second thing I did was to thank my innermost self for something so simple and yet so emotionally charged. I listened between father and son as they talked about the day, time and logistics. Had it been up to Frank Elias and had the Pegasus existed, he would not have hesitated to ride one!

"I left the information at home. I'll mail it to you as soon as I am back, on Monday, so you don't waste time."

He was captivated and touched his chin with one hand. Finally, he smiled and asked me, "Don't you plan to go?" Frank Elias seemed to assume I was going with him.

I couldn't because of personal commitments, including my son Alex's birthday, and work, so I shook my head. But he didn't have to wait any longer. I urged him to go right away.

"I'm sure it's part of destiny. Go! Isidoro is waiting for you."

He smiled and said, "I think Isidoro is waiting for you in New York." It was his subtle insistence. But he was determined, "I can go in a couple of weeks if that works better..."

I was thinking about the symmetry of the situation. A direct descendant of Bianca on the female side was giving the information to the direct descendant of Isidoro on the male side. It was like a representation of the two of them in a new consciousness, in the minds of two of their direct successors.

"Don't stop...you received the same calling as I did. This is what you must do for the family, for those of us who are here and for those who will come. To recognize this Isidoro as ours!"

My heart was filled with relief and infinite joy. Contemplating my cousin's expression, I knew he had the sensitivity to perceive the subtlety of things. We were witness to the change of the story and we both knew it. The mystery was about to end.

"When you arrive, present these death certificate documents to compare dates. When you confirm his grave, ask if there is anything else. Maybe there is an object stored somewhere, I don't know, a pocket watch, for example. I always thought Isidoro had one. Or something that someone left behind. And find out if there is any document that indicates who paid for his grave, who was the person who took his remains there...and if it was the undertaker himself, who made that payment...who was it?"

"Exactly," Frank Elias nodded. "Who buried him there? And why?"

"Oh, cousin! Don't forget to give me a description of the tomb, of the tombstone, of the material it's made of. Does it have a cross outlining it? I want to know who bought it...I want to know everything."

"Don't worry. I'll take care of it." And looking at my eager eyes, he added, "I'll take pictures and all."

I felt as if destiny had already mapped out that future moment of encounter.

I learned that when Frank Elias decides on something, he goes for it. And he had already decided he was going to make this happen! Father and son were quick decision makers. I thought it illustrated Isidoro's personality.

This encounter between ancestor and descendant would forever change the future of Isidoro's memory. I felt that I was going to find the true divine treasure.

"Come on, there's more to celebrate!" said my cousin, beckoning for me to go with him back to the party where our cousins where dancing or just having great conversation.

In a couple of days, when Frank Elias took flight, it would not be on a winged horse with a silver bridle, brandishing clouds or obstacles, as I imagined, but on a simple airplane. But maybe because I am myself my imagination easily overtakes me. I imagined him in an ultrasonic jet and on a direct trajectory, leaving behind a divine cloud of pink smoke that looked like cotton candy. The trajectory of a new future was mapped out for us. A future where there would be other new divine treasures.

The day he decided to travel, he wrote to me. He was about to leave. At that time, people did not chat by phone as they do now, but by email. Due to some inconvenience that I don't remember, I could not scan the letters with the map and describe it to him. I sent all this to him by email. So I did the best I could to describe it.

A few days later, he emailed back to tell me that he had left New York City for Myersville, north of Manhattan and past the Bronx, in search of the Kensico Cemetery. He informed me that, on that occasion, he was accompanied by a friend of his. He was a very funny and talkative man, who I understood was called Sultan. Later, I had a chance to meet him in person; he was a burly and handsome man who was very charming!

In that future when I met him, I asked him to recount with great detail the anecdote of their first visit to Isidoro's tomb when he went on that first scout with Frank Elias. Sultan did not make me beg and, with great pleasure, narrated and acted out the scene in amusing voices, including what each of the participants did and said, even the employees at Kensico. As I listened to him, I could not help but be fascinated with the vicissitudes of the feat. I was cracking up with laughter at everything he told me. Thanks to his eloquence and the magic of the details I could visualize Frank Elias, hero of the next story, and I could describe his face, his gestures and his laughter and thus, I built in my mind a novel episode in this love affair with our ancestors. Because so it was. Frank Elias did not hesitate, and the winds of destiny were in his favor to perform the ultimate feat of going after his great-grandfather, Isidoro. What follows is Sultan's account of their enjoyable adventure.

KENSICO CEMETERY

*T*hat morning, in the first week of September 2008 in New York, Sultan went to pick up Frank Elias in his black jeepeta. The license plate of the vehicle had only one word on it: "jefe". As I said before, he is a friend who accompanies and helps Uncle Frank's family when they go to New York. He told me that they drove across town until they found the northern highway. Then they followed a road that skirts the Hudson River on one side, and on the other, the countryside dressed in the first shades of autumn.

As they drove away from the skyscrapers of Manhattan, Sultan talked. The streets were narrow and curvy and enjoyed the warm, wooded summer that was about to end. He wanted to find out who this Isidoro was that Frank Elias was looking for. In his mind he wondered, *And what is this genealogy thing? Why is he looking for his great-grandfather? Why did this blessed great-grandfather pass away in New York City? Why didn't his people come for him sooner? Why this sudden interest? Why...?* Sultan seemed like a little child questioning everything while he made Frank Elias laugh.

"And so, this Isidoro..." Sultan began.

"He left Puerto Plata." My cousin answered.

"But it was a long time ago."

"One day in 1912, leaving Bianca alone..."

"And who is Bianca?"

"My great-grandmother, Isidoro's wife."

"And you're sure he didn't abandon her?"

Through the window glass, they could see the effervescent rapids of the Hudson. The road had a line of trees and bushes separating it from the river. The tame water that served as a mirror to the oak trees that, in September, dared to begin to change color timidly, their green paling slightly. Later, as autumn progressed, the greenish yellow would turn orange or bright red. Winter would sooth the trees to sleep, only to wake them up so they could be born again in spring.

"Isidoro went away and left your great-grandmother Bianca, pregnant. He disappeared..." Sultan was trying to understand.

"That's right," Frank Elias agreed. "But it wasn't that he left her on purpose. He...died."

Sultan pondered the information for a minute; then, questions poured out.

"And tell me something... why did he come to New York? Your great-grandfather, how did he end up here? How long has he been buried in that cemetery without the family knowing about it?"

"Since 1912," my cousin answered.

He was wearing sunglasses. The day was clear and warm, although the wind accompanied them and made them wink their eyes continuously.

"Almost a hundred years! Let's see, let me calculate... Ninety-four years buried and all that time without someone coming to pay the bill. Add to that the interest per year. That's going to be a lot of money! Did you bring your checkbook? They're going to be waiting for you with a bill the size of the cathedral. And don't laugh, I'm not joking! I'm warning you," continued Sultan in good humor. "Don't come to me asking for money, especially now, at the last minute!"

Frank Elias laughed but didn't find words to answer back. He continued to admire the oak trees on the road and the green grass on the side of the road. And he was distracted by the thoughts that wouldn't leave him alone.

What will I find after so long, after so many years lost to us without knowing his whereabouts?

But inside, he had the conviction that he was doing *the right thing.* That something big was happening with the *family angel*, probably rearranging the tree, making space for Isidoro back in the family again. Just as I had insisted.

"Isidoro...it's a very common name," Sultan finally said. But he didn't sound completely sure of his statement.

Frank Elias smiled again. He had never been so sure of anything.

"It has to be him. It's him," he affirmed.

"But how long has he been there, who has taken care of him in that cemetery? Has anyone paid anything? What happens if no one ever makes a payment?"

"That's part of what we don't know."

"Do you think he's still interred there? Who bought the lot? Who buried him so far away from home—did he have family here in New York?" Sultan insisted, talking almost to himself. The fascination of history and mystery had enveloped him too.

Amused by the conversation, but not paying much attention to Sultan's doubts, Frank Elias was fascinated by what he was about to discover and convinced that genealogy research was a complete adventure.

"We'll see, but I'm here to find it. That will be enough."

They both fell silent and continued their journey, admiring the route and what it offered in its path.

Sultan slowed down when he spotted the iron gate that bordered the cemetery grounds and he described everything he saw.

"Look! Look at all these dense trees, all this space...the entrance...the beautiful arches. I think this cemetery belongs to millionaires!"

Happy, Frank Elias smiled again.

"I still think you're going to get a bill. I'll ask again, did you bring your checkbook? Don't look at me like that, I'm not going to lend money to you," Sultan continued.

"Ha ha! Never mind."

"But I'm serious. You have to be prepared. Did you bring your credit card? What if they don't accept credit cards?"

My cousin could only laugh while his partner went on and on with his string of intrigues.

"They're going to catch you and charge you for the hundred years he's been buried here."

"Ha ha! We'll see!"

"I don't know why you people get into this business of looking for ancestors."

"Well, according to my cousin, we have to put in order the myths of our history so that we can heal the family spirit."

"I don't know what you're talking about. I only know that this cemetery is very impressive, that the office is not small, or rather, what you see on that hill in the distance is the office, but it looks like a mansion! So after you look at it and see, you can say that this ancestor, this Isidoro you have been looking for so long, and I admit I don't understand why, you can say he is not yours. Ready? I will support you. Your cousin will understand. No, really! Listen to me. It's an exit plan, just in case..."

"Ha, ha! Never. I'll never ever deny him."

"It's a good idea..." Think about it. "Yep. Think about it!"

"I'll never deny Isidoro. It would be to deny my roots, my history."

And then I think he said, *"Besides, I've got a cousin who'll give me a kick in the butt if I deny him."* Although I am not sure if he really said that.

Frank Elias had only the description of the map on which someone with a yellow marker and good will had marked number 25 for us. We didn't have a smart phone to pinpoint the exact location for us. Life was so different then!

The grove ended at the gates of the Kensico cemetery. The green grass was cut to perfection and the white marble tombstones were beginning to appear as rectangles of the same color among the flowering hills. Sultan stopped the cart at a quiet intersection to look around before continuing. Although there were no other car in the vicinity, they could not believe their eyes. The place was huge, with paths big enough they could be called streets! And there streets upon streets, crisscrossing like a small city. A few white crosses stood up, short and dignified. And on the corners were signs that seemed to indicate the names of the streets. The magnitude, power and beauty of the place left them speechless.

"This cemetery is huge. And it looks as neat as a silver cup. It must have been very expensive to bury him here. Are you sure?"

"I think the office is over there, in that group of buildings," Frank Elias said.

There were three buildings that looked like a country club because they were so big. Together they entered the office. Frank Elias introduced himself to a kind, grandmotherly-looking lady with short, silver hair in cute little curls. She was behind a wooden desk. He showed her the document with the information I had given him. The woman put on her glasses to read and examine what my cousin was handing her. She carefully read what it said.

"Where do you say your great-grandfather Isidoro is located?"

"In area 25," he answered, folding the paper again.

The lady stood up and left her desk. She asked him to follow her.

Meanwhile, Sultan (who had stayed near the door) gave Frank Elias a friendly nod as if he was watching him closely. He winked at him and silently promised him that, if necessary, in the blink of an eye, he would help him flee.

I don't know if my cousin laughed or not, I only know that what I thought was area 25 a tiny little square on my map, was no such thing! It had about 500 graves in the ground and was much bigger than the map had led us to believe. I thought it was a grave with the number 25 and that was it! It turned out to be a huge area in hectares! The land of this cemetery was immense.

"That is not a grave number...it's the lot number of a whole area —the oldest area in our cemetery!"

Frank Elias did not flinch. He felt an unshakable certainty. He followed the lady with granny eyes and the agility of an athlete. Together they entered a huge closet and searched through the hundreds of books.

"The lady told me that where number 25 is, it's a huge area! There may be dozens of graves there," he wrote me by email. I remember thinking: *Oh no, this looks really bad.*

In Virginia I was looking forward to the conclusion of this mystery, were we going to finally find him? And I wanted to believe it was going to be as easy. "Oh yes, the Isidoro, the only one named Isidoro, that one who died in 1912...yes, here it is!"

They searched through a volume of the 1912 register until they found the right place. The organization of the site was impressive, so, with a new map in hand, they pointed out where the grave was. But before Frank Elias and Sultan could leave to drive off in their car down the yellow-marked road, an old man dressed in overalls came through the door. After a brief conversation with him, the lady turned to my cousin.

"This is one of the gardeners who's been taking care of the place for years. He knows area 25 like the back of his hand. Follow him. He will take you there."

As they sat in the jeepeta, behind the gardener's pick-up truck, Sultan commented,

"He sent this two-hundred-year-old gardener in that torn-up van for us to follow in our car. Why? Is this grave that far away?"

As they followed the blue pick-up truck turning into each street up the hill toward area 25, Sultan continued, "That man we're following looks too strong. And how come he knows area 25 like the back of his hand? I bet he was the one who buried Isidoro in the first place!"

"Noooo! He doesn't look that old, Sultan!"

Frank Elias could not contain his laughter.

"I think he's about two hundred years old."

"No, he isn't!"

"Well, he looks strong. Aren't you afraid?"

"And now, you, so large, tell me *you're* afraid of him."

"Scared? No, no...I'm terrified! That guy with that shovel. What's that shovel doing back there? And with those big eyes. And that faded blue pickup truck. No, no. I think he's a ghost!"

"Ha ha ha! Stop making a movie. She said it's the gardener. I'm not afraid."

"You're not afraid of anything. But I am! Of ghosts."

"Ha ha! There's no such thing as ghosts."

"Tell that Isidoro guy when he comes out..."

"Ha ha!"

The gloomy blue van stopped next to an asphalt road, under a tree. The man with, according to Sultan, penetrating eyes and a suspicious shovel jumped out of the van. He walked towards them and pointed between some huge trees.

"You must climb this hill. It's up there. There are several, so, you'll have to check every gravestone because they are scattered and the names on some are not very clear."

The three of them set out raking the area, step by step, stopping at each headstone and reading. Frank Elias was going faster and got ahead of them.

Finally, Frank Elias stopped at one and read, then shouted, "I found the treasure!"

Later, he emailed the family, "I found it." He also attached a photo of a rectangular grave in the green grass. It was the first time I saw it. Years later, when I went to visit it, I don't think any gravestone had ever brought me so much joy!

Frank Elias also wrote to his dad, copying me in. He made the comment to him that Isidoro's tombstone was not stone or marble, but bronze. We thought that someone had been there before us, someone who cared enough to have the generosity to make it so.

Over the next few months after this discovery, all of Queco's family visited the site. They did it as a kind of pilgrimage. They also traveled to Italy to visit the house where Queco was born and raised, thus honoring that part of the lineage, and teaching the new descendants about their origins.

I found it highly significant that it was he, Frank Elias, from the direct line of Isidoro's surviving male descendant's got to see the grave for the first time. Frank Elias, son of Frank, son of Queco, son of Isidoro. I think that these are the designs of the family spirit.

In 2012, one hundred years after his death, Uncle Fernando, returned to Isidoro's grave with his brother Luis Manuel to commemorate his grandfather. They made a small personal tribute to him and shared it with everyone in an email. Thus, we were represented through them and we also honored his name.

A NEVER ENDING STORY

*O*nce, I received an image with a message from a person tracing his family tree. The caption said, "When in a family a seeker of his family tree emerges, it is because he embodies the desire of the whole tree of his clan, to rise in consciousness, to improve all descendants and move forward."

How is it that the unconscious spirit calls our attention to repair the repetitions of the family clan? A spirit that leads us to transform pain and sadness into union and compassion. There is no other way to define and explain that something that guides us to transform, transcend and transmute our common history into love. If we do not learn from our mistakes, we are doomed to repeat them. At some point in this research, I began to think that there is an angel for every family. An angel that protects all generations and has the central eye. A special being that calls us to improve ourselves. And every time a family member grows and heals emotionally and/or spiritually, his individual consciousness and that of all his descendants expands. He surrenders to love. If someone is exalted, his thought illuminates the path to the divine and thus exalts the family. And when I say the divine, I think of love, union, acceptance, friendship, good faith, brotherhood, and altruism. The whole clan benefits. This is possible for every family.

I visualize that tree as being at the top of the family trees, trees that serve as intercessors or, in other words, they are the guardians that correct our vision (of mistakes, negligence, unfulfilled dreams) so that we turn our gaze to love. And that is the angel of the genealogical tree that transmits a strong current of love to all its own. A winged creature that sees us and, gently, calls us to approach and to repair with love all that needs attention. It is an infusion of love. We are to turn our gazes to accept the good and the not so bad. As it was, it was perfect.

At the beginning, I did that and I felt like I was guided by an instinct. Then, I understood that I was guided by what I now call "the family angel" and whom I consider as the guardian angel that was instilled in us as children and with whose blessing we were favored. We all had our guardian. Didn't we?

I was not under any delusion that I would forever be the only one called a "bonding agent" for this family. I understood that there would likely be many others. Most importantly, the chosen ones are those who allow themselves to be guided and who investigate beyond the obvious. To find the blessings, which are the treasures. The essence of the ancestors is in every cell of our being. I know this because mine have traveled with me, walked with me, laughed with me, cried with me. They have even loved with me. A love of a thousand loves.

I have never felt so accompanied in this ancestral love and union as I did when Frank Elias approached me and told me what he knew. My heart rejoiced in the fullness of a closing circle. The relief of what was finished for now and the next that was beginning. Here and now, I understand and bless the realized dream of my ancestors. In that corner in front of the plaque, I felt the weight of this knowledge on my shoulders and chest. In front of that descendant with whom I share the genes of Isidoro and Bianca, I felt a union that I find beautifully poetic. His dominant, coming from male to male, is his father, Frank, followed by Queco and, from there, Isidoro. On my side, my dominant is my mom, followed by Chela, and from there, Bianca.

It seemed representative of my family. Strong women and equality are accepted, they are thought to be complimentary to the totality of each person's role in the family. I come from a family where the normal is this equality of virtues and values that are represented by our ancestors.

The next time I saw Frank Elias in person, a little more than three years had passed. I went to meet Carlotta, his firstborn. He and Claudia were all smiles, waiting for me in their house, which is almost right on the coast. The sea starts right there and extends all the way to the ocean. The blue was reflected on the white walls and when we opened the windows, the sound of the waves was subtle and became soft and constant until it emptied into a lullaby.

"I still remember the adventure you put me through that blessed day in New York. The truth is that many people don't understand this genealogy thing, but to me it's magic."

He was watching me sincerely, with those penetrating eyes that are not afraid of anything. I found myself thinking about destiny and everything that had happened. And what had been avoided.

"For me, tracing genealogy has all this power to heal. At the beginning of the story, my mom thought Isidoro had abandoned Bianca."

"But how come you couldn't tell her for sure?"

"When I managed to ask for the birth certificate thanks to Uncle Fernando's information, they sent me some information from Italy that indicated there were two Isidoros. I had to go to the genealogy offices of the Family Search organization. There I found the correct Isidoro. For a long time I thought that there were two persons called Isidoro, of the same age, and from San Secondo. Every time I found a document, I wondered if it pertained to the correct Isidoro, or was it the other one? Much later, I discovered that the *other one* turned out to be an uncle of Isidoro who had died as a child, right there, in that town."

"So in the end there was only one," he concluded, nodding.

"I have investigated so many things and found so many ancestral vestiges that I could write many books."

"I hope you do!" He smiled looking at me and I remembered Mami.

I explained that I always felt dissatisfied with the documents. After receiving the death certificate and before finding the cemetery, I searched in case there was another alternative, in case there was another Isidoro in the world. I had looked in other cemeteries: in Bologna, in Bogota and even in New York. One day, I found other similar names and I could not believe it. I even found an

Isidorus Raynier buried in Maryland and a family named Raineri in Pennsylvania, with names similar to ours, such as Francesco. When websites like *Ancestry*, *Geneanet* and others were opened, I kept searching endlessly.

"Because sometimes you're not sure what you know is all there is to it; I felt deep inside me that I had to lift every stone on the road, no matter how heavy it was, and check for myself every name, every possibility."

"But haven't you been to visit him?" My cousin asked me "There is an air of pilgrimage when one does it. Their encounter, for me, was unforgettable."

In 2014 I went to touch Isidoro's tomb. I spent the whole afternoon marveling at how peaceful and quiet the place was, and that made so many emotions well up in my chest. I wish, someday, I could find letters written by him, make more unforgettable trips in his name, arrive in Bogota and find the unimaginable now. I have dreamed of finding writings by him, how I would love to see the shape of his handwriting. And destiny was willing to please me in everything. But all that I leave for later.

"And, although my mother is no longer here, I will continue the research for her," I told Frank Elias. "And for the women of my lineage. The supposed "abandoned" ones, who in the end were not such, but who did not take that as an excuse to abandon themselves. No. They never abandoned themselves and this story taught them to be autonomous and sovereign over their own lives. There is no more beautiful legacy than that."

"And if there is anything I can do to help you, you can count on me," he said. "You know the story doesn't end here. It goes on."

"I'll keep searching because I'm fascinated with everything I find."

"So we go from the unknown by reason to the known by the heart."

"I wish I could have said that to my mom, with the evidence I have today! Although I suspect that Mami would contemplate me with her infinite patience and tell me, "For what it's worth...what difference does it make? Because all death, in the end, is abandonment."

"But it's nobody's fault, it's life!" Frank Elias answered.

"But at the moment you don't know that. Like in my grandmother's case: a two-year-old girl sees her father walk out the door, saying goodbye. She cries but he doesn't stop. He continues on his way. For her, the last memory she has of her father is like an abandonment. Even if it was unintentional, even if it's because we can't any of us know the future..."

"In the end, all these experiences feel like a collective experience, and I see it as positive," Frank Elias concluded. "He has given us knowledge about our grandparents. There is something that feels more complete. A strength and a living energy."

I felt it too. There was a new current of strength in me, encouraging me, sustaining me, filling me with love. I recognized that strength now, not only from my research, I knew that *something* was guiding me, *something* was showing me paths to take, places to look in daily life. For example, the memory of my grandmother instilled in me patience with my children. And also a love for what I do, both at work and at home, giving me a maturity and conscientiousness in household matters. I was becoming more and more organized! I've always been introspective, but I also loved enjoying the simple things in life. My children's voices seemed to me the most wonderful sounds, perhaps because I now knew that there was a father who didn't get to hear his daughters grow up. Even the colors of the sunset seemed brighter and more unusual to me. Perhaps, because I knew that this had united my ancestors on a boat?

"A strength that comes from our ancestors," Frank Elias said. "A support. Knowing what they went through, it gives me energy. I mean, look where we come from. So I think more needs to be done, for them and for us and our descendants."

We stood for a while contemplating the swaying of the sea until he spoke again.

"I'm sorry I couldn't find anything more than the information that he was cremated and that, of course, none of his belongings were recovered since he died far away from Puerto Plata. But I did understand that our great-grandmother was notified. Tío Colorao told me that she had learned of his death. It appears in the archives of the Masonic Temple too. There are documents there that seem to have commemorated her death in late August 1912. Although our great-grandmother was not present."

"Surely she was not inclined to nostalgia, but she was human. Sometimes I wonder if, in her pregnant state, she waited for some time for him to return. Like when she returned from one of her trips," I mused.

"And we can go on speculating if we want. But I say her personality led her to deal with the present and leave the past in the past. She must have buried the stories and refused to mention her sorrows. And thus, a family myth was formed."

"But the family spirit forgets no one. Isidoro was not going to be forgotten without explanation. This research was inspired by a force of that tribal spirit and a love far greater than my own self. I have been an instrument, and a happy instrument of this epic story. Just a messenger of a great love—a love that has transcended generations."

As I watched him his gaze was fixed on the sea. I thought of all those who lived before us. Are we really called by ancestors? I think we are. So I added, "And you are too!"

He looked up and said with a half-smile, "Then, cousin, we already know what the divine treasure is."

I took a deep breath.

"Yes, we know...what is it?"

"They. They are!" There was a pride in Frank Elias' tone when he said it.

"Yes," I agreed. I was happy because he understood. Because we came from the same love that once united to form a family. And that doesn't make us equal in the eyes of our ancestors.

"Our ancestors are our divine treasure." His voice vibrated with joyful emotion.

"Yes. And we...we are each of us their descendants." I wanted him to be the one to say the last word.

"We are their divine treasure."

FAREWELL

I picture Isidoro and Bianca at the threshold of the hotel entrance. Facing him and with her back to the street, she yells out her despair.

"You're leaving. You are leaving me."

"I would never leave you," he says, taking her by the hands and staring at her.

"What if something happens?"

"What will happen? This trip is essential."

"You always say that," Bianca answers, letting go.

Tenderly, he takes her hands again and, in a very intimate moment, whispers to her:

"Bianca. My *madame*. You are the bravest woman I know. You have always known what to do. Why should this be any different? The best decisions have been made by you, and often without me."

"It's better with you."

"This adventure, the adventure of our lives, we started it together. You and me. Look around you. Look at all that we have built here: a house and a big business. And beyond what is in sight, your house in Bologna. We've done it all together, side by side. With you, life is better, more joyful, fairer and safer. I would never abandon you. I will always be by your side."

"You say that because you've decided to leave."

314

"Look at my suitcase. You think I'll be gone for long? It's so small. It's my promise of a short trip."

"You've known how to survive on almost nothing, with your own insight. The way you find resources goes with your personality. You have achieved what you have wanted to achieve." This last statement he said more forcefully.

"With work!"

She knew it was her vision. The organization and the loving disposition in everything she did, but...

"I have a bad feeling...remember once you left and didn't come back in time."

She didn't want to tell him what she sensed. *Something's going to happen. You're going to end up leaving me.*

"I'll come back. I always come back. And I will one more time. Always."

What must have been the words spoken under that threshold of the white wooden door there in Puerto Plata? What must their hearts have felt on that misty morning when the ship waited and their desires converged? How did he go to see and say goodbye to the twins, his youngest daughters? They were so different in appearance, but both already saying "papa". One with dark hair and blue eyes like him as a child and the other with Bianca's platinum fluff and light hazel eyes.

"Look, it's you and me in a small way. Our youngest daughters represent us."

"You can think of anything!" she said.

"Yes, look. It's being born again...in each of our children. These little girls complete our treasure."

Bianca watched him come closer to kiss her on the forehead and then embrace the other children: Blanquita, Yolanda, Isidorito and Beatriz. Yolanda leaves before him. She wanted to see him walk away from the street and goes to the other corner. And from there, she stays contemplating her parents in their bitter farewell.

Bianca felt her sadness turning into anger and the rumbling in her chest warned her that everything was imminent. How could she avoid this departure? How could she endure him looking at her to say goodbye? She'd had a dream and had told him about it. It didn't have to be today. He could have avoided boarding in the face of that premonition.

How could she stop him leaving?

But she knew trying to stop such a tenacious and adventurous man was like trying to calm the anxieties of a sea in constant motion. An eternal swaying. A plea to the ocean. The sea...how it defined Isidoro! At times, it looks flat and calm, hiding the whirlwind that could happen at any moment. A metaphor for his boldness moving forward toward his next plan, and the constant current of his tenacity. That's how he was. Always industrious and busy, even when his friends were talking at meetings. Always encouraging further conversation, asking questions, and encouraging others to do so as well, to speak up, to express themselves, to laugh and enjoy their glasses of bubbly champagne. He loved to see everyone enjoying every moment. He gave himself completely to every task, whether it was work or recreation. Now, that whirlwind of love and spirit was leaving. She was annoyed by loved ones who seemed to abandon her, not irritated with life for forcing her to do everything alone. But she had promised herself not to let herself faint, least of all at such times.

"I haven't come this far to give up now," she had promised herself when she saw him off. Three months later, Bianca uttered this sentence again. Although she remembered the moment of his departure with pain, she was convinced that she had to move on.

Is this the end of the story between Isidoro and Bianca?

Or is it only the beginning of a new story? A new series of adventurous laughs. New epic stories that shape future memories for the family. A love that grows with family and down through the generations. And all this shapes the memories in our blood, in our minds and in the family mind that carries the angel, a true divine treasure.

ACKNOWLEDGMENTS

Writing a book about the mystery that surrounded my ancestors was an adventure of almost two decades. At first, it was a genealogy research to solve the mystery of an abandonment. However, love had its own designs.

Divine Treasure is a book guided by that love that transcended generations. I thank all the descendants of Isidoro Rainieri and Bianca Franceschini who encouraged me, supported me, and gave me their stories, dreams, suspicions and anecdotes. Especially my mother and Uncle Fernando, who, even from heaven, encouraged me. To my sisters, who accompanied me at all times, I love you with all my heart. To my cousins, the Harper Rainieri, Imbert Rainieri, Rainieri Marranzini, Ginebra Rainieri, Barletta Rainieri and Maltes Rainieri, who embraced me, always welcomed me and shared so much care and love with me. To the talented editors, Marian Ruíz and Veronica Cacharón, for their valuable and thoughtful comments. To Yoli Prado, who transcribed my scribbles. To my cousins Bonnelly Thomen, who enjoyed first drafts and encouraged me all the way. To Hilda Blanch, for accompanying, helping, caring and believing in me... I have no words.

ABOUT THE AUTHOR

Graciela Thomen Ginebra is a lover of her ancestors, a family researcher and genealogist author. Ever since she knew about the mystery in the family and the deep sorrow that it brought to generations, she set out to find and complete her genealogical tree. What she found was a love that transcended generations.

By female vein, she is a direct descendant of Isidoro Rainieri and Bianca Franceschini. Divine Treasure is an autobiographical novel with historical and spiritual traits.

The author was born in the Dominican Republic and lives in Virginia with her children near a forest enchanted with a white deer.

Made in the USA
Las Vegas, NV
13 July 2021